CONTROL FREAK

A real world guide to DMX512 and Remote Device Management

Wayne Howell

ENTERTAINMENT TECHNOLOGY PRESS

Systems Series

This book is dedicated to the "Grand Cru Crew"
Some of life's madder people!

CONTROL FREAK

A real world guide to DMX512
and Remote Device Management

Wayne Howell

by the same author:
Rock Solid Ethernet

Entertainment Technology Press

Control Freak
A real world guide to DMX512
and Remote Device Management

© Wayne Howell

First edition published June 2008
by Entertainment Technology Press Ltd
The Studio, High Green, Great Shelford, Cambridge CB22 5EG
Internet: www.etnow.com

ISBN 978 1 904031 55 0

A title within the
Entertainment Technology Press Systems Series
Series editor: John Offord

CODE / CF01-0608

Contents

Preface

Wayne starts the Introduction to this book with the words "there is no need for this book".

What is he talking about! Are those the words of a salesman - can you imagine him saying the same thing about any other of his products? What does his publisher think about that for a sales line right at the beginning of the book?

If you are standing in a bookshop reading this and deciding whether you should buy the book or not – then my advice is to take absolutely no notice of what the author says. That doesn't sound right either, does it? Let's try again. Dear reader, take no notice of Wayne's momentary aberration in his opening phrase; please skip that part but then go on to voraciously devour everything else in the book.

Fortunately, for those of us wondering if this is the same Wayne Howell we know, he quickly redeems himself and goes on to explain why there is actually a very strong need for this book. Here we are in total agreement.

The world of lighting control protocols is a complex and esoteric one mostly inhabited by beings that use words like 'Checksum' and 'UID' in everyday conversation and whose closest friend is probably a packet analyser. I can reveal a little secret here; Wayne Howell leads a double life. By day he's as geeky as they come and can bit wrangle with the best of them. However, he can transform 'at will' into his secret articulate alter-ego who is willing and able to pass on his arcane knowledge not only to fellow initiates but also to those of us who don't even know what a pocket protector is for. Most importantly he is able to explain his subject in words and language that make the complex topics he deals with clear and understandable.

Clarity is important. If there's one thing we need right now with lighting control it's clarity. The world of entertainment lighting is in a period of significant change; moving lights have become ubiquitous and we have two simultaneous disruptive technologies – the introduction of LEDs as truly viable light sources and the slow inexorable merger of video and lighting. The consequence is that new and improved control standards have become essentials rather than nice-to-haves. Those standards have been issued but just because a piece of paper with 'standard' written on it exists doesn't mean that anything will actually happen. It needs developers to adopt those standards and incorporate them into products; it needs users to connect those products together in a rig and make them work; and finally it needs everything to come together in a show that achieves the designer's artistic vision. Control protocols are an essential enabling technology to help achieve that artistic vision – that's what it's all about and why we are all so passionate about this industry.

If you are still standing in that bookshop and you've made it this far then I think you are hooked. Whether you are one of the cognoscenti who already knows all there is to know about DMX512A and RDM but needs a reference book as a refresher; or instead someone who needs a source book to explain how those protocols really work and to bring you up to date then this book covers your needs. Whatever I might have said, Wayne really does know what he's talking about!

Mike Wood
Mike Wood Consulting LLC

Welcome to Control Freak.

In principle there is no need for this book! Many people have spent what must now be several man years ensuring that the DMX512 & RDM standards contains every relevant fact, instruction and recommendation. On the other hand, as one of the standards' authors I can assure you that it is definitely not bedtime reading! Perhaps more importantly the purpose of the standard is to tell you the facts, not how to use or interpret them.

For many years, the PLASA 'Recommended Practice for DMX512' by Adam Bennette has been the master reference on the subject. However technology has continued to move forward. We now have the DMX512-A standard and the recent launch of Remote Device Management. Adam is currently writing the second revision and I am sure it will continue to be a definitive reference on the subject.

Control Freak is intended to provide a more in depth discussion of the subject. It is my hope that it will prove useful to both users and product designers whilst also offering an introduction to those who simply require an overview of the subject.

This book is not intended as a replacement for the ESTA Standards documents. If you are reading this as a product designer, you will certainly need copies of the actual standards.

I would like to thank the members of the ESTA DMX512 and RDM Task Groups for all their hard work on both standards. I also thank the staff at Artistic Licence for their assistance with numerous photographs and proofing sessions and in particular Kate Staines for finding the typo's, Tracey Patterson for the front cover, Simon Fraser, Simon Hobday, Tim Baarsch and Ian Airley for reviewing the manuscript and their incisive comments. Thanks also to Adam Bennette for finding time, during the writing of his own book, to review the manuscript. And finally to Scott Blair, chair of the RDM Task Group, for fielding a continuous stream of emails that often started 'Can you remember why we did this ...'

As ever, thanks to Jackie and John at Entertainment Technology Press for their hard work in getting the manuscript to print.

Wayne Howell
Hayling Island, May 2008

Chapter 1 Lighting Control Protocols

A Brief History

The lighting industry uses a remarkably diverse range of lighting control protocols. The reasons for this vary. In some instances, choice of protocol is cost driven, in others it is simply advancement in technology. Added to this equation is the inevitable group of manufacturers who attempt to foist proprietary control onto their customers in the hope of locking them into a specific product range.

In this chapter, I will attempt to describe the most significant protocols and discuss some of the benefits and drawbacks.

Analogue Control

Analogue control simply involves using a single wire for each control circuit. The voltage on the wire varies (usually between 0 to 10V) and the voltage at any given time sets the intensity of the dimmer. This is the oldest form of control. It is still in regular use today, primarily due to its simplicity. Any fault can be diagnosed easily with a voltmeter. The main drawback is that today's lighting systems use many channels, ranging from hundreds to tens of thousands. At this level, analogue becomes very cumbersome and expensive. It is worth noting that the analogue control protocol has just recently become an ANSI (American National Standards Institute) standard (ANSI E1.3 2001).

Early Multiplex

The limitations of analogue control led manufacturers to investigate methods of sending multiple control channels over a single wire. The generic term for this is multiplex. Two different types exist: Analogue Multiplex and Digital Multiplex.

Early developers of Analogue Multiplex include Strand Lighting with their D54 protocol and ADB with S20. These protocols are still in use today, although rarely used for new installations. Analogue Multiplex solved the problem of transmitting many channels over one wire. Unfortunately, these protocols are prone to problems such as interference, which is visible as flickering lights.

The next round of developments came with Digital Multiplex. The concept is similar, but the multiple control channels are transmitted over a single cable using digital information. Early developers include Avab and Colortran with similarly named protocols. The only drawback with this type of protocol is the fact that they are proprietary systems. This made it very difficult to interconnect equipment from differing manufacturers. Conversion products, called protocol converters were developed by companies such as Artistic Licence, ADB and Grey Interfaces (now Pathway Connectivity), but these were relatively expensive ways of solving a problem that should not have existed. The problem was solved in 1988...

DMX512

DMX512 was the first standard method of digital multiplex. It was invented by the USITT (United States Institute of Theatre Technology) in 1986. Adoption of the standard by manufacturers was exponential.

As the name suggests, DMX512 allows 512 channels to be Digitally MultipleXed on a single cable. It employs an electrical standard called RS485; this is a method of transmitting data over a pair of wires that are twisted together. The result is very high immunity from electrical interference.

In 1990, the standard underwent some improvements. That is why the term DMX512 (1990) is often seen on equipment marking.

In the decade to follow, DMX512 became the defacto standard and proved remarkably resilient. One potential drawback was the complexity of diagnosing faults on a digital system. This was quickly overcome as manufacturers developed sophisticated test tools such as the Goddard Design "Lil'DMXter" and the Artistic Licence "Micro-Scope".

DMX512 has just underdone a series of upgrades and a new standard 'DMX512-A' now exists. Happily, this is completely compatible with the earlier version. DMX512-A addressed a number of minor limitations in the original standard, along with adding a range of new functionality.

Talking Back

By the early 2000s, one of the biggest problems was the fact that DMX512 only 'talked' in one direction. That is from the control system to the dimmers or moving lights. There was no way to retrieve information such as status and temperature from the lights. More importantly, the DMX512 address of each light needed to be set manually, often using fiddly 'DIP Switches'. As channel counts rose into the tens of thousands, the need for a solution became urgent....

RDM

RDM stands for Remote Device Management and is a new standard recently published by ESTA (Entertainment Services & Technology Association). It operates on the same cable as DMX512 or DMX512-A and allows bi-directional communication.

This provides numerous benefits, key amongst them is the ability to remotely set the DMX512 start address. In large installations, this allows the task of 'patching' the lights to be totally automated.

RDM also allows diagnostics data to be retrieved from the lamps and dimmers. The range of information is wide and varied. It can include feedback such as operating temperature, moisture sensors, lamp hours and fault information.

Whilst RDM is very new, a number of manufacturers are already shipping RDM products. These include Artistic Licence, Doug Fleenor Design, Goddard Design, HELL, Wybron and EDI with major players such as High End and Vari-Lite set to join soon. The first fully integrated RDM control system, Colour-Tramp, was launched by Artistic Licence in 2003. By extensive use of RDM, it operates as both the lighting controller and also as a diagnostics and management system. Information retrieved from the lamps using RDM can be displayed on a PC screen or even emailed for evaluation and maintenance control.

The Ether

DMX512-A and RDM provide a solid workhorse that will be with us for the foreseeable future. There is only one limitation: Only a short time ago, 512 channels seemed sufficient. That is no longer the case. We now regularly talk about the number of Universes of DMX512 not the number of channels (Universe is the term used to describe a group of 512 channels or one 'cable' of DMX512).

Just as rising channel counts spurred the change from Analogue to Multiplex, a way to multiplex DMX512 Universes over the same cable was sought.

Most manufacturers agreed that Ethernet was the interface to use. The majority of implementations effectively multiplex multiple universes of DMX512 over the Ethernet cable. The first manufacturers to offer solutions were proprietary. Strand released ShowNet, ETC released EtcNet II and Artistic Licence released Art-Net.

ESTA started a programme called ACN (Advanced Control Network). Unfortunately, and almost 15 years on, the standard is still only partially complete. The concept is laudable; to invent an Ethernet control protocol that will provide a standard method of control for everything from lights to sound, video and even stage mechanics. In recent years, the programme has come under new stewardship, has goals that are more realistic and may soon see the light of day.

In an attempt to break the deadlock, Artistic Licence released Art-Net into the public domain and then included a range of free development tools and software. The concept seems to have worked. With over 90 manufacturers now supporting Art-Net, it is becoming the defacto standard. In 2007 Art-Net II was launched which overcame the maximum universe limit of 40 that existed in the original specification.

Ethernet protocols such as Art-Net do not replace DMX512 and RDM; they all work together. The Ethernet part is used to distribute many universes of data around a building, converting locally to DMX512/RDM for local distribution to lights and dimmers.

So, that is the background. Let's look at the details of DMX512 and RDM...

Chapter 2 The Data

The Basics

DMX512 is a way to move up to 512 channels of lighting data from a controller to the dimmers or moving lights. DMX512 is based on RS485, which is a standard that defines the electrical part of the protocol.

DMX512 can travel up to 300m in a single run. Up to 32 devices (dimmers, moving lights etc) can be connected to one cable by using the 'loop through' technique. If you need more than 300m or more than 32 devices, you can boost the line with a device known as a splitter.

The controller always connects to one end of the DMX cable. The cable then runs to the first device, loops through that and on to the second device. At the very end of the last device on the cable, you connect a terminator, which stops reflections and interference to the signal.

As you will see in the rest of the book, there is more to DMX than this brief summary. However, stick to the above and you won't go far wrong!

Addressing

DMX512 is a streaming protocol. It continuously sends a stream of data that is primarily used to describe the level or intensity of a lighting channel. Receivers of DMX512 obtain the information they require by reading the information at a particular offset from the start of the data stream. This offset is known as the Start Address.

Before continuing, a few definitions may be useful:

Start Address: This is the offset into the data stream that contains the data to be used by a receiver.

Slot: This is the name for each piece of data in the stream. There can be a maximum of 513 slots. Slot 0 is the Start Code. Slots 1 - 512 contain the data.

Data Slot: This term is used less frequently and is intended to differentiate between Slot 0 (Start Code) and all the data slots. Data Slots 1 - 512 relate to Slots 1 – 512. There can be a maximum of 512 Data Slots. Data Slots are often also called Channels.

Footprint: This is the number of Data Slots or channels consumed by a receiver.

Start Code: The data contained in Slot 0. This tells us the type of data contained in the remainder of the packet. A Start Code of zero means that the packet contains standard lighting level data.

A particular lighting fixture may consume any number of channels. An intensity dimmer may use only one channel to represent intensity. The dimmer then has a footprint of 1.

The drawing below shows the first 10 data slots of a DMX512 stream. Alongside, arbitrary fixtures are shown 'consuming' the data slots. The process of addressing fixtures is known as 'Patching'.

In this example, each fixture has a footprint of 1 and the fixtures are patched to consecutive start addresses.

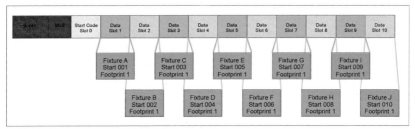

In the next example the fixtures have a range of different footprints. Fixture A has a footprint of 3 and may be an RGB colour changer. Fixture B has a footprint of 4 and could be a simple automated fixture with channels used for pan, tilt, colour and gobo. Again, these are patched consecutively and so the start address of each fixture increases by the footprint of the preceding fixture.

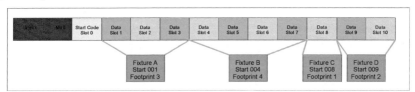

Fixtures can share the same start addresses although clearly this means that the lighting console will not have individual control of each fixture. The following diagram shows this concept which is called 'Multiple Patching'.

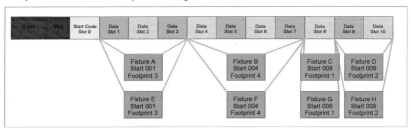

One of the most common errors when patching is to overlap the addressing of consecutive fixtures. The following diagram shows this:

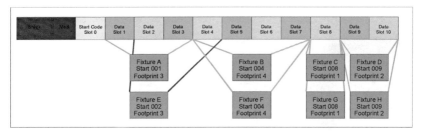

Fixture E has been patched so that it uses the last 2 data slots assigned to Fixture A and the first data slot assigned to Fixture B & F. Whilst perfectly legal in DMX512 terms, this is almost certainly not what is wanted. If Fixture A & E are RGB colour changers then when Fixture A is set to full green, Fixture E will be showing full red!

Bits and Bytes

A 'Bit' is the name given to the smallest possible piece of digital information. It can represent two different states. These are described in many ways: True – False, On – Off, One – Zero and so on. The name is derived from Binary digIT.

A Bit can be used to describe many real world items. A light switch can be described with on 'Bit' because it is either On or Off.

A Byte is a combination of eight Bits. Each Bit is assigned a binary value that allows it to describe decimal numbers up to 255. Each of the Bits in a Byte is numbered starting at zero as shown in the top row:

Bit	7	6	5	4	3	2	1	0
Decimal Value	128	64	32	16	8	4	2	1

Converting a binary Byte to decimal is simple using the following table.

Bit	7	6	5	4	3	2	1	0
Binary Value	1	0	1	0	0	1	1	0
Decimal Value	128	64	32	16	8	4	2	1
Add These:	128		32			4	2		166

If there is a '1' in the binary number, simply add the decimal value. In this example the binary 10100110 is in decimal 128 + 32 + 4 + 2 = 166

Wheels and Switches

The DMX512 Start Address can be set in numerous different ways. On the most modern equipment it is set by RDM (see Part 2) and there may be no user controls on the receiver.

Receivers that do have physical controls vary widely between manufacturers. The drawing below shows the most user friendly interface which consists of three rotary dials. The start address in the range 1-512 is simply dialled in.

Start Address 166

Many products also use DIP switches to set the start address. This means that the start address must be entered in binary (see side bar).

The drawing below shows the most prevalent system which uses 10 individual switches. Note that the manufacturers of DIP switches generally print numbers 1-8 on the switch. This should be ignored! Use the numbers printed on the product panel or the circuit board; these will tell you the binary significance of each switch.

In the example below white indicates the position of each switch; so white at the top is 'On' or a binary '1'. Ten switches are required to encode all the possible numbers in the range 000 to 512. In binary a start address of 1 is 0000000001. Equally a start address of 512 is 1000000000. This example is called 'Zero Based' because it is possible to encode the number '0'.

See Appendix F for a full table of binary conversion.

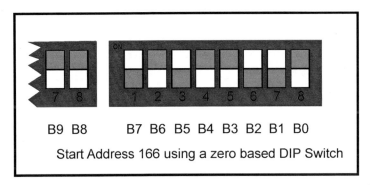

B9 B8   B7 B6 B5 B4 B3 B2 B1 B0

Start Address 166 using a zero based DIP Switch

Some manufacturers use a different system called 'One Based'. This has the dubious benefit of only needing 9 switches. However, the user must subtract one from the start address before converting to binary and then setting the switches!

Happily this system is used less frequently on modern equipment.

Some manufacturers use small circuit board links to achieve the same purpose. In this system each binary position is set to '1' or '0' depending on whether a shorting link is placed over the pins.

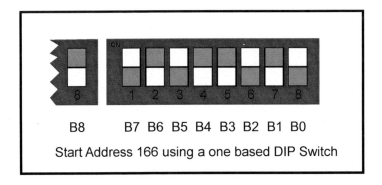

B8   B7 B6 B5 B4 B3 B2 B1 B0

Start Address 166 using a one based DIP Switch

Versions of DMX512

DMX512 has evolved through three versions (four if you consider RDM to be a new release of DMX512).

The protocol was invented in 1986 by the USITT (United States Institute of Theatre Technology). The basic structure of the protocol has not changed in the revisions that followed.

In 1990 the standard was upgraded. The key change was to increase the MaB time from 4uS to 8uS. The change was required because many microprocessors were unable to process the end of break and start receiving data in the 4uS allowed. Products which adhere to this standard are usually marked as DMX512(1990).

In 2005 the standard underwent a major upgrade to become DMX512-A. This upgrade laid the foundations for RDM and added some major new features to DMX512. See Chapter 7 for a full discussion of DMX512-A.

Anatomy of a DMX512 Packet

In this section we'll look at the make up of the DMX512 data. Before doing so, we need to look at the basics.

DMX512 is an asynchronous digital serial protocol that operates at a baud rate of 250Kbaud.

Let's start by breaking down that statement:

Protocol: A Protocol is analogous to a language or a set of rules. If two people speak the same language, they can communicate.

Serial: This means that the data is sent sequentially down the wire. The opposite of this is a parallel system where each bit of data has its own wire.

Digital: This means that the system only uses two states, on and off. The two states are also called 1 & 0 and also Mark & Space. Contrast this with an older protocol such as D54. D54 is an analogue serial protocol. D54 sends a sequence of variable voltage (analogue) pulses.

Asynchronous: This means that the transmitter and receiver are not synchronised to each other.

Baud Rate: This defines the 'speed' of the signal or the number of bits transmitted per second. The DMX512 baud rate is fixed at 250Kbaud. That can also be expressed as 250,000 bits per second.

So, now we've dealt with the definitions, let's take a look at the structure of DMX512.

The DMX512 Packet

The diagram below shows the structure of DMX512.

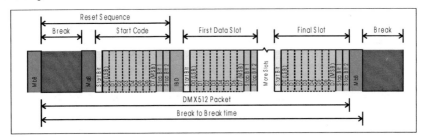

Break

The Break is the synchronisation that tells the receiver a new frame has started. The term Break is used in the communications industry to mean transmitting a continuous 'zero' state for at least the time required to transmit one character of data. In DMX512 the term Break is used in a similar way, but there is a greater minimum duration for the Break to be considered valid. Most microprocessors have built in Break detection which greatly simplifies the task of the receiver.

MaB Mark after Break

The Mark after Break or MaB is an idle period after the Break when the line is held in a 'one' state. The name comes from the terminology of 'Mark' equates to logic 'one' and 'Space' equates to logic 'zero'.

There are numerous interchangeable terms that may be used here. The following table may assist in their interpretation:

Names of 'Cable'	Names of 'One'	Names of 'Zero'
Cable	One	Zero
Wire	1	0
Line	True	False
	On	Off
	Mark	Space
	Marking	Spacing
	High	Low
	Hi	Lo

Thus the phrase 'The line is marking' simply means that transmitter is sending a continuous logic one.

Start Code

The Start Code is also known as 'Slot 0'. This is the first character or byte that is transmitted. It contains a number in the range 0 to 255. A value of 0 indicates that the data to follow is standard lighting level data.

Reset Sequence

Reset Sequence is simply an abbreviated method of describing the sequence Break – MaB - Start Code. More technically, it is the time from the leading edge of Break the end of the second stop bit of the Start Code.

DMX512 Packet

The DMX512 Packet starts at the falling edge of Break and ends at the end of the last stop bit of the last slot of data. A common misconception is that the Packet is a measure of the Break to Break time.

Break to Break time

The Break to Break time is as the name suggests a measure of the time between two consecutive Breaks. This time provides the refresh rate of the signal.

MbB Mark Before Break

The MbB is a measure of the time interval between the end of a DMX512 packet and the start of the next Break. The above three timing parameters are related by the following equation:

$$\text{Break to Break time} = \text{Packet time} + \text{MbB}$$

It is worth pointing out that the MbB does not include the two stop bits of the preceding data slot. This is particularly important when measuring this parameter with a scope as the preceding stop bits and the MbB are both logic one.

IBD Inter-Byte Delay

The IBD is also often called the ISD or Inter-Slot Delay. This is a measure of the time between two consecutive slots. The DMX512 standard allows this value to be zero. However this is probably the largest cause of compatibility problem as there are numerous receivers on the market that cannot handle a zero IBD. In addition the new RDM standard places a minimum constraint on the Average IDD.

DMX512 Timing

The timing requirements of DMX512 are different depending on whether they are viewed from the transmitter or the receiver. The reason is simply that transmitting the data over a cable will cause small changes is the signal timing. If the minimum MaB time (for example) was specified as the same value at both transmitter and receiver, these minor variations in timing could cause the receiver to discard a perfectly good packet. For this reason the transmitter timing specification is always tighter than the receiver timing.

The RDM standard places additional constraints on some timing parameters. See Chapter 9 for details.

Transmitter Timing

Item	DMX512(1986)		DMX512(1990)		DMX512-A	
	Min	Max	Min	Max	Min	Max
Packet Time	1,192uS	1S	1,196uS	1S	1,204uS	1S
Break to Break	1,192uS	1S	1,196uS	1S	1,204uS	1S
Break	88uS	<1S[1]	88uS	<1S[1]	92uS	<1S[1]
MaB	4uS	<1S[1]	8uS	<1S[1]	12uS	<1S[1]
Data Bit	3.92uS	4.08uS	3.92uS	4.08uS	3.92uS	4.08uS
Slot	43.12uS	44.88uS	43.12uS	44.88uS	43.12uS	44.88uS
MbB	0uS	<1S[1]	0uS	<1S[1]	0uS	<1S[1]

Note 1: These maximum times must be set such that the Packet Time does not exceed 1S.

Receiver Timing

Item	DMX512(1986)		DMX512(1990)		DMX512-A	
	Min	Max	Min	Max	Min	Max
Packet Time	1,192uS	1S	1,196uS	1S	1,196uS	1.25S
Break to Break	1,192uS	1S	1,196uS	1S	1,196uS	1.25S
Break	88uS	<1S[1]	88uS	<1S[1]	88uS	<1S[1]
MaB	4uS	<1S[1]	8uS	<1S[1]	8uS	<1S[1]
Data Bit	3.92uS	4.08uS	3.92uS	4.08uS	3.92uS	4.08uS
Slot	43.12uS	44.88uS	43.12uS	44.88uS	43.12uS	44.88uS
MbB	0uS	<1S[1]	0uS	<1S[1]	0uS	<1S[1]

Note 1: These maximum times must be set such that the Packet Time does not exceed 1S.

Loss of Signal

A receiver should define 'Loss of Signal' when it has received no DMX512 packets for 1.25 seconds or more. The standard requires that the receiver should hold the last state that it received. In practice, many manufacturers implement variations on this. Some lamps simply black out on loss of signal and there are a few that reset and go open white! It is often worth performing a loss of signal test during rehearsal; that way you know what to expect in a fault condition.

Asynchronous Communication

Asynchronous serial communication is a method of communication used in many environments ranging from printers to DMX512. It is called Asynchronous because the clocks of the transmitting and receiving devices are not synchronised.

The Diagram below shows two examples of a character.

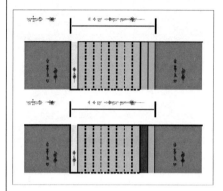

Each character consists of the following parts:

- Start Bit. This is a logic zero that indicates to the receiver that a new character is starting. There is only ever one start bit.
- Data Bits. The data follows the start bit. The number of data bits is application dependant and can range from 5 to 8. Most systems including DMX512 use 8 data bits.
- Parity Bit. The parity bit may or may not be transmitted. In DMX512 parity is not used. Parity is a simple form of error checking. The parity bit can take on five forms:
    o Odd Parity: The number of preceding data bits, of logic one state, are counted. If the number is odd; a parity bit of logic one is transmitted.
    o Even Parity: The number of preceding data bits, of logic one state, are counted. If the number is even; a parity bit of logic one is transmitted.
    o Mark Parity: A logic one is transmitted in the parity bit position. This serves no useful purpose and is rarely used.
    o Space Parity: A logic zero is transmitted in the parity bit position. This serves no useful purpose and is rarely used.
    o No Parity: The parity bit is not sent.
- Stop Bits: The stop bits indicate to the receiver that the character has finished. Depending on application there may be 1, 1.5 or 2 stop bits. This rather odd allowance of a variable number of stop bits dates back to electromechanical teleprinters. The number of stop bits was set to allow time for the actual character to be printed. DMX512 uses 2 stop bits.

It can be seen that there are numerous valid combinations. These are usually abbreviated in shorthand of 'Data-Bits, Parity, Stop Bits'. For example 8E1 means 8 data bits, Even Parity and 1 stop bit. The code shorthand for DMX512 is 8N2, 8 data bits, no parity, 2 stop bits. The start bit is not included in the shorthand as there is only ever 1 start bit.

The time taken to transmit each bit is defined by the Baud Rate. The Baud Rate of DMX512 is 250,000. The reciprocal of this gives us a bit time of 4uS or 4/1,000,000 seconds.

Between characters the signal or line is in a logic one state. This is usually called a Mark or Marking State. A logic zero is called a Space.

Start Codes

The start code is the first byte of information that is transmitted after the break. It can take any value from 0 to 255. The start code defines the meaning of the remainder of the packet. This is a very powerful feature of DMX as it allows different types of data to be interleaved on the same cable.

The most important start code is zero. This means that the remainder of the packet contains standard lighting data. Zero start code data makes up the majority of the traffic on a DMX cable and usually consumes in excess of 90% of the bandwidth.

As the zero start code data is so important, start codes that are not zero are often called Alternative Start Codes or ASC.

There are two types of ASC. Those that are either part of or reserved by the DMX512-A standard and those that have been allocated to manufacturers. Before the advent of DMX512-A, numerous manufacturers were allocated ASCs for specialist control functions. This has now been stopped as the available stock of ASC numbers would have quickly run out.

The table below shows the current allocation of standardised ASCs. See Appendices A & B for a detailed listing of all ASCs. In the table below the symbol '0x' is used to denote a hexadecimal number.

Name	Decimal	Hexadecimal	Purpose
Lighting Data	0	0x00	Lighting level data in this packet.
Text Packet	23	0x17	Packet contains a text message
Test Packet	85	0x55	Packet is used to check network integrity.
Manufacturer	145	0x91	Contains manufacturer specific information.
RDM	204	0xcc	Used for Remote Device Management compatibility testing. See Part 2
System Information Packet	207	0xcf	Contains control and checksum information.
Prototype	241-247	0xf1-0xf7	Can be used by manufacturers for prototype tests but should not be used in any products that are released.

Chapter 6 contains a more in depth discussion of Alternative Start Codes.

Chapter 3 The Wire

DMX512 is based on a standard called EIA-485. This standard was previously known as RS485 and this term is still widely used. The two terms can be used interchangeably. RS485 defines the electrical interface including the voltages used, the topology (way in which devices can be connected), currents and the style of data transmission. These items are termed 'The Physical Layer'.

Different protocols using the same physical layer can be safely interconnected, however there is little chance the devices will understand each other. A common language which sits on top of the physical layer is required. That is the purpose of DMX512, it defines the actual language so that devices can understand each other.

In this chapter we shall focus on the physical layer.

The Basics

A DMX512 system has a transmitter (lighting console) at one end of the cable. A maximum of 32 receivers (dimmers, moving lights) can be connected to the cable. The far end of the cable is then terminated (see below). The following drawing shows a basic DMX512 interconnect.

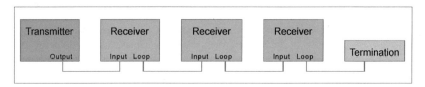

DMX512 receivers have an input connection and a loop connection. Internally these connectors are simply wired together.

Resistors and Resistance

The purpose of a resistor is to limit the flow of current in a circuit. The operation of this statement is governed by the best known law of electronics: Ohm's Law.

Ohm's Law states: $V = IR$

V is the voltage across the resistor measured in Volts (V). I is the current through the resistor in Amperes (Amps - A) and R is the value of the Resistance measured in Ohms. The symbol for Ohms is the Greek upper case character Omega (Ω). In many cases, particularly in circuit diagrams, an uppercase 'R' is used instead.

It is worth just pointing out some semantics: A Resistor is a physical component that exists in a circuit. A Resistor has a Resistance, but also a circuit has a Resistance. So if we consider a circuit made up of a length of wire and an 120Ω Resistor, the total Resistance of the circuit is calculated by adding the Resistance or the Resistor and the Resistance of the wire,

The equation for Ohm's Law shows that for a given resistance, the current flow will increase with voltage. It is common sense that two resistors connected is series with each other will lead to a combined resistance that is the sum of the two resistors. In the drawing below, the combined resistance of the two series resistors is 240Ω.

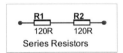

Series Resistors

The situation is slightly less intuitive with parallel resistors. In the drawing below, we have two paralleled resistors R3 and R4 both of value 120Ω. The combined Resistance of this circuit is 60Ω.

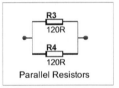

Parallel Resistors

This is calculated using the equation $1/R = 1/R3 + 1/R4$. This is in fact the circuit of a DMX512 cable. The drawing below is electrically identical, simply redrawn in a more conventional way.

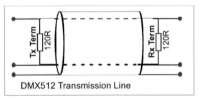

DMX512 Transmission Line

With this drawing it becomes easy to see why a value of approximately 60R is measured across pins 2 & 3 of the DMX512 connector *when both ends are connected.*

Termination

Termination of a DMX512 cable is achieved by connecting a 120R resistor across the data pins (2 & 3). Some receivers have a switch (usually labelled 'Terminate' or 'End of Line') that allows a termination resistor to be enabled. However the norm is to connect a 'Terminator' to the final receiver's loop connection. Terminators are available commercially but are also very easy to build. Simply take a cable mounting male XLR 5 pin connector and solder a 120R resistor across pins 2 & 3. The resistor should be approximately 1W rated and should be insulated such that the pins cannot touch each other or the shell of the connector.

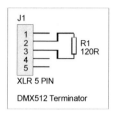

Termination of the DMX512 cable is very important. Its purpose is to absorb the energy at the end of the cable which stops energy being reflected back up the cable. If reflections occur, they travel back along the cable and cancel out the real signal, causing data corruption.

An un-terminated cable will not cause any physical damage but is likely to be unreliable.

It is very easy to check whether the cable is terminated. Simply disconnect the cable from the transmitter and use a meter to measure the resistance between pins 2 & 3 of the cable connector. If the line is terminated, the reading will be approximately 120R. A value in the range 100R to 130R is OK. The reading will depend on the total length of cable in use.

If the reading is very high or open circuit, there is no terminator fitted. If the reading is approximately 60R, the line is double terminated. This can happen if a receiver has a 'Terminate' switch engaged and also there is a termination plug connected. The following table summarises the readings:

Resistance of Pins 2 & 3 of transmit end cable	Conclusion
Less than 50R	Cable is shorted or terminator faulty.
From 50R to 65R	Cable is double terminated.
From 100R to 130R	Good Termination.
Greater than 1KR	No termination fitted.

It is important to note that these values assume measurement with the transmit end unplugged. If the cable is connected at both ends, divide the values above by two (see side bar). This is because the transmitter or lighting console (should) contain a transmit termination resistor.

Ohm and Cavendish

In 'Resistors and Resistance' we discussed Ohm's Law, but why is it so named?

The law is named after Georg Simon Ohm, a German physicist born in 1789. Ohm was schooled in science and philosophy by his locksmith father. Finding university below the level of his father's teachings and apparently preferring to play billiards, Ohm dropped out.

An enraged father packed him off to Switzerland there he took up a teaching post. After a number of years moving from one teaching position to another along with private tutoring, Ohm returned to Bavaria to complete his education. His years of private study resulted in a degree which he followed with a book on geometry. The book resulted in his appointment by King Wilhelm III of Prussia to the Jesuit Gymnasium of Cologne. Here his interests moved from mathematics to physics. Ohm started his best know research with the then recently invented Voltaic Cell or battery. This led to the publication of the engagingly titled 'Die Galvanische Kette, mathematisch bearbeitet' (Mathematical investigation of electric circuits) which contained the now famous Ohm's Law.

Meanwhile, some seven years prior to the birth of Ohm a British physicist had already discovered 'Ohm's Law'!

Henry Cavendish was born in 1731, grandson to the Duke of Kent. He was painfully shy and somewhat eccentric. Cavendish is better known for other milestones of science such as discovering the composition of the Earth's atmosphere and calculating the density of the Earth. He is sometimes incorrectly credited with calculating the mass of the Earth and the gravitational constant. In fact these calculations were not performed until after his death, but were based directly on his original calculations. There remains a sign near his house in Clapham Common saying 'Here the World was weighed'.

Many of his discoveries, particularly relating to electricity, were not found until after his death as his shyness led him not to publish. Indeed had he published, many well known laws of physics and electrical terms such as Coulomb's Law, Charles' Law, Dalton's Law, Dielectric Constant, Wheatstone Bridge and of course Ohm's Law would carry his name.

Ironically, one of the discoveries that is attributed to Cavendish – that hydrogen and oxygen react to form water – is contested and many believe it should be attributed to James Watt.

Cable Length

The maximum cable length from the transmitter to the terminator is 300m or 1000ft. If greater cable lengths are required, then a splitter is needed (See next chapter).

That was a nice simple and unambiguous statement. Not everyone agrees with this. Some manufacturers say it is 500m. Some argue that as RS485 allows 1000m, and there is no reason to limit DMX512 to 300m.

The reality is that there are numerous products on the market that cannot drive cables over 300m and there are some that can. The cautious engineer will consider 300m a maximum and only consider exceeding this if they have no other option and have tested the equipment beforehand! Also keep in mind that whether a long cable works will be dependent upon the number of loads connected and their spacing on the cable. When pushing the boundaries of cable length, it is sensible to use a point to point configuration. That is: make the receiver a single splitter. It is also sensible to use cable with bigger conductors (lower AWG number). Most standard data cable is 24AWG. Consider 22AWG (such as Proplex™ or Datasafe™) if you plan to exceed 300m.

The picture shows just such a case. French engineer Philippe Monlong needed (I never did ask why!) to control this castle from over 500m away. It seems that the Micro-Scope is one of the products that will driver long cable distances.

Y Cables

A Y-Split cable consists of one male XLR and two female XLR 5 pin connectors. All pins 1, 2 and 3 are simply wired to each other respectively. Y-Split cables must not be used with DMX512. The following drawing shows the reason:

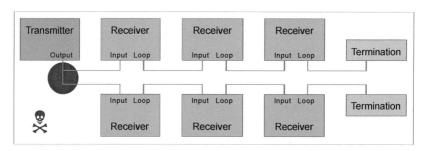

Here a 'Y-Split' cable, shown in the red circle, has been used. The problem is obvious; the transmitter now has two terminators connected, which will overload the transmitter's driver electronics. The correct solution is to replace the Y-Split cable with a DMX512 splitter.

Cable Runs

It is important to give thought to how DMX512 cables are physically laid. It is advisable to avoid running DMX512 cables parallel to mains cables or dimmer output cables. To do this is to form a transformer between the two types of cable which can result in increased noise pickup in the DMX512. Where mains and control does need to cross, do so at right angles when possible.

Connectors

The standard DMX512 connector is the 5 pin XLR. There are three exceptions, detailed below, where different connectors are allowed. It should be noted that the 3 pin XLR is not and has never been allowed. The reason is simply to avoid the potential for data and audio (which use 3 pin XLR) to become mixed.

The drawing below shows the pin layout for both the female and male connectors. The female connector is the transmitter or console end. The male is the receiver or dimmer end. Both are viewed from the connector side (not the 'solder' side).

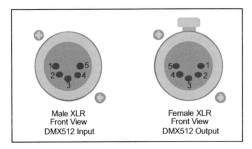

Male XLR
Front View
DMX512 Input

Female XLR
Front View
DMX512 Output

XLR5 Wiring

Pin	Colour *	Function
1	Screen	Signal-Common
2	Black	Data A-
3	White	Data A+
4	Green	Data B-
5	Red	Data B+

* Colour coding does vary by cable manufacturer. This is for guidance only.

Making a DMX512 cable

Making a good quality DMX512 cable is very simple if some basic rules are followed:

- First and most important – choose a good quality twisted pair data cable.
- Don't connect the connector shell to the cable screen, the screen must connect to pin 1 only.
- Ensure that the outer jacket is clamped by the strain relief.
- Don't untwist the pairs of wires more than necessary.
- Insulate the screen with silicon sleeving to ensure it does not touch the shell.
- Do not attempt to crimp the solder bucket.

Connector exceptions

There are three exceptions where connectors other than the 5 pin XLR may be used:

- • 1. RJ45
- • 2. Miniature connectors
- • 3. Screw terminals and punch downs

RJ45 Connector

The RJ45 connector is allowed as a DMX512 connector in certain circumstances. It is acceptable to use the RJ45 in patch bays, installation splitters and areas that are mainly used by 'technical staff'. It is not acceptable to use them on 'end user' products such as moving lights.

The drawing below shows the pin numbering for a female RJ45:

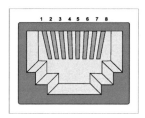

RJ45 Wiring

Pair	Pin		Colour	Function	XLR Pin
2	1		White/Orange	Data A+	Pin 3
	2		Orange	Data A-	Pin 2
3	3		White/Green	Data B+	Pin 5
	6		Green	Data B-	Pin 4
1	4		Blue	Not Assigned	
	5		White/Blue	Not Assigned	
4	7		White/Brown	0V	Pin 1
	8		Brown	0V	Pin 1

CAT5 Cable

CAT5 (including CAT5e, CAT6 & CAT7) cable is valid for installation cables but not portable cables.

Two types of CAT5 exist: UTP (Unshielded Twisted Pair) and STP (Shielded Twisted Pair).

The DMX512 specification says that UTP should only be used inside metal trunking and that STP should be used in other circumstances. When UTP is used for DMX512 it is important to ensure that it is kept clear of power and load cables to avoid interference.

Miniature Connector

The DMX512 standard accepts that there will be some circumstances where it is not physically possible to fit an XLR on the product. An obvious example is a PC card. The standard allows the designer the flexibility to choose a connector that fits, subject to the caveat that a conversion cable between the non-standard connector and a 5 pin XLR be included with the product.

Screw Terminals & Punch Downs

Products designed for control room / permanent installation may use screw terminal blocks or 'punch down' connectors as applicable.

The 4 pin XLR

Unfortunately the DMX512 standard did not address the use of the 4 pin XLR. This connector is widely used as a method of sending DMX512 and power to devices such as colour scrollers and LED colour changers.

There is general consensus on the following wiring:

Pin	Function
1	Signal-Common
2	DMX Data A-
3	DMX Data A+
4	DC Power 24-48V

That said, use caution: Early Wybron and current Colour Kinetics products reverse pins 1 and 4. It is very simple to construct a small tester to identify the polarity, circuit diagram below:

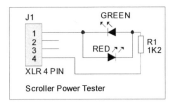

Scroller Power Tester

If pin 4 is positive relative to pin 1 (normal) then the green indicator will illuminate. Conversely if the pins are reversed the red indicator illuminates. In the unlikely event that one of the pins contains an AC component, the indicator will show orange (as both colours will alternate at the AC frequency).

Pins

The first three pins of the XLR connector do all the work. The specific use of pins 4 and 5 has never been defined by the DMX512 standard. Over the years some manufacturers have used pins 4 and 5 for proprietary protocols, DC power and numerous other functions. Given this history of incompatibility, there is a school of thought that says the safest plan is to leave these pins disconnected.

The standard requires these pins to be connected in the cable; however this mandate is widely ignored. Conclusion: don't make any assumptions about the signal to be found on these pins!

Cables

The first and most important point on cables is that it does matter! From time to time you hear people say they've been using Mic(rophone) cables for years and it works fine. Such comments are misguided and those who utter them are flirting with disaster. Let's look at why.

DMX512 is a digital signal. This means that the waveform is fundamentally square in shape. For those of you who can remember the school physics lesson, a square wave can be made by starting with a sine wave and then adding each odd harmonic to the original. The drawing below shows this for the first few harmonics of a sine wave. You can see that the waveform is getting closer and closer to becoming a square or digital waveform.

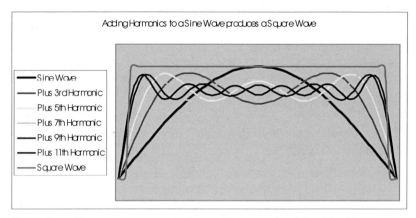

Adding Harmonics to a Sine Wave produces a Square Wave

- Sine Wave
- Plus 3rd Harmonic
- Plus 5th Harmonic
- Plus 7th Harmonic
- Plus 9th Harmonic
- Plus 11th Harmonic
- Square Wave

In the audio world, square waves are bad news. They sound awful and tend to make cones part from speakers. The audio world also dislikes high frequencies; anything above about 22KHz is outside the human hearing range and is just electrical noise.

Mic cable and audio cable is designed to pass the low frequency audio information and filter out or at least attenuate the high frequencies.

So, what happens when you pass DMX512 down a Mic cable? The cable treats it as audio, attenuating the high frequencies. However, we have just concluded that those high frequencies of harmonics are the difference between a sine wave and a square wave.

The result is simple: mic cable tries very hard to turn our nice square digital signal into a sine wave. The results can be disastrous. The drawing below shows what can happen.

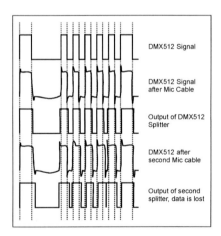

DMX512 Signal

DMX512 Signal after Mic Cable

Output of DMX512 Splitter

DMX512 after second Mic cable

Output of second splitter, data is lost

The cable problem is compounded when the data gets to the first splitter. It tries to turn the data back into a square wave. However, the Mic cable has turned our nice straight lines into curves. This results in a new digital waveform, but the vertical edges have now moved. When the process is repeated through a second Mic cable and a second splitter, we see that sections of data have been lost.

Cable Choices

Numerous cables are available for use with DMX512; in fact any quality cable designed for RS485 will work. The recommended minimum core size is 24 AWG (7/0.2) both for physical strength and to minimise voltage drop over long cables. Below is a table of cables found in regular use. In many cases the choice of cable is based on its physical attributes such as rugged sheath, rodent proofing, fire safety and regulatory requirements.

Man / Part	Make-up	Zc	Capac-itance	Sheath	Conductor	Outer Dia	Temp Range	Smoke Fume	Weight per 100m	Primary Use
AC Lighting Datasafe Ultra 1	1 Pair	120R	39pF/m 66pF/m	PVC Black	22AWG 19x34AWG	5.9mm	-30 +75C	n/a	15.24Kg	Portable cables / Installation
AC Lighting Datasafe Ultra 2	2 Pair	120R	39pF/m 66pF/m	PVC Black	22AWG 19x34AWG	7.4 mm	-30 +75C	n/a	22.56 Kg	Portable cables / Installation
TMB ProPlex PC224T	2 Pair	110R	43pF/m 89pF/m	PVC Black	22AWG 19x34AWG	8.2mm	-20 +60C	n/a	8.63Kg	Installation cables
TMB ProPlex PC222P	1 Pair	80R	72pF/m 135pF/m	Polyur-ethane Black	22AWG 19x34AWG	5.5mm	-40 +105C	n/a	4.32Kg	Portable cables
TMB ProPlex PC224P	2 Pair	110R	43pF/m 82pF/m	Polyur-ethane Black	22AWG 19x34AWG	7.3mm	-40 +105C	n/a	6.70Kg	Portable cables
TMB ProPlex PC244T	2 Pair	100R	41pF/m 134pF/m	PVC Black	22AWG 19x34AWG	8.2mm	-20 +60C	n/a	8.63Kg	Installation cables, outdoor/ portable
TMB ProPlex PC224RAT	2 Pair	110R	42.7pF/m 82.0pF/m	PVC Black	24AWG 7x32AWG	8.1mm	-20 +60C	n/a	8.63Kg	Installation cables (rodent proof)
TMB ProPlex PC224 LSOH	2 Pair	120R	40pF/m 84pF/m	LSOH	22AWG 7x22AWG	7.1mm	-20 +70C	Low smoke/ zero halogen by design	6.20Kg	Installation LSOH cables
TMB ProPlex PC222 LSOH	1 Pair	100R	45pF/m 95pF/m	LSOH	22AWG 7x22AWG	5.5mm	-20 +70C	Low smoke/ zero halogen by design	4.1Kg	Installation LSOH cables
Belden 9842	2 Pair	120R	42.3pF/m 75.9pF/m	PVC Grey	24AWG 7x32AWG	5.9mm	-30 +80C	n/a	9.4Kg	Installation

Notes on capacitance: The first figure stated is conductor to conductor. The second figure is screen to conductor.

Wire Size

Describing the size of a wire conductor can cause immense confusion due to the number of systems in use.

The important information about a conductor is its cross sectional area and its conductivity or resistance. To generalise slightly, most cables are made of copper conductors and copper's conductivity is pretty much constant. This allows us to focus on the cross sectional area of the conductor. Continuing to generalise, most conductors within cables are of a circular cross section. That means that we can use conductor diameter and cross sectional area (CSA) interchangeably as they are related as follows:

$$CSA = \Pi r^2 \text{ where r = radius}$$

We can also describe this as:

$$CSA = \Pi d^2/4 \text{ where d = diameter}$$

The symbol Π is a constant value 'pronounced pi' of approximate value 3.14. (For those who cannot remember: 'How I Wish I Could Calculate Pi'. The number of letters in each word gives the value 3.141592).

The above makes it fairly simple to describe conductors which are solid. However flexible cables are stranded which means they are made up of a number of much smaller conductors (called strands) which are twisted together.

As the strands are also circular, the above calculation needs to be modified. The reason is that we must allow for the air gaps between the strands. In Europe, stranded cable is usually designated in the form '7/0.2mm' or '16/0.2mm'. This short form means Strands/Diameter so the first example is 7 strands each of diameter 0.2mm.

We can use the above equation to calculate the CSA of each strand:

$$CSA = \Pi d^2/4 \text{ where d = 0.2mm}$$

$$\text{Therefore CSA} = 3.14 \times 0.2 \times 0.2 / 4 = 0.0314 mm^2$$

As there are 7 strands, we multiply by 7 for the total conductor CSA = $0.2198 mm^2$

When comparing stranded and rigid conductors, it is important to use the above calculations. Simply comparing the diameter would yield incorrect results as shown by the following drawing. The green areas represent the conductor.

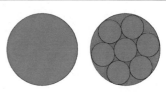

Solid Conductor   Stranded Conductor

The US system uses a different system of units, although the concept discussed above remains valid. The US description is called AWG or American Wire Gauge. This number is neither a diameter nor a CSA. To add to the confusion the AWG number increases as the CSA decreases. The equation for converting AWG is shown below and Appendix K details the conversion.

$$D(inch) = 0.005 \times 92^{(36-n)/39} \text{ where n is the AWG number}$$

$$D(mm) = 25.4 \times 0.005 \times 92^{(36-n)/39} \text{ where n is the AWG number}$$

$$CSA(mm^2) = 0.0126441 \times 92^{(36-n)/19.5} \text{ where n is the AWG number}$$

RS485

The RS485 standard defines the method of data transmission using three wires to connect transmitter to receivers. There is a Data+ wire, a Data- wire and a Signal-Common wire. There are numerous variants on these names which are shown in the table below:

Pin 1	Pin 2	Pin 3
Common	Data-	Data+
Ground	Complement	Data
0V	Return	Send

RS485 is a balanced transmission system that uses twisted pair cable. (See the Balancing Act side bar for details). This means that the Data+ and Data- signals travel down conductors that are twisted together.

The Common signal connects to the screen or shield of the cable which provides a barrier against external interference.

The RS485 signals are generated and received by silicon chips called line drivers. The most common part used in DMX512 is called a 75176. These devices deal with converting the data into a balanced signal that can be transmitted over the cable. The transmitting end drivers send the signal with approximately 5V range between the Data+ and Data- wires. The receivers can detect a signal with as little as 200mV (0.2V) between Data+ and Data-. This allows a significant amount of voltage to be lost in the cable and explains why it is possible to transmit DMX512 over such relatively long distances.

Common Mode Voltage

Common Mode Voltage (CMV) is an important term to understand before we go on to discuss drivers and isolation. The Common Mode Voltage is the common voltage on the data wires relative to the common wire. It is easier to visualise this in the opposite sense; it is also defined as the difference in voltage between the transmitter and receiver commons.

RS485 sets a CMV limit of -7V to +12V. Given the many hundreds of amps flowing around a large stage rig or architectural installation, it is easy to exceed these limits. It is for this reason that many DMX512 receivers are designed with isolation.

I first experienced the problems that common mode voltage can cause at the Live Aid concern at Wembley. During rehearsals there was a stage mains fault which caused an earth differential of some 50V between stage and the lighting tower. A huge instantaneous current flowed through the screen of the DMX512 cable and the cable literally vaporised. The RS485 drivers were not too pleased either!

Testing Common Mode Voltage

CMV can exist as both a DC and AC component. Testing is very simple. Disconnect the DMX512 cable and use a voltage meter connected between pin 1 of the transmitter (lighting desk) and pin 1 of the receiver (dimmers / moving lamps). Do the test with both the DC and AC range. A reading of more than around 5V on either range indicates a potential CMV problem. In the first instance you should check for an actual electrical fault. Assuming the CMV is not caused by an electrical fault, an isolated splitter can be used to solve the problem.

A Balancing Act

Numerous data transmission systems use a balanced line. The DMX512 protocol uses the RS485 balanced line system. Ethernet uses transformer coupled balanced lines.

The balanced line concept provides noise immunity. This simply means that a balanced line resists electrical noise, which in turn allows the signal to be transmitted over longer distances.

The concept is best understood by considering an un-balanced line, such as RS232.

Electrical noise can generate spikes that cause data to be lost. In the drawing above, a binary 1 is received as a binary zero because of the noise.

The balanced line solves this problem by transmitting both the main signal and an inverted copy or complement signal. As the two wires are twisted around each other, any interference will be picked up equally in both wires as shown below:

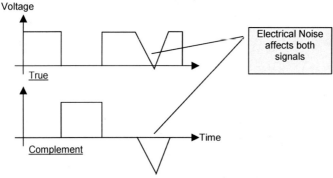

The clever part comes at the receiver. The two signals are subtracted from each other. Remembering that two minuses make a plus, the spike voltage disappears whilst the data signal is amplified by a factor of two:

Isolation

Isolation is one of the more complex aspects of DMX512. The purpose of isolation is to protect equipment from damage due to excessive voltages and specifically Common Mode Voltages.

It is a common misconception that isolation is related to safety. This is not the case. DMX512 isolation is about protecting the equipment and network from damage. The safety of operators and users is paramount and is addressed by correct electrical installation and earthing of the equipment. Engineers must never look upon the Signal-Common of a DMX512 cable as a safety connection.

Ground & Earth Connections

The DMX512(1990) standard did not address isolation or earthing which has led to numerous incompatibilities between manufacturers. DMX512-A attempts to address the situation by defining three categories:

- Preferred Topologies – Do it this way.
- Allowed Topologies – If you have good reason, you can do this.
- Non-preferred Topologies – You can do this but we would prefer it if you didn't.

We will discuss all of these in detail in the next section. The following table summarises the position:

Transmitter	Preferred	Allowed	Not Preferred
Transmitter – Ground Referenced	YES		
Transmitter – Isolated		YES	
Receiver – Isolated	YES		
Receiver – Non Isolated		YES	
Receiver – Grounded			YES
Transceiver - Floating		YES	

Before going any further it is worth clarifying some confusing terminology. In the US, the term 'Ground' is used to mean the safety connection of electrical equipment. In the UK, the term 'Ground' is usually understood to be the Signal-Common of electronics and the term 'Earth' means the safety connection. The reader will doubtless see the huge potential for confusion!

In an attempt to resolve this confusion, the DMX512 Task Group invented the word 'Earth-Ground' for the safety connection. Whilst this term is used in the body of the DMX512 standard it is not used as part of the names for different driver schemes.

In order to avoid confusion I have chosen to not use the word 'Ground'. I use the term 'Earth-Ground' and 'Signal-Common'. As with all rules there is an exception: I have used the DMX512 standard names for each of the allowed topologies in the hope that it will allow the reader to cross reference between this book and the standard. I apologise for the confusion, but it was not of this author's making! For the avoidance of confusion: Earth-Ground = Mains Earth.

Transmitters

Two forms of transmitter circuit, or topologies, are allowed by the standard. The preferred topology is Ground Referenced. An alternative is Isolated.

Ground Referenced Transmitters

DMX512-A strongly suggests that transmitters should be connected (optionally via a resistor) to Earth-Ground. The drawing below shows a block diagram.

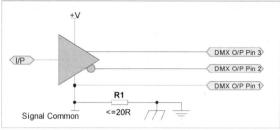

Ground Referenced Transmitter

The key point to note is the resistance which connects Signal-Common to Earth-Ground. The standard requires this be of a value of 20 ohms or less. This configuration keeps the shield of the DMX512 cable at the same potential as the chassis of the transmitter. This is good for noise immunity as the shield acts as a Faraday Cage around the twisted pair conductors. The DMX512-A standard actually says that the preference is for this resistance to be zero ohms when possible. Most designers ignore this rather dubious statement for one simple reason: In a fault condition, significant current can flow though the shield and so through this resistance. It is better to fix a blown resistor than attempt to repair tracks on a circuit board.

The standard does not require manufacturers to label this type of transmitter. To confirm the type, disconnect the DMX512 cable and meter resistance between Earth-Ground and the XLR pin 1. If the resistance is 20R or less it is a Ground Referenced transmitter.

Isolated Transmitters

DMX512-A allows isolated transmitters but does not recommend them. In the drawing below, the green dotted lines represent an electrical barrier between the internal electronics (on the left) and the output driver (on the right).

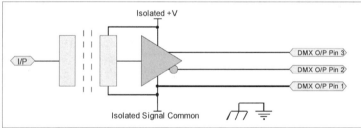

Isolated Transmitter

Notice that there is no connection between Signal-Common and Earth-Ground. As the driver is isolated from the internal electronics, the screen of the cable will be at an indeterminate voltage. This is the reason that DMX512-A does not recommend this topology; the screen cannot act as a Faraday Cage and is therefore more prone to noise and interference. That said, the standard does not preclude its use for a very good reason: There are some special circumstances when this topology solves real problems, particularly when driving Grounded Receivers. We will discuss this in more detail in the next chapter.

The standard requires manufacturers to label this type of transmitter as either 'ISO' or 'ISOLATED'. Unfortunately this requirement is widely ignored. To confirm the type, disconnect the DMX512 cable and meter resistance between Earth-Ground and the XLR pin 1. Also meter resistance between all other DMX512 input and output pin 1 of the product. If all readings are > 22MR then the output is isolated.

The following table indicates the main uses of the two transmitter topologie

Transmitter	Use
Ground Referenced	Lighting Consoles
Isolated	Specialist Splitters

Receivers

Three forms of receiver circuit, or topologies, are allowed by the standard. The preferred topology is Isolated although Non-Isolated and Grounded are allowed.

Isolated Receiver

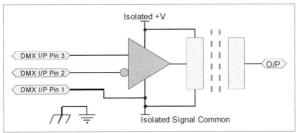

Isolated Receiver

Isolated Receiver is the preferred circuitry. It perfectly complements the preferred transmitter topology of 'Ground Referenced'. Notice that the Isolated Receiver has no connection between Earth-Ground and Signal-Common. In fact the standard allows there to be a resistance of 22MR or greater, but in data terms that is the same as no connection. This means that the Signal-Common will settle at a voltage defined by the transmitter, but no current will flow and there will be no Common Mode Voltage.

This topology requires some relatively expensive components and uses more space than the alternatives. Those are the only reasons that this circuit is not used in all receivers.

The standard does not require manufacturers to label this type of receiver. If a label does exist, the recommended text is either 'ISO' or 'ISOLATED'. To confirm the type, disconnect the DMX512 cable and meter resistance between Earth-Ground and the XLR pin 1. Also meter resistance between all other DMX512 input and output pin 1 of the product. If all readings are > 22MR then the input is isolated.

Non-Isolated Receiver

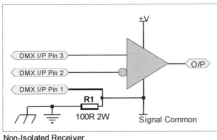

Non-Isolated Receiver

Non-Isolated Receivers are allowed in DMX512-A, but not the best solution. However, they are much lower cost to implement and therefore widely used.

Note the 100R resistance between Signal-Common and Earth-Ground. This resistance is used to limit the current that can flow through the screen of the DMX512 cable. These screen currents are caused when multiple receivers are looped on a DMX512 cable. Each receiver makes a connection between the cable screen and Earth-Ground through a resistor. Common Mode Voltages may exist between each receiver. Without the resistance, potentially damaging currents could flow through the cable screen.

The standard requires manufacturers to label this type of receiver as 'NON-ISO'. To confirm the type, disconnect the DMX512 cable and meter resistance between Earth-Ground and the XLR pin 1. If the resistance is approximately 100R it is a Non-Isolated receiver.

Receiver – Grounded

Some manufactures produce DMX512 receivers that have the Signal-Common (pin 1) connected to Earth-Ground. The DMX512-A standard allows this, but recommends against it.

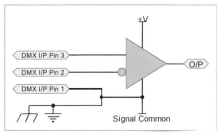

Grounded Receiver

The standard requires manufacturers to label this type of receiver with a triangular warning symbol containing an exclamation mark. To confirm the type, disconnect the DMX512 cable and meter resistance between Earth-Ground and the XLR pin 1. If the resistance is less than 10R it is a Grounded Receiver.

The only reason that DMX512-A allows this style of receiver is that one such company was part of the working group that developed DMX512-A. To put it bluntly, an impasse was reached and the only way forward was to allow this exception!

(Earth-)Grounded receivers are bad news for the following reason: In large systems the transmitter and receivers will be geographically distant from each other. They may even be powered by different sub-stations. If the DMX512 Signal-Common is connected to Earth-Ground at both ends, it is entirely possible that the screen of the DMX512 connector will provide a lower impedance path between the two sub-stations than the Earth itself. If this is the case, a massive current will flow through the screen of the cable and untold damage will occur.

When faced with using (Earth-)Grounded Receivers, always use an (output) isolated splitter.

Transceivers

A third variation on the theme exists for transceiver circuitry and is called 'Floating'. The significance of this topology is that it is a combined input – output topology. It is primarily designed for battery powered in-line processing equipment. Electrically, the notable point is that the voltage at the Signal-Common of this equipment is defined by the equipment to which it is connected. Any given product can only have one floating transceiver circuit as to have more would cause potentially damaging ground conflicts.

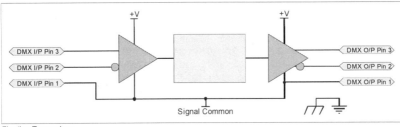

Floating Transceiver

Real World Circuits

In the previous section we discussed transmitter and receiver topologies; however the drawings I've used are intentionally simplified to identify the key differences. Let's now look at a real world circuit for an isolated receiver.

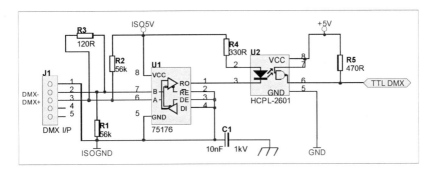

On the left we have the 5 pin XLR input connector to the receiver. On the right is the internal data signal 'TTL DMX' which will connect to the product's microprocessor.

The first point of note is that the receiver has two separate DC power supplies which are isolated from each other. The product's main power supply is labelled '+5V' and 'GND'. The second power supply is labelled 'ISO 5V' and ISO GND'. This power supply is only used to power the receiver's line receiver chip (U1). The 'ISO' power supply is most often generated from a device called a DC to DC converter. These devices convert one DC power voltage to another and importantly introduce electrical isolation.

The DMX512 signal arrives at the line receiver U1 at the pins marked 'A' and 'B'. These are the differential inputs to the line receiver. There are three additional resistors connected to these terminals. R3 is the DMX512 terminator. In reality R3 will only be connected if this is the last receiver on the line.

R1 & R2 are called 'pull apart' resistors. They are not required by the DMX512 standard but are implemented by many manufacturers. Their purpose is to keep pins 2 and 3 of the DMX512 connector in a known state when there is no signal present. These resistors are usually a minimum of 56KR and in some products much higher. The reason that they must be of a high value is that the effective resistance will reduce as more receivers are connected to the DMX512 cable. If a value of 56K is used in 32 receivers on one cable, the effective resistance will be 1.75KR.

The line receiver converted the balanced DMX512 into a single logic level signal. This signal appears on pin 1 of U1. This is referenced to the isolated power supply which in turn is referenced to the cable screen. The signal must be electrically isolated before it can be used by the product.

Isolation is achieved using a device called an opto-coupler. In theory it is possible to use a transformer but I do not know of any manufacturers who do this. An opto-coupler does exactly as the name suggests: it uses light to transfer the signal. The non-isolated logic signal arrives at pin 3 of U2 which is the cathode (negative terminal) of a light emitting diode (LED) inside the opto-coupler. The resistor R4 connects the other side of the LED to the isolated power supply and also limits the current that can flow through the LED.

When the DMX512 signal is at a logic zero (space) current flows through the LED and it illuminates. Conversely, when the DMX512 signal is a logic one (mark), no current flows and the LED is off.

Inside the opto-coupler, a tiny light guide directs the light from the LED to a photo diode. If the photo diode is illuminated, it switches on and current flows through resistor R5. The output at pin 6 of U2 is a logic low (0V). Conversely, when the photo diode is not illuminated it switches off and no current flows at the output (pin 6 of U2). The resistor pulls up the signal and the output is a logic 1 (5V). This output signal is now a direct copy of the DMX512 signal but is referenced to the product's internal power supply and isolated from the DMX512 cable.

The final component is C1. This is an RF (Radio Frequency) bypass capacitor. It s purpose is to filter high frequency noise from the cable screen into Earth-Ground of the receiver. DMX512 does not require this component but it is to be found on almost all receivers for the simple reason it is almost impossible to pass CE or FCC tests without it.

The drawing above is much closer to a real world circuit but it is still simplified for clarity. For example I have omitted decoupling capacitors and transient protection circuitry.

Common Errors

Having discussed at length the 'good' topologies, let's take a look at the 'bad' and the 'ugly'. The purpose in discussing these is simply that these do exist in the real world. Every now and then you will come across one of these products and the problems they cause can waste hours in fault finding. Knowing where the product designer messed up can really help!

Signal-Common resistance - transmitter

A common error to be found in numerous legacy products is the misplaced Signal-Common resistor. This situation was exasperated a few years back when the German DIN organisation issues a copy of the DMX512 standard that contained this error in a drawing, indicating it was good practise.

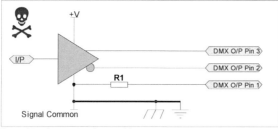

Transmitter - Incorrect resistor position

At first glance this looks very similar to the 'Ground Referenced Transmitter' circuit discussed above. Look carefully at the position of R1, it is between Signal-Common and Pin 1 of the XLR. This is very bad news as it injects a Common Mode Voltage onto the cable at the transmitter. The resistor should be in the connection between Signal-Common and Earth-Ground.

Signal-Common resistance - receiver

A similar design error can be seen in some receiver designs.

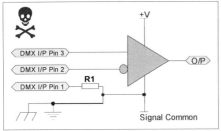

Receiver - Incorrect resistor position 1

At first glance this looks very similar to the 'Non-Isolated Receiver' circuit discussed above. It is not; look carefully at the position of R1, it is between Signal-Common and Pin 1 of the XLR. This is very bad news as it injects a Common Mode Voltage onto the cable at the receiver. The resistor should be in the connection between Signal-Common and Earth-Ground.

A variation of this error is shown below:

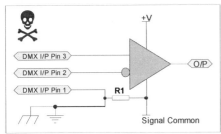

Receiver - Incorrect resistor position 2

This is even worse. Not only is the resistor in the wrong place, but this has now become a 'Grounded Receiver' because the cable screen is now connected direct to Earth-Ground!

Chapter 4 DMX512 Networks

In the previous chapter we discussed the physical layer of DMX512. Let's now connect this all together and see how it relates to DMX512 networks. As we have seen the DMX512-A standard provides us with a number of transmitter and receiver topologies. What happens as we interconnect them?

DMX512-A recommends Ground Referenced transmitters and Isolated Receivers. The reason is simply that this is the best technical solution and resolves all concerns over ground loops and common mode voltage faults. In reality, numerous topologies exist including those banned by DMX512.

The chart below gives an overview of the potential concerns when different topologies are connected. The abbreviations Tx and Rx are used for transmitter and receiver respectively in this chapter.

	Isolated Receiver	Non Isolated Receiver	Grounded Receiver
Ground Ref Transmitter	Best	OK	Problem
Isolated Transmitter	Caution	OK	Problem

Let's look at each combination in detail:

Ground Referenced Tx to Isolated Rx

This is the topology recommended by the DMX512-A standard. Looking at the drawing below, it is easy to see why.

The drawing shows a Ground Referenced Transmitter connected to two Isolated Receivers. The thick green lines represent the DMX512 cable from the transmitter to first receiver and then the DMX512 cable that loops out of receiver 1 into receiver 2.

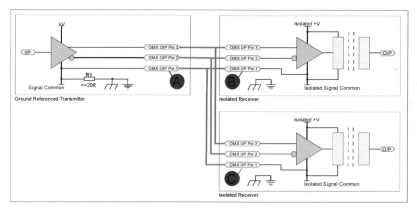

The transmitter is referenced to Earth-Ground by the resistance R1. This means that the voltage at position 'A' and therefore the DMX512 cable screen is referenced to Earth-Ground. The screen of the DMX512 cable connects positions 'A' and 'B' together. As there is no resistance to Earth-Ground in the first receiver, the voltage at position 'B' is free to follow the voltage at 'A' without causing current to flow in the screen.

The same is true of the loop connection to the second receiver. The result: 'B' and 'C' voltages follow the screen voltage set by 'A'. No screen current flows and there is no common mode voltage.

Conclusion: This is the best arrangement and no problems are to be expected.

Ground Referenced Tx to Non-Isolated Rx

This is a topology allowed by the DMX512-A standard and is probably the most widespread topology encountered in the real world.

The drawing shows a Ground Referenced Transmitter connected to two Non-Isolated Receivers. The thick green lines represent the DMX512 cable from the transmitter to first receiver and then the DMX512 cable that loops out of receiver 1 into receiver 2.

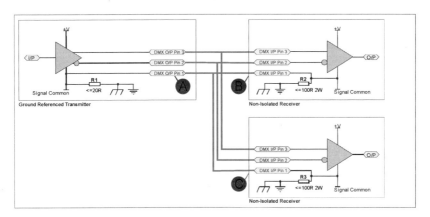

The transmitter is referenced to Earth-Ground by the resistance R1. This means that the voltage at position 'A' and therefore the DMX512 cable screen is referenced to Earth-Ground.

The screen of the DMX512 cable connects positions 'A' and 'B' together. Position 'B' is referenced to Earth-Ground of the receiver. If there is a difference between the Earth-Ground potential of transmitter and receiver, current will flow through the cable shield. This is not disastrous as resistances R1 and R2 will limit the current. However the current flow will develop a voltage across R2. The available common mode voltage range allowed by RS485 will be reduced by this voltage.

The same occurs in the loop through connection to the second receiver. If all three Earth-Ground potentials are different, three fault current flows will occur.

Conclusion: Normally there is no problem if all equipment is powered from the same distribution board. If it is not, or very long cables separate the equipment, consider using an isolated splitter.

Ground Referenced Tx to Grounded Rx

This is a topology that the DMX512-A standard strongly recommends against. Interestingly it is not the connection to the transmitter that causes the biggest problem; it is the receiver loop through connections.

The drawing shows a Ground Referenced Transmitter connected to two Grounded Receivers. The thick green lines represent the DMX512 cable from the transmitter to first receiver and then the DMX512 cable that loops out of receiver 1 into receiver 2.

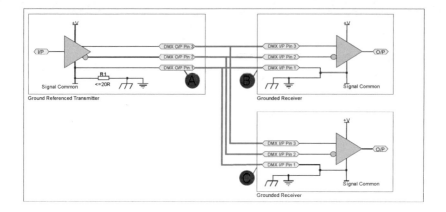

The transmitter is referenced to Earth-Ground by the resistance R1. This means that the voltage at position 'A' and therefore the DMX512 cable screen is referenced to Earth-Ground.

The screen of the DMX512 cable connects positions 'A' and 'B' together. Position 'B' is connected to Earth-Ground of the receiver. The DMX512-A standard allows R1 in the transmitter to be in the range 0R to 20R. If it is 0R then there is a direct connection to Earth-Ground. The screen of the DMX512 cable will then connect Earth-Ground of the transmitter to Earth-Ground of the first receiver. If there is a difference in these voltages, potentially destructive currents will flow in the screen. It is for this reason that I believe the DMX512-A standard to be incautious in allowing R1 to be zero and recommend designers use the value of 20R.

The situation is worse when looking at the looped receivers. Positions 'B' and 'C' are both connected directly to their respective Earth-Grounds. Keeping in mind that we may have 32 receivers rather than 2, the potential for damage is massive.

Conclusion: Avoid this topology at all costs. This is one instance where the use of output isolated splitters is the best solution.

Under no circumstances should the safety Earth-Ground of the receivers be disconnected in order to resolve the problem. This is an exceedingly dangerous practise.

Isolated Tx to Isolated Rx

This is the topology that is unlikely to present any electrical problems but can be prone to interference.

The drawing shows an Isolated Transmitter connected to two Isolated Receivers. The thick green lines represent the DMX512 cable from the transmitter to first receiver and then the DMX512 cable that loops out of receiver 1 into receiver 2.

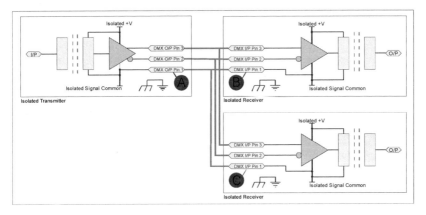

The transmitter and receivers have no reference or connection to Earth-Ground, so there is no potential for common mode voltages or screen currents. However, the screens of all cables are at an unknown potential. This actually means that the cable screens will act as an aerial, picking up local interference. The fact that the data wires are twisted pairs will limit the extent to which the interference becomes a real problem.

This topology can be a real problem in areas prone to lightning as the floating screen not only offers no protection, but actually acts as a transformer channelling voltage spikes into the electronics.

Conclusion: Use some caution. Many people assume that isolating both ends must be better because you get twice the protection. This is simply not true!

Isolated Tx to Non-Isolated Rx

This topology is allowed by the DMX512-A standard. The drawing shows an Isolated Transmitter connected to two Non-Isolated Receivers. The thick green lines represent the DMX512 cable from the transmitter to first receiver and then the DMX512 cable that loops out of receiver 1 into receiver 2.

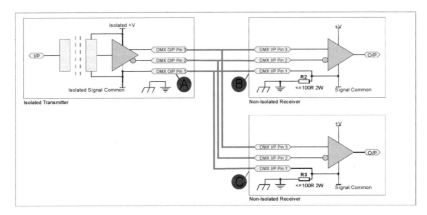

The transmitter has no reference to Earth-Ground, but receiver 1 is referenced to Earth-Ground by the resistance R2. This means that the voltage at position 'B' and therefore the DMX512 cable screen is referenced to Earth-Ground.

The screen of the DMX512 cable connects positions 'A' and 'B' together so the screen takes on the potential of 'B'. There is no potential for current to flow through the screen of the cable connecting the transmitter and first receiver.

The receivers are both referenced to Earth-Ground through R2 and R3. There is a potential for current flow but the magnitude is limited by the resistance.

Conclusion: Normally there is no problem if all equipment is powered from the same distribution board. If it is not, or very long cables separate the equipment, consider using an isolated splitter.

It is worth comparing this to the previous example of Ground Referenced Tx to Non-Isolated Rx. The additional expense of transmitter isolation has bought us very little.

Isolated Tx to Grounded Rx

The DMX512 standard recommends against the use of Grounded Receivers. However, when faced with using them, Isolated Transmitters can help.

The drawing shows an Isolated Transmitter connected to two Grounded Receivers. The thick green lines represent the DMX512 cable from the transmitter to first receiver and then the DMX512 cable that loops out of receiver 1 into receiver 2.

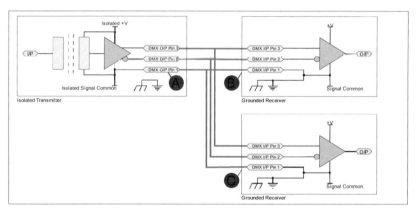

The transmitter is not referenced to Earth-Ground so there is no problem with common mode voltage between the transmitter and the first receiver.

The problem is with the looped receivers. Positions 'B' and 'C' are both connected directly to their respective Earth-Grounds. If the receivers are powered from different distribution boards, there may well be a significant fault current flow through the screen.

Conclusion: The use of an isolated transmitter only gives us a benefit in the first cable. This is one instance where the use of output isolated splitters is the best solution, but limit the number of receivers per splitter output to the minimum to avoid building up CMV between the looped receivers.

Splitters

Splitters are known by a range of different names including repeaters, buffers, line amps, distribution amplifiers and boosters. They all fundamentally perform the same functions which are:

•   Allow us to drive more than 32 receivers.

- Extend the 300m cable distance limit.
- Optionally insert isolation between different segments of the DMX512 network.

A splitter usually has one DMX512 input which is usually isolated. It then has any number of outputs which may or may not be isolated from each other. The significance of this statement will become clear as we look at some examples.

Driving more than 32 receivers

We have already discussed the fact that there is a maximum of 32 receivers per DMX cable. To drive more, we need multiple DMX512 cables. As we are not allowed to Y-Split the cable, we need a splitter. The diagram below shows a simple splitter configuration.

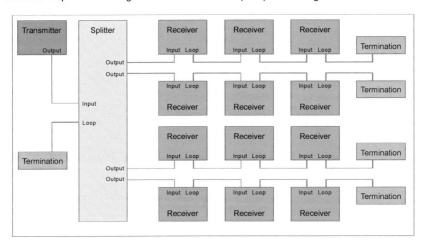

In this example we use a four output splitter. Each output of the splitter is able to drive up to 32 receivers over 300m of cable. Note that splitters usually have a loop through connection which if unused must also be terminated. Each output of the splitter must also be terminated. The drawing below shows a similar configuration which uses the splitter loop connection.

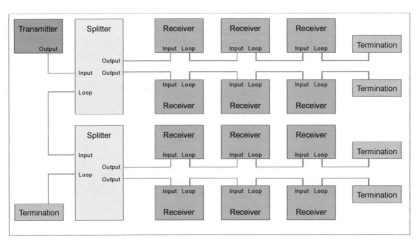

The Loop connection of the splitter can be treated in the same way as a receiver as is shown by the following drawing. Note that in this situation, the second splitter is a 'receiver' and counts as part of the total number of devices connected to the transmitter.

Splitter Loop Through

The Splitter Loop connection can be used to connect directly to the receivers as shown in the diagram below. Care should be taken in calculating the maximum number of receivers. In this example, the transmitter is driving four receivers as the splitter must be included in the calculation.

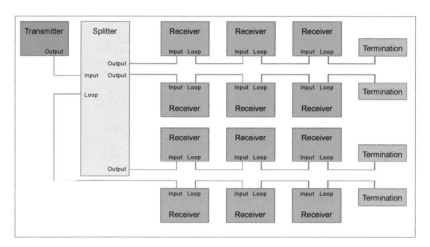

The above configuration is not as good as the previous examples because the bottom line of receivers is not optically isolated from the transmitter.

Extending Cable Distance.

Splitters can also be used to extend cable distance. When used in this way, splitters are often called boosters or repeaters.

The drawing below shows a simple configuration that can achieve a total cable distance of 900m using two splitters. It is important not to push this concept too far; as a rule of thumb, consider four cascaded splitters to be the maximum. The reason is that each splitter can introduce minor timing variations to the signal. These variations are compounded by each cascaded splitter.

In fact if a network design calls for many cascaded splitters, then there is probably a better way to achieve the same result. For example: convert to fibre optic which can provide many kilometres of transmission distance.

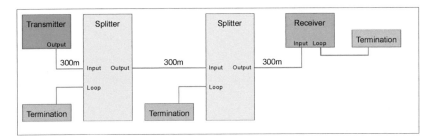

Splitter Isolation.

In the previous chapter we discussed the different transmitter – receiver Earth-Grounding topologies. Splitters provide us with a tool that allows us to keep different areas of power distribution isolated, avoid ground loops and ensure the network stays within common mode voltage limits.

There are two main types of isolation regime to be found in splitters:

- Isolated Receiver – Ground Referenced Transmitter
- Isolated Receiver – Isolated Transmitter

The former is by far the most common type of splitter. It is often simply called an 'Input Isolation Splitter'. The latter is usually called a 'Fully Isolated Splitter'. Fully Isolated Splitters are significantly more expensive than Input Isolated Splitters.

The majority of DMX512 networks can be implemented using Input Isolation Splitters. Fully Isolated Splitters are a more specialist tool. They are most useful when dealing with either very large networks or receivers that are referenced to Earth-Ground.

We have discussed in detail the reasons that we need isolation but the key question is 'How do we implement this in the real world?'

The key consideration is power distribution. Lighting control often involves switching significant amounts of electrical power. This in turn can lead to varying earth-neutral voltages which if not resolved will present common mode voltage problems. The decision on which type of splitter to use and where to place them depends upon the type of receiver input (isolated, non-isolated, ground referenced etc) in use.

When to use Input Isolated Splitters

Input Isolated Splitters are the general workhorse of DMX512 distribution. As a rule of thumb they are used with isolated and no-isolated receivers (but not with ground referenced). Consider the following drawing which shows a simple stage and control position layout.

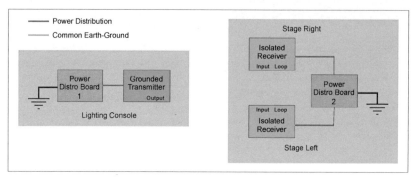

For the purposes of the example we are assuming that the two positions are powered from different distribution boards. This means there is a possibility that there will be common mode voltage differences between the two positions.

The drawing below adds the DMX512 cables, without using splitters.

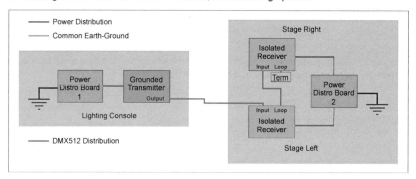

As the receivers are isolated, there is no need for an isolated splitter. The receivers are already providing isolation and protecting the transmitter from common mode voltages. It may be that a splitter is required for other reasons, such as if there are more than 32 receivers.

When adding splitters to this arrangement it is worth doing so in a manner that will be most useful in a fault condition. The drawing below shows an input isolated splitter added to the network. It is powered from the stage power (Distro Board 2). This provides a second level of protection in the event that the receiver isolation is compromised (perhaps by a DMX512 cable with the screen shorted to the shell). In that fault situation, an input isolated splitter powered from the lighting console end would provide no protection against common mode voltages.

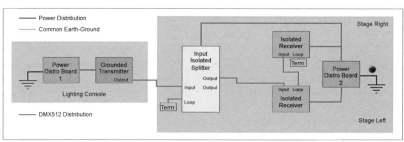

The drawing below shows the same topology but with non-isolated receivers.

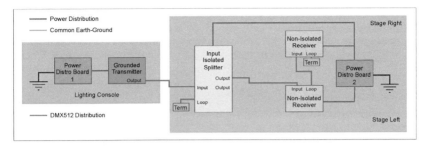

In this situation the splitter is providing the first line of isolation and it is very important that the power fed to the splitter is from the stage. This ensures that the Earth-Ground to which the splitter outputs are referenced and the Earth-Ground to which the receivers' non-isolated inputs are referenced are identical.

When to use Fully Isolated Splitters

Consider the following drawing: at this stage we are simply looking at power distribution. The drawing shows three areas from a large stadium gig. The lighting tower, the stage and a truss full of audience blinders rigged at the rear of the stadium. Each of these areas takes a power feed from a different distribution board.

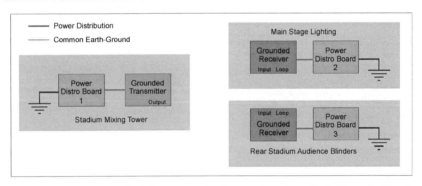

For the sake of this example, let's assume that the receivers have Earth-Grounded inputs. Whilst this would be unusual, it does mimic a situation where the receivers are isolated but a cable fault has led to a connection between Signal-Common and Earth-Ground. Clearly this is an artificially worst case scenario, but it serves to highlight the pitfalls.

In the drawing below, we simply connect these areas together without splitters.

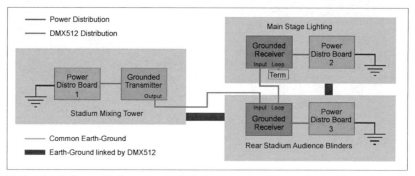

This is potentially very bad news – why? We have made a connection, via the screen of the DMX512 cable, between the Earth-Grounds in each position (shown by the red bars). In theory this should not matter. All three power distribution boards are earthed, so our DMX512 cable screens are simply making parallel connections. The reality is that there will almost certainly be differences between the Earth-Ground potential at each board, particularly once the show starts. A difference in potential means that current will flow. If the DMX512 cable presents a lower impedance path, the current will flow through the screen with potentially disastrous results.

Now let us add a splitter. We will use an Input Isolated Splitter as this is the most common type. The drawing below shows the common sense place to put the splitter:

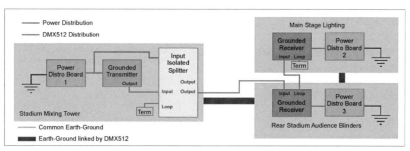

In fact, we have achieved very little. The splitter is powered from the same power source as the transmitter or lighting console. Most Input Isolation Splitters have Earth-Ground referenced outputs. This means that we still have cable screens linking Earth-Ground points between three different power distribution boards. In reality, the splitter will most likely have a resistance between Earth-Ground and its outputs, so there is benefit. However there is a better method.

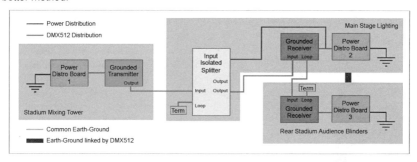

The drawing above is subtly different: The splitter is now powered from 'Distro Board 2'. The outputs of the splitter are now referenced to the same Earth-Ground as the 'Main Stage Lighting. The grey shaded areas show equipment on the same power distribution. Note that one of the red blocks has gone. The splitter is now providing some useful isolation. However we still have the DMX512 loop cable bridging Earth-Ground between 'Distro Board 2' and 'Distro Board 3'.

This is one situation where a fully isolated splitter is a benefit. The drawing below shows the layout:

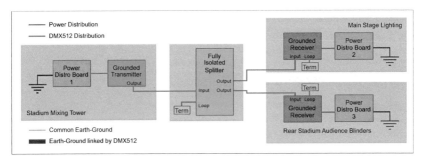

Note that the power source of the splitter is not shown on this drawing. The reason is that it does not matter; the DMX512 inputs and outputs are fully isolated from each other and Earth-Ground. There is no longer any secondary connection between Earth-Ground in different areas.

In the description above I have used the example of a large stadium gig. The concept is also very relevant to large installations.

Splitter Functionality

In the previous section we discussed the most important aspect of splitters – isolation. It is, however, also important to understand what the splitter is doing internally. There are three key types of Splitter:

- Buffering.
- Regenerative.
- Cleaner.

Buffering Splitters

A Buffering Splitter is one that simply transfers a direct copy of the input DMX512 to the output(s). The majority of splitters on the market are of this type.

The Buffering Splitter is usually a purely electronic design. It provides the benefit of relatively low cost and a negligible insertion delay. On the down side: they have no ability to correct any received errors.

Insertion delay is critical in fast response DMX512 networks such as video streaming. The term describes the extent to which the product delays the DMX512 signal. As Buffering Splitters are electronic rather than software based, the insertion delay is usually just a few nanoseconds.

Regenerative Splitters

Regenerative Splitters are characterised by retransmitting the DMX512 data. This implies that the product uses software to receive a DMX512 frame and then re-transmit. The major benefit of this approach is that the splitter can error check and even corrects data errors. The down side is that the insertion delay will be relatively large, normally an entire DMX512 frame.

Cleaners & Fixers

Arguably Cleaners & Fixers are a special case of Regenerative Splitter. However, I have treated them as a separate category as they offer significant benefits.

The term 'Clean' is used in different ways by different manufactures. Some use it to mean fix any 'true' errors. Others also remove perfectly valid data such as Alternative Start Codes. This allows the product to be used to both 'fix' bad data and also solve compatibility problems with receivers that cannot handle more advanced forms of DMX512 and RDM.

Some standard splitters now provide an additional output with this functionality. The output may be labelled 'Safe', 'Clean' or 'Fixed' depending upon the manufacturer.

Splitter Marking

The DMX512-A standard has improved on the previously confused situation by defining labels to define the grounding of inputs and outputs. Unfortunately the improvements stopped at that point and there remains no standardised method of describing splitter functionality and isolation.

Some years ago, Artistic Licence designed a set of symbols to address this problem. The symbols are in the public domain and the 'art-work' is available to any manufacturer that wishes to use them.

Input: Isolated
Output: Ground Referenced with common grounds
Number of outputs: 5
RDM Capable: Yes

Input: Isolated
Output: Ground Referenced with common grounds
Number of outputs: 5
RDM Capable: No

Input: Isolated
Output: Independently isolated
Number of outputs: 5
RDM Capable: No

Input: Isolated
Output: Independently isolated
Number of outputs: 5
RDM Capable: Yes

Input: Non-Isolated
Output: Ground Referenced with common grounds
Number of outputs: 5
RDM Capable: No

Input: Non-Isolated
Output: Ground Referenced with common grounds
Number of outputs: 5
RDM Capable: Yes

Input: Isolated
Output: Ground Referenced with common grounds
Number of outputs: Multiple
RDM Capable: Yes

Input: Isolated
Output: Independently isolated
Number of outputs: Multiple
RDM Capable: Yes

Splitter Termination

Termination of splitter outputs follows exactly the same rules as a DMX512 transmitter: the end of line must be terminated. It is worth noting that there is no purpose in terminating the unused outputs of a splitter.

Real World Splitters

The table below shows a feature matrix for a range of popular splitters.

Manu	Product	Isolated Input	Number Outputs	Individually Isolated Outputs	Connectors	RDM	Features	Format
Artistic Licence	Rack-Split RDM	YES	9	NO	XLR5	YES	HES Safe output	1U 19"
Artistic Licence	Iso-Split RDM	YES	10	YES	Ethercon-RJ45/XLR5	YES	HES	1U 19"
Artistic Licence	DMX-Split RDM	YES	5	NO	XLR5	YES	HES	Truss / Desk
Artistic Licence	DMX-Fix	YES	5	NO	XLR5	NO	Fix & Clean	Truss / Desk
Artistic Licence	Rail-Split RDM	YES	6	NO	Screw Terminal	YES	HES	Din-Rail
Doug Fleenor	DMX-OPTO5	YES	1	N/A	XLR5	NO		XLR
Doug Fleenor	125EE	YES	5	YES	XLR5	NO		Boxed
Doug Fleenor	BIDI8	YES	8	YES	XLR5	YES		1U 19"
Goddard Design	Hub 5	YES	5	1 output	XLR5	YES	Safe output	1U 19"
Goddard Design	FD CC05	YES	5	NO	XLR5	NO		1U 19"

HES = Supports High End Systems talk back protocol

Artistic Licence DMX-Split RDM

DMX-Split RDM is an RDM capable splitter with input isolation. Five independent outputs are provided.
In addition to supporting both RDM Draft and RDM Standard, the product also supports the High End Talkback protocol.

The product is powered from 9-24VDC using a 4 pin XLR. This is designed to allow Scroller power supplies to be used to power the splitter.

The product has an optional truss mounting adapter.

Artistic Licence Rail-Split RDM

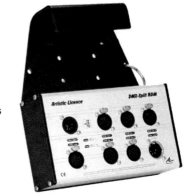

Rail-Split RDM is an RDM capable splitter with input isolation. Six independent outputs are provided.
The product supports RDM Draft, RDM Standard and the High End Talkback protocol.

All connections are via screw terminals and the product is designed for permanent installation.

Artistic Licence Rack-Split RDM

Rack-Split RDM is an RDM capable splitter with input isolation. It provides Eight independent outputs in a 19 inch rack form factor. The product supports RDM Draft, RDM Standard and the High End Talkback protocol.

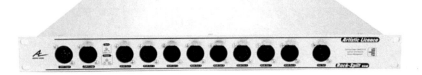

A ninth 'Safe' output is provided. This output strips all non-zero start code packets from the data stream as an aid to interfacing with non-compliant products.

The product is mains powered with an auto-sensing power input.

Artistic Licence Iso-Split RDM

Iso-Split RDM is an RDM capable splitter with both input isolation and output isolation. Ten independent outputs are provided. In addition to supporting both RDM Draft and RDM Standard, the product also supports the High End Talkback protocol.

The product is mains powered with an auto-sensing power input.

Doug Fleenor Design DMXOPTO-5

The DMXOPTO-5 is an inline DMX512 opto-isolator that is built into an XLR connector. A mains adapter (US only) is hardwired to the product.

Doug Fleenor Design BIDI8

The BIDI8 is an RDM capable splitter with both input isolation and output isolation. Eight independent outputs are provided. The product supports RDM plus the High End Talkback protocol and the Martin protocol.

The product is mains powered with an auto-sensing power input.

Goddard Design Hub5

The Hub5 is an RDM capable splitter with input isolation. Five outputs are provided. The product offers the option of setting any output to 'Clean' mode, filtering out non-zero start codes. Additionally these outputs can be set to continue to retransmit last data in the event of an input failure.

The product is mains powered with switch selected voltage range.

Artistic Licence DMX-Fix

DMX-Fix provides an isolated input with five independent outputs. The outputs are a 'cleaned' version of the input.

DMX-Fix provides the following functionality:

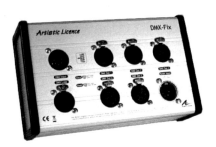

1. Outputs continuous DMX512 with fixed timings of:
    *   Break 250uS
    *   MaB 30uS
    *   MbB 30uS
    *   Break to Break 30mS
    *   Data Slot Count 512
2. Accepts Receive parameters of:
    *   Break in the range 56uS to 1000uS
    *   MaB in the range 5uS to 1000uS
    *   MbB in the range 0uS to 1000uS
    *   Slot Count of 0-513
    *   Packet time of 23mS to 1000mS
    *   Accepts 1 or 2 stop bits
3. Filters out consecutive Breaks
4. Filters out all non zero start codes.

Chapter 5 Fault Finding & Common Faults

It's all going horribly wrong!

This chapter is intended to help you fault find when it starts hitting the fan! If you are reading this, you think there is something wrong with the DMX but don't know what.

Remember three things:

1. Don't panic yet
2. Be logical about fault finding
3. Look for simple and dumb problems first

Divide & Conquer

Is the same problem happening everywhere? If you designed the DMX distribution system well, you will have a small number of devices on each cable and splitters driving different zones of DMX. If all your zones driven from one splitter have a common problem then the fault is upstream (upstream means on the controller side) of that point.

Free Tools

Remember to use the free tools that manufacturers designed into the products. Many splitters have data activity lights. Check that the data lights are showing similar status on each splitter. It is often possible to locate a fault by simply studying the indicators on splitters.

Moving Lights and dimmers often have data indicators that can provide a wealth of information. For example, let us say you have 10 lamps on a bar with one DMX cable looping through them all. Look up for the data good indicators. If the indicators change state between two lamps, it points to a dead link cable.

Simple Tools

A very simple tester can be built into a male XLR connector. It uses a bi-colour LED which can be pushed through the connector's strain relief. The drawing below shows the circuit:

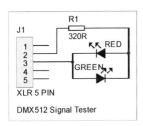

It can be seen that when pin 3 is positive relative to pin 2, the green LED will illuminate. Conversely, the red LED will illuminate when pin 2 is positive relative to pin 3.

This simple tester can provide a wealth of information. It can be connected directly to the output of a lighting console and then gradually moved along the network to identify the position of a fault:

Colour	Analysis
Not illuminated	Either console disconnected or a broken data wire.
Constant Green	Line is marking, so console has active drivers but no data is being sent.

Colour	Analysis
Constant Red	Either a continuous Break is being transmitted, or more likely pins 2 & 3 are swapped. If previous network connection was showing Constant Green then it is definitely swapped pins.
Flickering	This represents data being transmitted – the constant switching from red to green produces orange.
Flickering Green	If all channels on console are set to full, this indicates good data. If all channels are set to zero, check for a pins 2 & 3 miswire.
Flickering Red	If all channels on console are set to zero, this indicates good data. If all channels are set to full, check for a pins 2 & 3 miswire.

Terminate

Make sure that all the end of run points has a DMX terminator. It is worth coding terminators in a bright colour such as red. This allows you to do a visual check that all the terminators are in place, from the ground.

Cables

In my experience, most DMX problems are eventually traced to a bad cable. Look for the first place that the problem occurs and test the cables at that point. Open the connectors and visually inspect the solder quality. A cold solder joint on a screen can cause hard to trace problems.

Symmetry

Look for symmetry in a fault and think laterally.

Does it work perfectly all day and then flicker madly for a few minutes at a particular time? It could be power interference when the street lights switch on or catering powers up the ovens!

Is the fault cyclic? If so, it could be a design problem with the fixture. I have recently seen a number of instances where a moving light judders every 3 seconds or so. It turned out that the (reputable) manufacturer had neglected to test that the DMX start code was zero before using the data. We temporarily solved the problem by disabling the RDM data.

Still not working

Time to bring out you DMX tester. If you are doing this level of fault finding, you should really have a DMX tester such as a 'Micro-Scope' or 'Lil'DMXter' in your tool kit.

Each DMX tester has different features, but the way in which you use them is very similar. A tester will fundamentally do three things:

- Transmit
- Receive
- Cable and network test.

How you use the tester will depend upon where you suspect (or guess) the fault may lie. Below are some pointers. I'm assuming you are tracking down a problem with a flickering rig of lights. That said, the methodology is good whatever type of fault you are tracking:

Use the tester in Transmit mode and plug it in instead of the console. If you can control the lamps without flicker, you know the console has a problem.

Use the tester in Receive mode at the input to the first splitter. If you see data errors on the tester, suspect the main cable. Pull out the cable and test it.

Use the tester in receive mode on an output of the splitter. If that shows data errors when the input was good, you should suspect the splitter. Double check other outputs to see that you get the same result. If you do suspect the splitter, confirm it by connecting the input cable to one of the output cables.

That takes the splitter out of circuit for one cable. If the lights on that cable start behaving then you have confirmed the splitter is faulty. If not, look again!

Use the Network Test facility on your tester. To do this, you need to plug a cable into your (preferably farthest) splitter and run it back to the console position. The tester replaces the console and transmits network test packets. The tester then receives data from the splitter and compares the two.

If the network test fails, you know the problem is somewhere between those two cable ends. Now narrow the search, plug one end into a position that is slightly nearer to the console.

Keep doing it until you find the faulty cable of equipment.

Test Equipment

As you would expect, commercially available test equipment for DMX512 equipment comes in a wide range of shapes and sizes. Below is a list of the most important kit. Note that this is specifically for DMX512 and that RDM test equipment is covered in Part 2.

Artistic Licence Line-Light

The Line-Light is a very simple tester built into an XLR connector. It monitors the two data pins (2 & 3) and shows activity on a bi-colour LED. See previous page for a circuit diagram to build your own. It differs from the 'Line Tester' below in that it only makes connection to pins 2 & 3.

it

Doug Fleenor Design Line Tester

The Line-Tester is another tester built into an XLR connector. It differs from the Line-Light above in that it monitors the state of the data lines relative to Signal-Common.

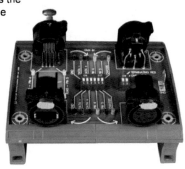

Artistic Licence DMX-Break

DMX-Break is an adapter that makes it easy to access the pins of the DMX512 cable. It also allows each pin to be individually isolated to aid testing.

Both 5 pin XLR and Ethercon RJ45 are used for input and output so it can also be used as a connector adapter.

Finally it has a switch to terminate the input and a simple LED data test (identical to Line-Light) that can be switched into the data path.

Artistic Licence Micro-Scope 3a

The Micro-Scope 3a is a feature rich DMX512 tester. It
is small and battery powered making it useful for site
and installation work. Key features are:

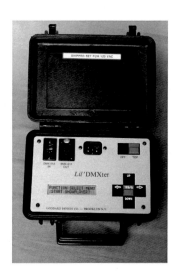

- Receive and display DMX512 in
  numerous formats including
  decimal, hexadecimal,
  percent, bar-graph and binary.
- Receive and display SIPs,
  Text and any start code data.
- Display all receive timing
  parameters.
- Analyse received checksums.
- Snapshot received data to
  memories.
- Flicker-Finder allows slots with flicker to
  be identified.
- Transmit data in both static and dynamic modes.
- Playback memories individually and in variable rate sequence.
- Configurable lamp libraries allow moving lamps to be tested easily.
- Single and double ended cable test.
- Network test allows both cables and splitters to be tested.
- Auto-backup mode that plays back a memory in the event of DMX512 loss.
- MIDI receive and display.
- Scope trigger output.
- Optional PC software allows configuration and programming of lamp library.

Goddard Design Lil'DMXter

The DMXter is a full featured DMX512 tester. It is battery
powered but significantly larger than Micro-Scope
making it more suited to the workshop environment. A
key benefit of this product is the ability to vary transmit
timing parameters. Key features are:

- Receive and display DMX512 levels in
  decimal, hexadecimal and percent.
- Display all receive timing parameters.
- Snapshot received data to memory.
- Transmit data with either single channel or all
  channel control.
- Transmit consecutive channels with autofade.
- Vary all transmit timing parameters including
  setting illegal values.
- Double ended cable test.
- Optional module for auto-backup (ShowSaver).
- Scope trigger output.

Artistic Licence DMX-Workshop

DMX-Workshop is a software package that is available free of charge from Artistic Licence. It operates with any Art-Net compliant DMX512 converter such as Net-Lynx or Data-Lynx and provides a wealth of test facilities for both transmitting and receiving DMX512.

Key features include:

- Transmit dynamic or static data.
- Replay recorded test memories.
- Receive and display data in numerous formats.
- Sophisticated flicker-finder identifies any change in slot level and logs information with a date and time stamp. This feature is incredibly useful when tracking down occasional data errors in an installation. DMX-Workshop can be left in place and log any errors.

Chapter 6 DMX512-A

DMX512-A is the colloquial name for a recent standard called ANSI E1.11. (American National Standard).

The development of DMX512-A was managed by ESTA. The group volunteers that did the bulk of the development work, the DMX512 Task group, includes:

Mitch Hefter (Chair / Rosco), Wayne Howell (Artistic Licence), Tim Bachman (Leviton), Scott Blair (HES), Bob Goddard (Goddard Design), Doug Fleenor (Doug Fleenor Design), Ted Paget (Jones & Philips), Peter Willis (Howard Eaton). This list is not exhaustive and many others have been involved in the work.

The advent of DMX512-A ushered in a host of new features. Some are incredibly useful whilst others are best described as esoteric! This section discusses these new features, ordered by my view on their importance.

Possibly the most important fact about DMX512-A is that it has been designed to be backwards compatible with earlier versions of DMX512. That means DMX512-A equipment should work seamlessly with DMX512(1990) equipment. That statement does of course assume that the products were designed in accordance with the standard; which sadly is not always the case.

Safety

The DMX512-A specifically states that the standard is not suitable for use with dangerous equipment such as stage machinery and pyrotechnics.

Protection

The DMX512 (1990) standard simply referenced the EIA-485 (colloquially known as RS485) standard for all electrical parameters. EIA-485 only defines protection against transients (such as voltage spikes) and not continuous fault conditions.

DMX512-A attempts to address this limitation by defining preferred grounding regimes for the cable screen and also defining the requirements for higher levels of protection.

Earthing

The DMX512 (1990) standard did not address the relationship between the XLR pin 1 and mains earth (Earth-Ground in DMX-Speak) or chassis. This led to numerous incompatibilities between manufacturers.

The DMX512-A standard addresses this by defining the grounding arrangements for transmitters and receivers that are preferred. We discuss this in detail in Chapter 3.

Isolation

DMX512(1990) did not address electrical isolation, also called optical or galvanic isolation. DMX512-A defines and recommends isolation but doesn't mandate optical isolation. However, it does define the requirements for isolated equipment. It also suggests that the DMX512 receiver should be isolated, whilst the transmitter is grounded. Again, we discuss this in detail in Chapter 3.

RDM and Enhanced Functionality

DMX512-A lays the foundations for Remote Device Management which is discussed in detail in Part 2.

Error Checking

The DMX512 (1990) standard provided no reliable method for error checking the data. As DMX512 packets are transmitted continuously and relatively quickly this was never perceived as a problem. In the unlikely event of some data corruption, a new packet appears and the error disappears.

In a simple DMX512 system that only transmits zero start code data and refreshes continuously, this remains largely true. However modern systems make use of 'delta' transmission algorithms. This involves only sending a packet when its contents have changed. In this system data corruption can be much more visible.

DMX512-A offers a mechanism for transmitting checksums to prove data integrity. The checksums are part of the SIP packets discussed below. Interestingly there has been little interest from manufacturers in supporting this. Perhaps the fact that a well designed DMX512 distribution system is very robust goes some way to explain this! None-the-less, the facility is now available in the standard.

Manufacturer ID

The DMX512-A adds the concept of Manufacturer ID codes. These are 16 bit numbers that are registered via ESTA. (See Appendix C).

Start Codes

The DMX512-A standard defines ESTA as the body responsible for allocating both Alternative Start Codes (ASC) and Manufacturer ID's (See Appendix A-C).

Connectors

The DMX512-A reaffirmed that the 5 pin XLR was the standard connector and that the 3 pin XLR must not be used. It also clarifies the fact that the spare pins 4 and 5 may only be used for EIA-485 data and cannot be used for power.

BASES for beginners

Computer based numbers are often represented in hexadecimal. Hexadecimal means Base 16, or to put it another way, there are 16 digits in the number sequence.

Humans use Base 10 most of the time, presumably because we have ten fingers and thumbs. In Base 10 there are 10 digits 0 to 9. When counting, upon reaching 9 we move to 10. The number 10 actually means one ten and zero units. I do appreciate that this is obvious!

Base 16 uses 16 digits. 0 to 9 and A, B, C, D, E, F. Counting is analogous to Base 10. Upon reaching 9, continue through A, B, C, D, E and F. From F, we move to 10. In Base 16, 10 means one 16 and zero units.

Base 16 of Hexadecimal is used widely for computer based numbers because it is simple to convert to and from binary. Each digit in Hexadecimal represents 4 bits in binary.

The following table shows the relationship:

Decimal			Hexadecimal		Binary							
100	10	1	16	1	128	64	32	16	8	4	2	1
0	0	1	0	1	0	0	0	0	0	0	0	1
0	0	2	0	2	0	0	0	0	0	0	1	0
0	0	3	0	3	0	0	0	0	0	0	1	1
0	0	4	0	4	0	0	0	0	0	1	0	0
0	0	5	0	5	0	0	0	0	0	1	0	1
0	0	6	0	6	0	0	0	0	0	1	1	0
0	0	7	0	7	0	0	0	0	0	1	1	1
0	0	8	0	8	0	0	0	0	1	0	0	0
0	0	9	0	9	0	0	0	0	1	0	0	1
0	1	0	0	A	0	0	0	0	1	0	1	0
0	1	1	0	B	0	0	0	0	1	0	1	1
0	1	2	0	C	0	0	0	0	1	1	0	0
0	1	3	0	D	0	0	0	0	1	1	0	1
0	1	4	0	E	0	0	0	0	1	1	1	0
0	1	5	0	F	0	0	0	0	1	1	1	1
0	1	6	1	0	0	0	0	1	0	0	0	0

Network Test Packet.

Start Code 0x55 (85)

You can look upon this as an advanced 'cable tester'. The big benefit is that it can test the entire data distribution path, including splitters. Here is how it works:

If data errors are going to occur, they are most likely to be when you are sending DMX512 at the maximum data rate and with the largest number of signal transitions on the wire. What do we mean by that?

Keep in mind that DMX512 has a very wide range of allowed timing. A console transmitting the maximum 512 channels can send a frame of DMX every 23mS; the fastest rate. At the other end of the spectrum, a console sending 24 channels may choose to update once every second (this would not be very useful but it is legal DMX)! There is a huge difference between these two situations regarding the number of signal transitions per second. The more signal transitions, the more likely it is that a potential fault will become visible. The drawing below illustrates the difference.

The refresh rate of the DMX is only half of the story. The actual data sent also has an impact on the amount of signal transitions seen on the wire. Consider three examples where we send all 512 channels at the same level. Levels of zero and full (0 and 255) cause few transitions on the wire. Yet sending all levels as 85 produces the maximum possible number of transitions. The reason is that the number 85 is expressed in binary as 01010101. Every consecutive bit changes state, which produces the maximum number of transitions on the wire. The diagram below illustrates this:

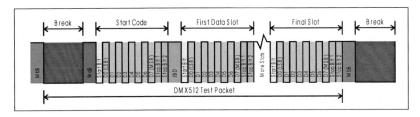

Why does the number of transitions matter?

The more transitions per second, the harder you are making the electronic work. It follows that if a fault is likely to occur you will see it more quickly.

Many if not most data distribution faults are caused by capacitive effects. These can range from the worst case of someone using Mic cable, to a dodgy solder joint. Capacitive faults become more of a problem as the frequency of the signal increases.

The Network Test Packet (NTP) is a DMX frame that uses Alternative Start Code (ASC) number 85. In addition, it is defined as containing all 512 channels set to level 85.

DMX512 testers such as Micro-Scope and DMXter can generate and analyse the NTP. This means that you can inject NTP into the cable at the console position and then analyse them at each possible outlet position or splitter output.

The result is a very high level of confidence that your cables, connectors and splitters are all working correctly.

System Information Packet.

Start Code 0xCF (207)

The System Information Packet or SIP is a new feature aimed at large installations. SIPs are transmitted at low frequency, by the lighting console, interleaved with normal lighting data. The SIP contains information about the console such as software revision, but also provides information such as the number of times the DMX signal has been processed. This could be passing through a merger or patching system. The SIP data can then be monitored at any point in the distribution chain.

The table below shows the structure of the SIP.

Slot	Name	Description
1	Byte Counter	This field represents the number of bytes within the SIP (SIPs are variable length). Valid values are in the range 24 to 255.
2	Control Bit Field	The control bit field contains flags that show whether the SIP contains checksum information. Field values are as follows:<table><tr><td>Bit</td><td>Description</td></tr><tr><td>7</td><td>Reserved and zeroed</td></tr><tr><td>6</td><td>Reserved and zeroed</td></tr><tr><td>5</td><td>Reserved and zeroed</td></tr><tr><td>4</td><td>Reserved and zeroed</td></tr><tr><td>3</td><td>Reserved and zeroed</td></tr><tr><td>2</td><td>Reserved and zeroed</td></tr><tr><td>1</td><td>Set to indicate that previous packet was an ASC.</td></tr><tr><td>0</td><td>Set to indicate that the receiver should await packet checksum information prior to using zero start code information.</td></tr></table>
3	MSB16 Checksum	The most significant byte of the 16 bit additive checksum of the previous packet. The checksum is calculated by adding together all 513 slot values in the previous packet (i.e. include the start code).
4	LSB16 Checksum	The least significant byte of the 16 bit additive checksum of the previous packet.
5	SIP Sequence Number	This field contains an 8 bit counter that increments for each SIP packet. The purpose of the field is to allow equipment to check that SIP's are arriving in sequence without loss of data.
6	DMX512 Universe Number	This field contains the number of the original universe output of the lighting console. In installations where the lighting console outputs a large number of universes, this field provides a simple method to identify cables in the patch bay. The valid range is 1 to 255. A value of zero indicates that the field is unused.
7	DMX512 Processing Level	All consoles and originating devices send this field as zero. Any inline processing devices such as merges and Ethernet transcoders can increment this value when the SIP is regenerated. This provides an indication of the number of times that the data has been post processed. This field is useful in very large installations where the data may have been processed several times. This field is analogous to an Ethernet 'Hop' count.
8	Software Version	This is the software version of the device that generated the SIP. The valid range is 1 to 255. A value of zero indicates that the field is unused.
9/10	Packet Length	This field shows the number of data slots transmitted in standard zero start code frames. The value is 16 bit and is displayed in hexadecimal. The values are shown below:<table><tr><td>Value</td><td>Meaning</td></tr><tr><td>0x0000</td><td>The packet length has not been declared.</td></tr><tr><td>0x0001– 0x0200</td><td>Fixed length packet in the range 1 to 512</td></tr><tr><td>0x0201- 0x7fff</td><td>Unused values</td></tr><tr><td>0x8000</td><td>The packet length is variable.</td></tr><tr><td>0x8001- 0x8200</td><td>The packet length is variable and the last packet was of a length in the range 1 to 512. (subtract 0x8000).</td></tr><tr><td>0x8201-0xffff</td><td>Unused values</td></tr></table>

Slot	Name	Description
11/ 12	Number of Interval Packets	This field shows the number of packets transmitted by the originating device since the last SIP. This number excludes the two SIP packets (at the start and end) but includes all other packets irrelevant of the start code. If the count reaches 0xffff it locks at that value and does not roll over to zero.
13/ 14	Originator's Manufacturer ID	This is a 16 bit manufacturer identification number. It is always the number assigned by the device that originally generated the DMX and is not altered by any post processing devices. A value of 0x0000 indicates that the manufacturer does not have a code allocated. A value of 0xffff is a temporary code indicating that the manufacturer has applied for a number. Where possible the number is assigned as two ASCII characters that represent the company initials.
15/ 16	2nd Device ID	The second device to process the DMX (which is the first to post-process) inserts it's manufacturer ID in this field.
17/ 18	3rd Device ID	The third device to process the DMX inserts it's manufacturer ID in this field.
19/ 20	4th Device ID	The fourth device to process the DMX inserts it's manufacturer ID in this field.
21/ 22	5th Device ID	The fifth device to process the DMX inserts it's manufacturer ID in this field. Any further post processing is not logged in the SIP
23	Spare	Sent as zero
24	SIP Checksum	The SIP checksum is calculated by adding the start code to the first 23 data slots of SIP data.

Text Packet

Start Code 0x17 (23)

Another new feature is the Text packet. This allows text information to be sent via the DMX512 signal. The key benefit is that 'black box' products that do not contain a screen are able to display text information such as operating status and software revision numbers.

The Text Packet was originally defined by Artistic Licence using a registered Alternative Start Code (ASC). The ASC has now been handed back to ESTA such that Text Packets can form part of the standard.

The table below shows the structure of the Text Packet.

Slot	Name	Description
1	Page Number	This field defines the page number of the text packet being sent. The value is in the range 0-255. Page number has no intrinsic meaning and is usually implemented as zero.
2	Characters per Line	This field indicates the number of characters per line that the transmitting device used for formatting the text. A value of zero indicates that the text is free form and unformatted.
3- 512	Data	Text data formatted in ASCII characters. The text is null terminated which means that a zero value must follow the last valid character. A total of 509 characters can be encoded within a single text packet.

Manufacturer Specific Packet.

Start Code 0x91 (145)

During development of DMX512-A it became clear there was a real risk that the supply of unused Alternative Start Codes (ASC) could simply run out. It was therefore decided that no more ASCs would be allocated to manufacturers and a new scheme would be used. The new scheme simply involves transmitting the Manufacturer ID in the first two slots. The remaining 500 slots contain the manufacturer specific data.

The table below shows the structure of the Manufacturer Specific Packet.

Slot	Name	Description
1	MAN ID MSB	This field contains the most significant byte of the Manufacturer ID.
2	MAN ID LSB	This field contains the least significant byte of the Manufacturer ID.
3-512	Data	Manufacturer specific data of up to 500 bytes length.

Prototyping Packets.

Start Codes 0xf0-0xf7 (240-247)

This range of start codes is reserved for manufacturers to use whilst testing and prototyping new products. Note that the start code 0xf0 was used for development of RDM. Generally this start code should be avoided as numerous products support Draft RDM using this start code.

Chapter 7 Conversion & Specialist Products

In this chapter we look at some of the products that are available for converting DMX512 to and from other interfaces and protocols.

Protocol Converters

A Protocol Converter is as the name suggests a device which converts from one protocol to another. The number of companies manufacturing this style of product has gradually reduced as demand has dropped.

Artistic Licence: Protocol-Converter

The Protocol-Converter is a rack mount unit which can convert and merge two separate input streams and then provide an output in yet another protocol. Supported protocols include: DMX512, DMX512(1990), DMX512-A, CMX (Colortran), S20 (ADB), Avab, AMX192, D54 (Strand).

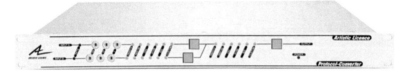

Pathway Connectivity: Ultimate DMX512 Converter

The Ultimate DMX512 Converter is a rack mount unit which can convert DMX512, DMX512(1990), DMX512-A, AMX192, K96 & K100 (Kliegl), CMX & D192 (Colortran), D54 (Strand), Micro-Plex 1 & 2 and EC Mux.

Digital to Analogue

A Digital to Analogue converter is also often called a Decoders or a Demux. The purpose of the product type is to convert DMX512 into analogue control voltage. Numerous manufacturers provide such products in a wide range of different form factors.

Artistic Licence: Rail-Demux

The Rail-Demux converts 16 consecutive channels to 0-10V analogue outputs. The outputs can also be configured to provide the 0-370uA current loop output used to control some European dimmers.

Rail-Demux is housed in a Din-Rail case with all connections made via screw terminals. RDM is used to set the product's Start Address.

Doug Fleenor Design: DMX24ANL

The DMX24ANL converts DMX512 into 24 channels of 0-10V analogue control. The output connection is via a 25 pin 'D-Sub' wired with pin 25 as common.

Analogue to Digital

An Analogue to Digital converter is also often called an Encoder or Mux. The purpose of this product type is to convert analogue control inputs into DMX512. This is useful for both upgrading older control consoles and also providing triggering of audio visual devices. The range of manufacturers offering these products is gradually reducing as the requirement to encode analogue control consoles reduces.

Artistic Licence: DMX-Mux

The DMX-Mux is a rack mount product that converts up to 72 analogue inputs into DMX512. In addition, the product can merge the analogue data into an existing DMX512 stream.

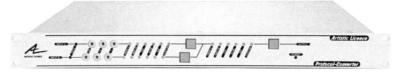

The product also offers a special 'Hog Trigger' mode which encodes the inputs in binary for remote triggering a Whole Hog lighting console. Inputs are via 25 pin D-Sub connectors wired with pin 25 as common.

Relays

DMX512 controlled relays can be used for a wide range of applications from triggering stage practical's to remote controlling breakers.

It is important to appreciate that relays should not be used to control dangerous loads such as firing pyrotechnics or non-constrained stage mechanics. This is because DMX512 contains minimal error checking and dangerous misfires could occur.

Always check the manufacturer data sheet before using this type of product to control inductive loads. Few DMX512 controlled relay products are designed for inductive loads and using them without external snubber protection networks will result in damage.

Artistic Licence: Rail-Switch
The Rail-Switch provides 6 mains voltage change-over relays. Each relay is switched on when its control channel exceeds 50%.

Rail-Switch is housed in a Din-Rail case with all connections made via screw terminals. RDM is used to set the product's Start Address.

Output rating is 230VAC at 8A non-inductive.

Artistic Licence: Rail-Tran
The Rail-Tran provides 6 Darlington transistor drive outputs designed to drive the coils of external relays. Each output is switched on when its control channel exceeds 50%.

Rail-Tran is housed in a Din-Rail case with all connections made via screw terminals. RDM is used to set the product's Start Address.

Output rating is 120mA per channel at 5 to 50VDC.

XTBA: Relay8
The Relay8 is supplied as a module for mounting inside the customer's equipment. The product provides 8 normally open relays with a rating of 24V at 500mA.

Mergers

A Merger takes one or more DMX512 inputs and merges them to form a composite output. Usually one of the inputs will have an offset control which allows the inputs to be concatenated rather than merged.

Take for example two lighting consoles which both output 30 channels. We wish to connect both lighting consoles to the same dimmer rack.

We can merge the two control sources which will result in an output containing 30 channels with each channel controlled by both consoles. Alternatively we can concatenate the inputs by offsetting the second console by 30 channels. This will provide an output of 60 channels with the first console controlling channels 1-30 and the second controlling 31-60.

Clearly a combination of merging and concatenation can also be used as the application demands.

When data from two or more sources is merged, the merging can occur in two distinct ways:

HTP

HTP or Highest Takes Precedence is most useful when combining channels that will be used for controlling intensity. In this scenario, the console which outputs the highest level will 'win'.

LTP

LTP or Latest Takes Precedence is most useful for controlling moving light attributes such as pan and tilt. In this scenario, the console to make the latest (or most recent) change 'wins'.

Artistic Licence: DMX-Merge

The DMX-Merge is a rack mount product that can merge or concatenate two DMX512 inputs. Both inputs are optically isolated with loop connections. Merging is by HTP.

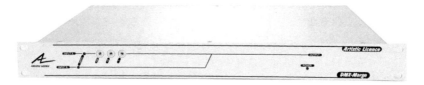

Doug Fleenor Design: DMX512 Combine 221E

The 'DMX512 Combine' is a modular product that can merge two DMX512 inputs. Both inputs are optically isolated and internally terminated. Merging is by HTP.

Patching Computers

A Patch is used to re-order the sequence of channels between the input and output. Patching products often add additional functionality such as cue replay and automatic backup.

Artistic Licence: Cue-Patch

The Cue-Patch provides a soft patch across 1024 channels using two DMX512 inputs and two DMX512 outputs. Additionally it can record and playback cues and sequences, automatically fade to a backup show on failure of an input and also provides built in splitters.

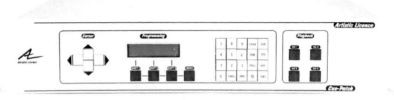

Backup Systems

Backup systems come in a wide range of shapes and sizes. All are aimed at saving the show in the event of an equipment failure. The key approaches that exist are as follows:

1. Automatic switching or 'Fail-Over'
2. Tracking Backups
3. Backup Consoles

Fail-Over: Artistic Licence Rail-Flip

The Rail-Flip is essentially an intelligent relay. Its purpose is to switch between a main and a backup console in the event of a failure. This can be done automatically as the product monitors the inputs for a fault condition. Equally it can be done manually using a remote switch-over control. The product supports 4 universes but this can be increased by linking multiple products.

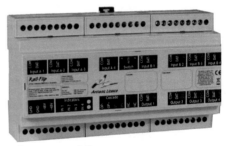

Rail-Flip uses a mechanical relay which ensures that the primary data will pass through the product in the event that Rail-Flip suffers a power failure.

Tracking: Artistic Licence Four-Play

Four-Play is a four univers disc recorder for both DMX512 and Art-Net Ethernet.

It can operate as a stand-alone show controller replay unit but can also operate a: tracking backup.

Console: Artistic Licence Dimmer-Switch

Dimmer-Switch is a single universe DMX512 controller. It provides a DMX512 input with master fader which allows the main console to be merged into the output stream.

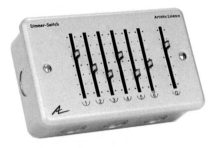

In the event that the main console fails, the operator simply cross fades to the recorded scenes and sequences.

Console: ETC SmartFade

SmartFade is a sophisticated lighting console in its own right. It also offers a DMX512 input allowing it to operate as a backup to a master console.

Additionally, SmartFades can be linked with MIDI allowing additional universes to be backed up.

MIDI Conversion

MIDI is a low cost protocol used widely in the music industry. Interfacing between MIDI and DMX512 can be useful for two types of application:

1. Music Synchronisation
2. Remote Control

Music Synchronisation: Artistic Licence MIDI-DMX

MIDI-DMX can operate as either a MIDI to DMX512 or a DMX512 to MIDI converter. MIDI sends audio information encoded as 'Note On' commands. These commands encode a seven bit number representing the musical note and a seven bit number representing the velocity (or weight) of the note.

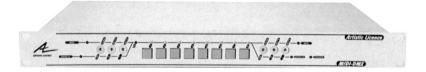

This means that both variables range from 0 to 127. MIDI-DMX makes the translation by encoding the MIDI Note as a DMX Channel (or Slot) number and using the Velocity to represent the intensity.

The product also provides eight low voltage relays and eight push buttons for general purpose interfacing.

Remote Control: Artistic Licence Common-Sense

Common-Sense is an event based triggering system that, amongst many other protocols, can trigger from both MIDI and DMX512.

The product operates by programming a cross point matrix of input events, such as a specific MIDI command, that will trigger specific outputs.

Common-Sense also integrates RS232, RS485, Matrix panels, Contact Closures, MIDI Time Code, Real Time Clock and Infrared remote control.

DALI Conversion

DALI is a low cost protocol used widely in commercial and retail lighting. Converting DMX512 to and from DALI can be useful as it allows a wider range of choice in the specification of both controllers and fixtures.

However, a word of warning is needed: DALI is some 200 times slower than DMX512. This means that much care must be taken at the system design stage if the application intends to achieve smooth fades from the DALI system. This is particularly true when using DALI to control colour mixing products.

Artistic Licence Rail-DALI

Rail-DALI can operate as either a DALI to DMX512 or DMX512 to DALI converter.

A total of 256 channels is supported, spread over 4 DALI buses. The DALI bus channel count is configurable allowing the user to trade refresh rate against cost.

Chapter 8 Design Considerations

This chapter discusses some of the questions faced by product designers. It is in no way intended to be a replacement for the thorough understanding of the standard that is needed by the product designer. However there are numerous aspects of the standard which do not immediately make the 'correct' implementation obvious. Careful consideration of the items below will provide you with a robust and compatible product design.

Baud Rate

The question of baud rate accuracy used to be moot; simply pick a microprocessor crystal value that gives an accurate division to 250KBaud. There is an increasing move to support both DMX512 and Ethernet on a single microprocessor. Numerous modern microcontroller platforms, such as Freescale and Microchip force the designer to use a modulo 25MHz crystal in order to drive the Ethernet PHY. This can often mean that in order to support both on one platform, 250KBaud cannot be achieved.

The DMX512 specification calls for a 2% accuracy of baud rate. Asynchronous serial communications and DMX512 in particular is pretty forgiving over baud rate accuracy. The reason is that the receiver restarts its internal clock at the start bit.

I've tested baud rate accuracy with a range of products running out 300m of nasty non-balanced cable. My conclusion is that most receivers start to error when the baud rate error exceeds 3%.

The maths is as follows:

- Each bit of the DMX slot is 4uS at 250KBaud.
- There are 11 bits (1 start, 8 data, 2 stop) in a slot. That equates to 44uS.
- Modern asynchronous receivers tend to sample each bit 3 times and then take a majority decision on whether the bit is high or low. This means that the sampling occurs 25%, 50% and 75% through each bit.
- The receiver resynchronises at the start bit of each slot. We expect receive errors to occur when a baud rate error pushes the final stop bit out of range.
- The 'normal' time from the start of start bit to end of second stop bit is 44uS. The error will then occur if this length reduces by more than 25% of one bit time, i.e 1uS.
- We therefore expect errors if the inaccuracy exceeds 1/44uS = 2.27uS.

Conclusion: Stay within the 2% limit required by the standard.

Stage Robotics & Pyrotechnics

This one is very simple: Don't! DMX512 has no intrinsic error checking. The standard is very clear that it is not to be used to control dangerous items.

Interpreting Timing Parameters

The DMX specification lays out the minimum timing for numerous parameters such as Break and MaB. Keep in mind that these are minimums; there are no awards for designing a product that uses the minimum values. If your product has a MaB of exactly 8uS and the receiver has a 0.1% error in its timing, your product's data will be rejected.

Below is a table of transmitter timing values that provide a good middle ground that reduce the risk of good packets being discarded:

Parameter	DMX512	DMX512(1990)	DMX512-A	RDM	Recommended Transmit
Break	88uS	88uS	92uS	176-352uS	250uS
MaB	4uS	8uS	12uS	12-88uS	20uS
MbB	0uS	0uS	0uS	176uS	200uS

The Minimum Packet Length

This is a concept that has led to numerous compatibility issues over the years. The standard states that the minimum packet length is 1,204uS.

This can be calculated as follows:

Parameter	Quantity	Unit Time	Total Time
Break	1	92uS	92uS
MaB	1	12uS	12uS
Start Code	1	44uS	44uS
Data Slots	24	44uS	1,056uS
Total			1,204uS

You may infer from this that the minimum number of data slots for a valid DMX512 packet is 24. A number of products on the market make this assumption; however it is wrong! The standard neither states nor implies this. An equally valid DMX512 frame is:

Parameter	Quantity	Unit Time	Total Time
Break	1	92uS	92uS
MaB	1	12uS	12uS
Start Code	1	44uS	44uS
Data Slots	1	44uS	44uS
Inter-slot delay	1	Variable	1,012uS
Total			1,204uS

Conclusion: It is a common misconception that the minimum valid number of data slots is 24. The DMX512 specification simply requires that the packet time is not less than 1,204uS.

It is worth noting that RDM complicates this matter slightly: In DMX512 the minimum requirement for MbB is zero. This means that the minimums for 'Packet Time' and 'Break to Break Time' are identical. RDM institutes a minimum MbB of 176uS and which means that the minimum Break to Break time increases to 1,380uS.

End of Packet Detection

One of the more frustrating aspects of DMX512 is the lack of a specific way to identify the end of packet. Numerous (minor) product incompatibilities have grown out of this.

Flaw 1: Assume that the following break can be used to terminate a packet. This is not valid as the DMX512 specification allows up to one second between packets. If you make this assumption you could inadvertently introduce a 1 second delay in your receiver. This is a real issue as many modern DMX512 transmitters use 'delta' transmission. That is: they transmit a packet only when data changes or every second, which ever is the shorter. A receiver that assumes break is the end of packet marker connected to a 'delta' transmitter will most likely not work correctly.

Flaw 2: Assume a consistent number of data slots will be transmitted in consecutive packets. The DMX512 specification does not require this. Modern controllers, particularly video streamers do transmit variable numbers of data slots to make bandwidth gains.

Conclusion: The only safe way to define the end of packet is 'when the receiver receives the last data slot in its footprint'.

Loss of Data Detection

The standard requires a packet be transmitted at least every second. Loss of data detection is best implemented by timing 1.25S from the start of break. If a second break is not received in that time, data is lost.

Fluctuating Timing

There are numerous controllers on the market which exhibit fairly wild fluctuations in timings such as Break and MaB. This is because in many implementations, a microprocessor uses the Break or MaB as time to either update its buffers or perform housekeeping.

Conclusion: Ensure your receiver design can handle the full range of allowed timings and do not hard code time delays on the assumption that you will receive consistent timing parameters.

Mark before Break

The DMX512 specification does not require there to be any time between the end of the last data slot's second stop bit and the start of the next break. The RDM standard mandates a minimum delay of 176uS. There are three reasons that this change was introduced:

1. Damaged stop bits: Numerous processors flag when the data has been transferred to the transmit shift register. Remember that the firmware needs to be sure that the second stop bit has completed before starting break. Otherwise you end up with a negative MbB. This will at minimum cause the last data slot to be lost to the receiver and in some receivers will cause the entire packet to be discarded.
2. What is the receiver doing? In RDM, product microprocessors have more work to do at the end of a packet. This time delay gives them time to process the frame and decide whether the bus direction needs to change.
3. Switching direction. Changes in the direction of transmission occur during the MbB. The 176uS provides a 'dead space' that allows the signals to stabilise.

Video Streaming

The standard does not address synchronisation of multiple DMX512 universes. However this is an issue of increasing importance with the growth of pixel based products and video streamers.

Consider a pixel wall driven by multiple DMX512 universes. The potential problem is usually seen as a form of 'ripping' whereby different sections of the wall update at different times. The result is aesthetically displeasing and designers of both the transmitting and receiving devices need to give this careful consideration.

In the DMX512 receiving device it is necessary to ensure that the modulation of the lights is synchronised to the received DMX512 break signal. That is: Do not run DMX512 receive and output refresh as asynchronous threads within your firmware.

The transmitting device then needs to ensure all of its DMX512 outputs are transmitted with their Breaks synchronised. If all the DMX512 outputs are from the same console this is a simple task. If they are (as is likely) being converted from an Ethernet protocol, then the converters need to implement synchronisation. For example: The Artistic Licence range of Art-Net to DMX512 converters all ensure that the transmitted break is synchronised to the ArtDmx Ethernet packet carrying the data. This ensures that the data does not 'rip' when used for video streaming.

Harry Nyquist – The Father of Information Theory

Nyquist was a major contributor to modern communications. His mathematical work forms the basis of efficient digital communication from mobile phones to DMX512.

Born in Sweden in 1889, he emigrated to the USA in 1907 and received a PhD in Physics from Yale in 1917.

He worked at AT&T's R&D department for the first seventeen years of his professional life. AT&T changed to Bell Telephone Laboratories in 1934. He stayed with Bell until his retirement in 1954.

At AT&T he helped develop the first facsimile machine, launched in 1924. His seminal work; "Certain factors affecting telegraph speed" was also published in 1924. In this he proved that the bandwidth of a carrier must be twice that of the sample frequency of the data in order that the signal can be accurately reconstructed. This is called the Nyquist Theorem (sometimes Nyquist-Shannon Theorem). This theoretical work laid the foundations for further advances by Claude Shannon and was the precursor to what we now call Information Theory.

Nyquist died in Texas in 1976.

Video Content

The comments above provide a data infrastructure capable of carrying video content. However careful synchronisation of the video content is required to make this work. Looking at the maths:

- Nyquist tells us that the bandwidth of a carrier must be at least twice that of the data. In this situation DMX512 is the carrier and the video to be streamed is the data.
- The minimum DMX512 packet length when sending all 512 channels is 22,668uS. That equates to a packet rate or bandwidth of 44.12Hz.
- Video content rates range from 24Hz for film to 25Hz for UK to 30Hz for US. Using Nyquist we see that we need a minimum carrier bandwidth of 48Hz to 60Hz.

On the face of it this tells us that it is not possible to stream video content over DMX512. There are three possible solutions:

1. Use a slower video frame rate. Unfortunately the product designer cannot control this so it is not a viable solution.
2. Send less than 512 data slots per DMX512 packet. This is a viable solution although rather frustrating. Video streaming is by definition channel hungry. 'Wasting' channels by design is not likely to look good on the specification.
3. Synchronising content to carrier. Without doubt this is the best solution. It simply means that a DMX512 packet is transmitted only when a video frame is received. Taking this approach 'cheats' Nyquist by synchronising the carrier and the data. Keep in mind that you must not break the one second refresh rule. This means that a timeout will be required such that should video stop, the product will continue to transmit a DMX512 packet at least every second.

Using Text Packets

Text packets are particularly useful when designing a transmitting device without a user interface such as converters and splitters. Consider implementing a text packet that is sent once at power on. This can contain human readable information such as software revision, custom configuration data and where relevant real time clock.

Termination

Keep in mind that the termination requirements for RDM are stricter than DMX512. To future proof the design, implement the RDM termination circuit even if the product is initially only to support DMX512.

Software selection of port direction

In DMX512 software selection of a port's direction was trivial. RDM complicates this as transmitter and receiver have different termination circuits. These two termination circuits are critical to the operation of RDM and must be honoured. This means that a design which implements software selection of port direction will need relays or switches to manipulate the termination circuitry.

Termination Detection

It is sometimes useful for a transmitting device to be able to detect whether the end of the line is un-terminated, terminated, double terminated or shorted. This is best achieved by monitoring the current consumed by the line driver. The table below shows approximate values for two common RS485 driver chips.

State	National Semi 75176 Average Current	MAX483 Average Current
Open	33.1 mA	31.6 mA
Terminated	47.7 mA	42.7 mA
Double Terminated	57.9 mA	48.9 mA
Shorted	88.0 mA	68.0 mA

Active Loop Through

Most DMX512 receiving devices have an 'Input' and 'Loop Through' connector. A common design error is to make the Loop Through active, i.e. retransmit the data. The flaw in doing this is that if the receiver loses power, all devices downstream will lose data.

It is better to make the Loop Through connection totally passive by connecting it directly (with short wires) to the input connector.

This approach also simplifies the firmware as active buffering of RDM data is a non-trivial piece of software!

RDM Timing

The RDM standard has significantly tightened the allowed range of packet timing. The reasons are discussed in more detail in Part 2. Even if a transmitter design is not intended to support RDM, it is worth implementing the RDM timing rules. The headline changes are detailed below:

Transmitter

Parameter	DMX512	DMX512(1990)	DMX512-A	RDM	Recommend Transmit
Break	88uS	88uS	92uS	176-352uS	250uS
MaB	4uS	8uS	12uS	12-88uS	20uS
MbB	0uS	0uS	0uS	176uS	20uS
Average Interslot	Not specified	Not specified	Not specified	0-76uS	0uS
Maximum Interslot	Not specified	Not specified	Not specified	2.0mS	0uS

Receiver

Parameter	DMX512	DMX512(1990)	DMX512-A	RDM
Break	88uS	88uS	88uS	88-352uS
MaB	4uS	8uS	8uS	8-88uS
MbB	0uS	0uS	0uS	0uS
Maximum Interslot	Not specified	Not specified	Not specified	2.1mS

Optical Isolation

The DMX512 standard does not mandate use of electrical isolation. It does however strongly suggest that when isolation is used, it is used at the receiver end and not at the transmitter end. The reason for this recommendation is an attempt to avoid having isolated transmitters driving isolated receivers. When this situation occurs it is possible that excessive common mode voltages will be seen as the pin 1 ground line has no reference to the outside world. Anecdotal evidence suggests this can lead to significant voltage spike being injected into the DMX512 receiver when the cable is first plugged.

Ground Loops

Grounding errors are one of the biggest problems in DMX512 networks. This is primarily because the DMX512 standards prior to DMX512-A did not give any direction. The preferred grounding arrangement is that the transmitter is referenced to Earth-Ground (mains earth) and the receiver is floating.

In numerical terms:

- The resistance between transmitter pin 1 and chassis or Earth-Ground must be 20 ohms or less.
- The resistance between receiver pin 1 and chassis or Earth-Ground must be 22 mega ohms or more (measured at 42VDC).

Use of Connectors

The standard connector is the 5pin XLR.

You are allowed to use an RJ45 only if the product is designed for permanent installation in a control room. You can use screw or punch down terminals in products designed for permanent installation. You can use a non standard connector only if it is physically impossible to fit an XLR in which case you must supply an XLR adapter with the product.

Finally: Never ever use 3pin XLR or stereo jack plugs.

DALI Conversion

Over the last few years a number of products that convert between DMX512 and DALI have come to market. There is absolutely no technical problem with this; however user perception can be a problem. Keep in mind that DALI is approximately 200 times slower than DMX512. The user who expects to convert from DMX512 to DALI and control multi-channel smooth crossfades is likely to be disappointed!

Mechanical Issues

I have seen numerous product designs with a very simple mechanical fault. Many electronic designs use a pcb mounted XLR connector for DMX512. This connector then 'pushes' through the metal panel. The problem is the eject tab on the female XLR. If the panel thickness is much greater than 2mm, the eject tab will not have room to move and the cable mounted male XLR cannot be released!

Radio Links

A simple rule of thumb can significantly reduce DMX512 network problems: Only use radio links when there is absolutely no way to run a cable. Cable is, by definition, more reliable than radio!

The Foundations

DMX512 (1986) and DMX512 (1990) were both designed as unidirectional protocols. This simply means that they are designed such that the data flows only from transmitter (lighting console) to receivers (dimmers and moving lights). DMX512-A remains fundamentally a unidirectional protocol, but lays the foundations for bidirectional data flow. Bidirectional data flow means that the dimmers and moving lights can talk back to the console.

These foundations take the form of 'Enhanced Functionalities' or EF's. DMX512-A defined a number of possible Enhanced Functionalities, giving each an EF number. The standard stopped short of defining how these EF's should be used.

The Enhanced Functionalities defined by DMX512-A are:

EF Number	Symbol	Primary Pair	Secondary Pair
1	←→ ----	Half duplex EIA-485-A (RS485) signal. The return signal (towards controller) is controlled by a registered Alternative Start Code (ASC).	Not used.
2	→ ←	Unidirectional DMX512 signal.	EIA-485-A (RS485) unidirectional signal in direction towards controller. The standard does not define the content or arbitration method.
3	→ ←→	Unidirectional DMX512 signal.	Half duplex EIA-485-A (RS485) bidirectional signal. The standard does not define the content or arbitration method.
4	←→ ←→	Half duplex EIA-485-A (RS485) signal. The return signal (towards controller) is controlled by a registered Alternative Start Code (ASC).	Half duplex EIA-485-A (RS485) bidirectional signal. The standard does not define the content or arbitration method.

Note that the term Primary Pair means the twisted pair connected to pins 2 & 3 of the XLR and the Secondary Pair is the twisted pair connected to pins 4 & 5. As will be seen from the table above, DMX512-A really only gives us the tools to describe these different schemes but does not tell us how to use them.

What is RDM?

RDM stands for Remote Device Management. This is the colloquial name for the ANSI E1.20 standard developed by ESTA. RDM allows bi-directional communication over the DMX512 cable using the twisted pair connected to pins 2 and 3. This same pair of wires is used to transmit data from the console to the dimmers or moving lamps.

What does RDM do for me?

The ability to remotely set the DMX512 start address is the most useful feature for the largest group of users. It is useful in an entertainment environment; removing the need to climb the truss or bring the truss in to resolve one incorrectly set dip switch.

In architectural lighting it is a massive aid. Consider in-ground and waterproof fixtures; it is no longer necessary to have a waterproof door to access local controls. Many large scale installations would become impossible without this ability. I recently worked on a project with approximately 20,000 channels of pixels fitted to the outside of a building. We calculated that setting the pixel addresses with dip switches would have required over one man year. Doing the same task automatically with RDM took around 30 minutes. It is therefore not surprising that architectural lighting manufacturers are amongst the first to support RDM.

RDM devices can send status and fault information back to the console. There are already products on the market (such as the Wybron InfoTrace and the Artistic Licence Colour-Tramp) that can monitor this information and send maintenance a daily report on any service issues.

All RDM products contain a unique electronic serial number. This provides potential benefits to hire companies for both inventory control and scheduling maintenance such as lamp replacement.

RDM products contain electronic signatures defining their manufacturer and model type. This allows consoles to accurately match and download lamp personalities.

RDM provides a more intelligent protocol that makes it much easier to mix DMX installations with sophisticated Ethernet protocols such as Art-Net or ACN.

History

As with so much of this industry it all started in a bar. This particular bar was in a hotel in Dallas used for the quarterly ESTA standards meetings; the year 2001. DMX512-A had just been completed and was in its public review stage. Scott Blair and I were pondering, over a drink, why the concept of bidirectional DMX had been discussed so much over the years but never come to anything.

We reached a surprising conclusion: the problem was not technical but marketing. All of the previous discussions and ideas had centred on the idea of getting sensor style feedback from the dimmers; fuse fail indication, lamp blown, fog liquid low etc. Whilst useful, the majority of people simply shrugged: "If the lamp is blown I'll know because it will be dark!" A bit of a simplification and not true in architectural applications. None-the-less that was the ground swell of opinion to date and so bidirectional DMX512 looked as though it would remain one of those useful paper ideas.

We quickly concluded that it was the ability to remotely set the DMX512 start address that would get people interested. The bar conversation expanded as others finished their meetings for the day: Bob Goddard, Doug Fleenor, Tracy Underhill and Peter Willis joined the fray. It soon became clear there was enthusiasm to get this idea up and running.

It took a little effort to convince ESTA to turn RDM into a fully fledged standards programme as initial perception was that the effort may detract from the functionality that ACN was expected to offer. The DMX enthusiasts won the day; RDM was born. Of course back then it wasn't yet called RDM; we were working under the snappy little title of "Polled Talkback Sub Task Group!"

The Pins 4 & 5 Question

In the first formal RDM development meeting I think it fair to say that we all entered the room assuming that RDM would be designed to use the spare pins 4 & 5 of the DMX512 connector. Some eight hours later we had all converted each other to using a half duplex protocol on the primary pairs (pins 2 & 3).

Using the spare pair for the data to return from the dimmers seemed most logical at the start of discussions. The idea would simply be that DMX512 would be transmitted from console to dimmers on the primary pair (pins 2 & 3) and that the dimmers or moving lights could send data back to the controller on the spare pair (pins 4 & 5). All we needed to do was define the message structure and a way of controlling when a specific dimmer (or any DMX512 receiver) should send back its data.

RDM did not develop this way as this apparently obvious solution had some down sides. In no particular order, the reasons are as follows:

- Many existing installations used single pair cable and did not wire pins 4 & 5. If RDM used those pins then many existing installations would need to be rewired before RDM could be used. In reality this meant that they would never use RDM.
- A very large base of existing products used the 3pin XLR and so pins 4 & 5 simply did not exist. Again if RDM used the spare pair, these product designs could not be easily upgraded.
- The design of the chip (75176) used by many product manufacturers for their DMX512 interface makes it a simple electronic upgrade to implement half duplex bidirectional data on the primary pair.
- Using the spare pair for RDM would increase the amount of driver electronics required and therefore product cost.
- Numerous manufacturers had used the spare pair for proprietary purposes ranging from power to custom sensors. To use the spare pair for RDM opened the potential for major compatibility problems with 'non-compliant' legacy products. (Legacy products are those designed before the advent of DMX512-A and RDM).

The issues listed above were deemed to be a significant barrier to the likely take up and support for RDM in the industry. Given that all the people working on standards development at ESTA are volunteers we did not want to run the risk that our efforts would be wasted and no one would use RDM!

So the decision was made that RDM would be a half duplex bidirectional protocol using the primary pair (pins 2 & 3).

Let's briefly look at what that means:

- Bidirectional: That data can travel in both directions; from console to dimmers and dimmers to console. (Note that when I use the term 'dimmers' in this context I really mean any DMX512 receiver).
- Primary Pair: The twisted pair connected to pins 2 & 3 of the 5pin XLR connector.
- Half Duplex: That data can only travel in one direction at a time. If we are only using the primary pair this is obvious in the sense that data can only travel in on direction at a time.

RDM is therefore an EF1 extension of DMX512-A.

RDM Addressing and the UID

Before we look at how RDM actually works, we need to explore the concept of addressing. In pure DMX512 addressing is really controlled at the dimmer end of the wire. The console sends up to 512 channels (or more correctly data slots). The dimmer has a Start Address that defines the starting channel that it will use. To describe a dimmer one could say 'the dimmer patched at channel 345'.

In RDM the above remains true for the lighting data - the actual channel levels. There is a 'but': RDM needs a way to send a dimmer a question or command and then receive an answer. If RDM were to reference dimmers by their start address confusion would quickly reign. Imagine sending this command:

"Set the start address of the dimmer with start address 23 to 145".

Or for that matter:

"What is the start address of dimmer at start address 145".

Clearly this does not work and the conclusion is that we can no longer use the DMX512 Start Address as the primary method of addressing a dimmer in the RDM world. RDM introduces the concept of an UID which stands for Unique Identification.

The UID is made up of six bytes of data in such a way that it is guaranteed that no two DMX512 receivers can have the same number. The UID is formatted as follows:

Byte	1	2	3	4	5	6
Function	Manufacturer ID		Product Serial Number			
	High Byte	Low Byte	High Byte			Low Byte

The Manufacture ID is a 16 bit number that is allocated to product manufacturers by ESTA. See Appendix C. The Product Serial Number is a 32 bit number that the manufacturer allocates uniquely to each product it manufactures. Note that there are some numbers in the product Serial Number that have special meaning; we will discuss these in the next chapter.

With the UID concept, let's revisit our example commands:

"Set the start address of the responder with UID 47:23:12:45:67:12 to 145".

Or for that matter:

"What is the start address of responder with UID 47:23:12:45:67:12".

Hopefully it is clear that this makes more sense! Notice that I have changed from using the term dimmer to 'responder'. In RDM speak a Responder is any device capable of responding to an RDM message. Equally I shall now use the RDM term for a lighting console which is Controller.

So how does RDM work?

The following drawing shows a typical flow of data between a controller and responder.

Normal DMX512 Data	1			7
Controller Sends RDM Message		3		
Responder Sends RDM Reply			5	
Idle Time		2	4	6
Wire Direction	Forward		Reverse	Forward

The row labelled 'Wire Direction' tells us the direction in which data is flowing. The RDM convention is to define Forward as data flow from Controller to Responder and Reverse as Responder to Controller.

Let's look at this in detail:

1. A 'normal' DMX512 packet is being sent from the controller to the responder. This is most likely a zero start code packet which is controlling the actual light levels. In any case this is a non-RDM DMX512 packet.
2. There may be idle time between the end of the DMX512 packet and the start of the RDM traffic.
3. The controller then sends an RDM message. This is a short DMX512 packet with the special start code of 204 (or 0xCC in hexadecimal). Contained within this packet is the UID that defines which responder must respond to the message.
4. There is then a pause during which time the Controller switches its DMX512 transmitter into receive mode, ready to receive a response. There are specific

timing requirements for this but at this stage I am simply focusing on the process.

5. The responder with a matching UID then transmits its response to the controller. It is important to understand that a responder only 'talks when asked'. A responder cannot initiate an RDM conversation.

6. There is a pause during which time the controller and responder switch back to forward direction.

7. Normal DMX512 packets then continue.

It is important to note that the drawing is not to scale. The RDM packets are generally very small compared to the normal DMX512 packets. In fact, even when sending continuous RDM data between each normal DMX512 packet, RDM consumes less than 3% of the available bandwidth.

If there is a standard DMX512 splitter between the Controller and Responder in the above example, it will not work. RDM requires a new breed of DMX splitter (such as the Artistic Licence Rack-Split RDM and the Goddard Design Hub5). This new type of splitter is intelligent as it must monitor the data for a command to reverse the direction of the splitter outputs.

Knock Knock - Who's There

We now have an understanding of how the data flows and how we address the responders. The key question is how does the controller know the UIDs of the responders to which it is connected? The controller could send a message to every possible UID and see whether a response was forthcoming. Unfortunately as the UID is a 48 bit number, there are 281,474,976,710,656 combinations. It would take the average lighting controller around 200,000 years to do that! Clearly a more elegant solution was needed; and one that did not involve the user typing a long list of UIDs into the controller!

The solution is a concept called 'Discovery'. We'll look at the details of packet structure in the next chapter; for now let's just look at the mechanism. In order to simplify the description we will pretend that there are only 8 possible UIDs which we number from 0 to 7.

The drawing below shows a binary search tree, this is used to discover which devices exist. The circles along the bottom of the drawing represent all the possible UID numbers in our limited world. For the purposes of our discussion, blue circles represent responders that are connected to our cable whilst yellow represents responders that could exist. At this point the controller does not know which of the possible responders exist.

The pink circles represent decision points in the tree. Inside the circle there is a letter (which is purely for description and a range of numbers. Looking at decision point 'C' we see that the number range is '4-7'. This tells us that possible UIDs 4,5,6,7 are below that decision point. The controller uses this binary search tree (or Btree) to discover which of the possible responders actually exist.

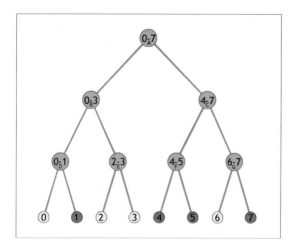

The discovery process starts with the controller sending a special discovery command called 'DISC_UN_MUTE' to all responders. It does this by sending the command to a special UID called the Broadcast Address. All responders listen for messages on both their own unique UID and also the Broadcast Address. This command tells all responders that discovery is about to start and most importantly that the controller does not know they exist.

The controller then starts to work through the Btree and discover which UIDs exist. It does this using another discovery command called 'DISC_UNIQUE_BRANCH' which is also sent to the Broadcast Address. The data associated with this command includes a range of UID numbers. When a responder receives this message it checks to see if its UID number is greater than or equal to the lower limit and less than or equal to the higher limit. If it is, it sends a response.

So in our example, the controller will start by sending a DISC_UNIQUE_BRANCH for the range 0-7 (because that is the largest possible range of UIDs). This is Decision Point A. In this situation, all responders should respond. The drawing below shows what happens.

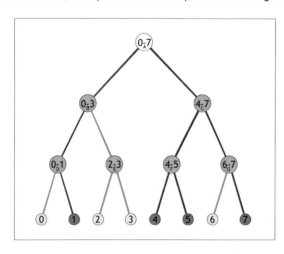

The red lines represent responses. This is called a collision because we have more than one responder transmitting at the same time. The responses will be garbled but the controller will see the errors and know that there are responders below.

The controller now reduces the range in order to identify which branch contains responders. It moves to Decision Point B and sends a DISC_UNIQUE_BRANCH for the range 0-3.

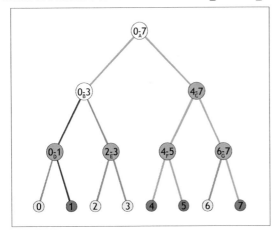

In this instance we can see from the red lines that there will be no collisions. Only responder 1 is below decision point B. The controller now knows that Responder 1 exists. The controller now sends a 'DISC_MUTE' command to Responder 1. This command tells Responder 1 that it has been discovered and that it should stop responding to discovery messages.

The discovery process makes use of collisions between responders transmitting at the same time. A collision is essentially an intentional fault condition. Because of this there remains the possibility that the controller has discovered Responder 1, but that there are actually other responders below that decision point. To guard against this problem, the controller will send the DISC_UNIQUE_BRANCH command for decision point B a second time.

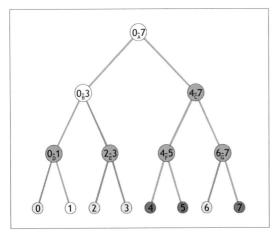

The controller receives no response (because it muted Responder 1) which confirms that there are no other responders below decision point B.

The controller moves to the next position in the Btree which is decision point C. It sends a DISC_UNIQUE_BRANCH for the range 4-7.

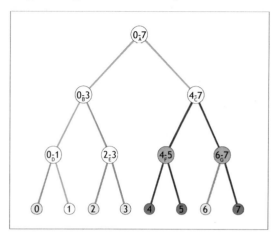

Again the controller sees collisions as shown by the red lines when responders 4,5 & 7 all attempt to respond at the same time.

The controller moves down the Btree to decision point F. It sends a DISC_UNIQUE_BRANCH for the range 4-5.

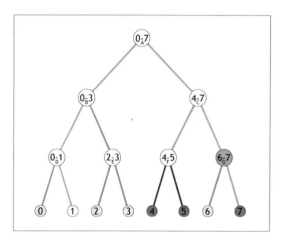

The controller still sees when responders 4 & 5 attempt to respond at the same time. The controller then sends a DISC_UNIQUE_BRANCH for the first of the two possible devices, i.e. a range 4-4.

Responder 4 responds and so the controller mutes it. The controller then sends a DISC_ UNIQUE_BRANCH for the second of the two possible devices, i.e. a range 5-5. Responder 5 responds and so the controller mutes it.

The controller has now discovered responders 1,4 & 5. The controller moves across the Btree to decision point G. It sends a DISC_UNIQUE_BRANCH for the range 6-7.

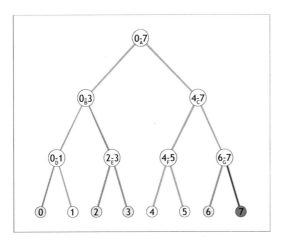

In this instance we can see from the single red line that there will be no collisions. Only responder 7 is below decision point G. The controller now knows that Responder 7 exists. The controller now sends a 'DISC_MUTE' command to Responder 7.

At this point we have exhausted the tree and so believe we have discovered all responders. To ensure that none has been missed, the controller will send a final DISC_UNIQUE_ BRANCH for the range 0-7. We expect to receive no response and no collision because we believe all responders have been discovered. Remember that when we discover a responder we mute it so that it stops responding to discovery.

The drawing below shows the final state with four responders (shown in white) discovered.

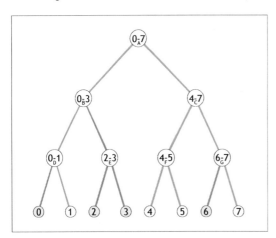

The controller now knows the UIDs of all the responders to which it is connected. It uses this information to talk directly to each device. From this point on, we should not see any collisions because each responder can be addressed uniquely by the controller.

Our simple example pretended that there were only 8 possible UIDs. Clearly this is not the case, but hopefully it is easy to see how the example scales to the real RDM world. The process is identical; it is just that the Btree is much much bigger.

Connecting responders after discovery

Discovery is generally performed when the controller starts up or during the patching process. Clearly it is possible that responders will be connected or disconnected after discovery has been performed. This means that the controller's list of responders can become out of date. This problem is resolved by a process called 'Ongoing Discovery' or 'Background Discovery'.

The controller will occasionally send a DISC_UNIQUE_BRANCH command to include all possible UIDs. Any responders that have already been discovered will not respond because they have been muted. Any responders that have been recently connected or powered on will then be discovered.

Detecting responders that have been disconnected can be done in two ways:

1. The controller can monitor responses from responders it has already discovered. If one of these responders fails to reply, it has most likely been disconnected and can be deleted from the list of discovered UIDs.
2. Alternatively the controller can periodically un-mute all responders and then mute each of the responders it has previously discovered. This method has the benefit of ensuring that unknown responders that were muted will now be discovered.

Generally the former option is easier to implement and use.

Swapping responders between controllers

There is one further scenario that can lead to a controller's list of UIDs becoming outdated. If a responder is moved from one controller or DMX512 port to another without being power cycled, there exists the possibility that it has already been discovered and therefore muted by the previous controller. In this situation, the responder will believe it has been discovered but the controller will not know of the UID. Option 2 above addresses this potential pitfall.

Chapter 10 Packet Structure

Overview

In the previous chapter we discussed the key concepts of RDM and reached a point where the controller has a list of connected responders. In this chapter we will look at the details of the RDM packet structure and data flow.

An RDM packet is just a DMX512 packet with a specific start code of 204. (There is one exception which is the discovery response packet which we will cover in the next chapter). The slots of the RDM packet are formatted in a specific manor that includes a header, a data area and a checksum. The following table shows this:

Data Type	Size
RDM Start Code	1 slot
Header	23 slots
Data	Variable
Checksum	2 slots

The first potential area of confusion is related to the RDM Start Code. In the table above I have shown this as distinct from the header. In DMX512 this would be the convention. However the RDM standard uses the convention that the Start Code is part of the header. It makes no real difference so in this book I have adopted the same convention as the RDM standard. So the revised table will be as follows, remembering there are 513 slots in a DMX512 packet.

Data Type	Size
Header	24 slots
Data	Variable
Checksum	2 slots

We can see that the smallest RDM packet, which has no data, takes only 26 slots. Many RDM commands are of this size which explains why RDM takes so little of the DMX512 bandwidth.

Packet detail

Let's now look at the packet in detail. The following table shows the contents of the header. Remember that slots number from 0 to 512.

Slot Number	Description	Values
0	RDM Start Code	204
1	Sub-Start Code	1
2	Message Length	24-255
3-8	Destination UID	
9-14	Source UID	
15	Transaction Number	
16	Port ID / Response Type	
17	Message Count	
18-19	Sub-Device	
20	Command Class	
21-22	Parameter ID (PID)	
23	Parameter Data Length (PDL)	0-231
	Parameter Data	
24*	Checksum high byte	
25*	Checksum low byte	

* The slot numbers of the checksum will change depending on the amount of parameter data. The table above shows slot numbers assuming there is no data.

Packet fields

There are two ways in which the detail of RDM can be discussed: We could look at all of the key concepts and then see how they fit into the packet structure. Alternatively we can discuss each field in the packet, describing the concepts to which they relate as they appear. I have chosen the latter approach.

The packet structure described above is used both by the controller to transmit to the responders and by a responder to transmit a reply to the controller.

RDM Start Code

The RDM start code is a value of 204 decimal that is transmitted as the first slot of the packet. (In DMX512 slots number 0-512 whereas Data Slots number 1-512). It is the RDM Start code that differentiates the RDM packet from all other DMX512 packets.

Sub-Start Code

The Sub-Start Code is always a value of 1 decimal. It is included to allow RDM to be expanded in the future. Currently, any RDM packet with a value other than 1 should be treated as an error and ignored.

Message Length

The size of an RDM packet is variable because different commands require differing amounts of data. This field tells us the length of the packet and implicitly tells us the length of the data.

The meaning of Message Length can be defined in two ways:

- The number of slots used by the packet including the start code and excluding the checksum.
- The slot number containing the checksum high byte.

These two definitions are interchangeable. We can see from the table above that the smallest possible value is 24. This corresponds to an RDM packet with no parameter data. As the field is 8 bits wide, the largest number it can hold is 255. This means that the maximum amount of parameter data that can be contained in an RDM message is 231 slots or bytes. This is calculated by subtracting the largest and smallest values: 255-24=231.

So we can use this field for three purposes:

- The packet size.
- The position of the checksum.
- The amount of parameter data in the packet.

Destination UID

In the last chapter we discussed UIDs in detail. To summarise, a UID or Unique Identifier is a 48 bit number.

The UID is made up of six bytes of data in such a way that it is guaranteed that no two RDM devices can have the same number. The UID is formatted as follows:

Byte	1	2	3	4	5	6
Function	Manufacturer ID		Product Serial Number			
	High Byte	Low Byte	High Byte			Low Byte
Individual Address	0x0001-0x7fff Appendix C		0x00000000-0xfffffffe			
Full Broadcast	0xffff		0xffffffff			
Manufacturer Broadcast	0x0001-0x7fff Appendix C		0xffffffff			

The Manufacturer ID is a 16 bit number that is allocated to product manufacturers by ESTA. See Appendix C.

The Product Serial Number is a 32 bit number that the manufacturer allocates uniquely to each product it manufactures using the range 0x0001 to 0x7fff.

Note that there are some numbers in the product Serial Number that have special meaning; these are the two broadcast addresses. Broadcast allows the controller to send a command to multiple responders. There are two broadcast addresses:

- Full Broadcast: All connected responders accept the communication.
- Manufacturer Broadcast: All connected responders with matching Manufacturer ID accept the communication.

When a responder accepts a broadcast message it never responds as this could cause collisions to occur. (Note that there are exceptions to this statement when the commands relate to discovery. We will cover these in the next chapter).

When a message is sent to a non-broadcast UID it is called Unicast.

To conclude, the Destination UID is the UID of the device to which this message is directed. If the packet is generated by a controller then this field will contain the UID of the responder to which it is directed. If the packet is a reply generated by a responder then this field will contain the UID of the controller that sent the request.

Source UID

The Source UID is the UID of the device that transmitted the packet. If the packet is generated by a responder then this field will contain the UID of the responder. When generated by a controller this field will contain the UID of the controller.

If an RDM field is larger than one slot, such as the UID, the order in which the bytes are transmitted is very important. RDM uses a system called 'Big-Endian'. This literally means that the 'big' or most significant end of the data is sent first. For example: If the Source UID is 0x414c01020304 then it will be sent as:

Slot Number	Description	Values
9	Manufacturer ID High Byte	0x41
10	Manufacturer ID Low Byte	0x4c
11	Product Serial Number High Byte	0x01
12	Product Serial Number Mid High Byte	0x02
13	Product Serial Number Mid Low Byte	0x03
14	Product Serial Number Low Byte	0x04

Transaction Number

The Transaction Number is an eight bit unsigned number that starts at 0x00 and is incremented in controller packets for every packet sent. A responder sets its Transaction Number to match that of the controller packet to which it is responding.

This field serves two purposes:

- Allows the controller to keep track of which response relates to which request.
- Provides a method for test equipment and 'packet sniffers' to marry requests and responses.

Port ID / Response Type

This use of this field changes depending upon whether the packet is generated by the controller or the responder.

If generated by the controller, this field is Port ID. If generated by the responder, this field is Response Type.

Port ID

The Port ID is used to describe the physical DMX512 connector on which the packet was sent. Values of this field range from 1 to 255. If the controller only has one DMX512 connector (port) this value is set to 1.

Generally RDM is designed to operate on a single DMX512 universe and does not support the concept of multiple universes. This field is the exception in that it accepts that RDM is likely to be used in a multi-universe environment. If you consider a two universe console with both DMX512 outputs connected to the same dimmer rack, its purpose is clear. Without Port ID the responder will see RDM messages arrive at both connectors with identical Source and Destination UIDs. This will make it difficult for the dimmer rack's software to identify upon which port it should reply.

You can consider the Port ID to be an extension of the UID that defines which universe transmitted the message.

The RDM standard does not mandate that controllers with multiple ports use this method. For example it is perfectly legal for the controller to allocate a different UID to each of its ports and set the Port ID to 1 on all.

Response Type

When the packet is generated by the responder, this dual function field becomes Response Type. Response Type is used by the responder to tell the controller how it is processing the command. The table below shows the allowed values and their purpose.

Val	Name	Description
0x00	ACK	The request has been processed correctly and any answer that the controller may have requested is contained in this response packet.
0x01	ACK_ TIMER	The responder must respond to a controller in a limited amount of time as defined by the RDM standard. In some instances a responder may not be able to retrieve the requested information in time to respond. In this event the responder sets the Response Type field to ACK_Timer and encodes a 16 bit number in the Parameter Data field. The 16 bit number is unsigned and represents an estimate of how long it will take to retrieve the data. The number is scaled such that each increment represents $1/10^{th}$ of a second or 100mS.

Val	Name	Description
		When the responder succeeds in retrieving the requested data, it adds the information to its list of queued messages so that the controller can retrieve the information. See Chapter 13 for details of the Queued Messaging system.
0x02	NACK_REASON	The responder is unable to comply with the request. There are numerous possible reasons why this may occur. Each possible reason is allocated a number and this 16 bit number is encoded into the first two slots of the Parameter Data in this packet.

Val	Name	Description
0	UNKOWN_PID	The responder cannot comply because the command was either not understood or is not implemented by this responder.
1	FORMAT_ERROR	The responder cannot comply because there is an error in the format of the command.
2	HARDWARE_FAULT	The responder cannot comply due to a hardware fault condition.
3	PROXY_REJECT	The responder is not in control of the DMX512 port required to forward this message and therefore cannot comply.
4	WRITE_PROTECT	The responder has write protection enabled and is not allowed to comply with the command.
5	BAD_COMMAND_CLASS	The COMMAND_CLASS field was invalid.
6	DATA_OUT_OF_RANGE	Some or all of the Parameter Data contained values that are out of allowed range for this responder.
7	BUFFER_FULL	The responder's RDM buffers are full and the responder is temporarily unable to comply.
8	PACKET_SIZE	The size of the packet containing the request exceeded the capability of the responder.
9	SUB_DEVICE_RANGE	The request was directed to a sub-device that does not exist.

Val	Name	Description
0x03	ACK_OVER FLOW	ACK_OVERFLOW indicates that the responder requires multiple messages to send the required answer. An example of this is when the controller requests a list of all the commands (PIDs) that a responder supports. When the controller sees this Response Type it knows to send additional identical requests in order to retrieve all the information. The controller detects when the multiple packet response has completed because the final packet in the sequence will have a Response Type of 'ACK' whereas all others will have 'ACK_OVERFLOW.

Message Count

Message Count is an unsigned 8 bit number that is set only by a responder generated packet. It indicates the number of Queued Messages that are waiting for the controller. Queued Messages occur for one of two reasons:

1. The responder has previously received a request with which it could not comply and had issues an ACK_TIMER. When the information becomes available in the responder, it queues a message containing the previously requested data.
2. The responder has an event that it wishes to report to the controller such as a temperature sensor error. As a responder cannot initiate an RDM conversation, its only recourse is to queue the relevant message.

A controller uses the QUEUED_MESSAGE command to retrieve these messages from the responder. The RDM standard does not mandate any order for retrieval of queued messages so it is down to the responder's software design to ensure messages are sent in an intelligent and prioritised order. The term 'Queued' implies that the controller may expect to retrieve messages in the order for which they were requested. Again the standard does not mandate this and the controller design should not make such assumptions.

Sub-Device

To this point we have discussed a responder as a single entity with which a controller can communicate. In fact RDM provides a two level hierarchy within the responder. The main entity is called the 'Root Device' and all RDM responders have a root device.

RDM also provides Sub-Devices. The controller can communicate with sub-devices by setting the Sub-Device field to a value other than zero. The following table shows how sub-device addressing works:

Sub-Device Field	Type	Description
0	Root	Communicate with root device.
1-512	Sub-Device	Communicate with sub-devices 1-512.
0xffff	Broadcast	Communicate with all sub-devices but not root device.

There some key facts to remember when dealing with sub-devices:
- Sub-devices are optional depending upon the design of the responder.
- All sub devices are identical. So it would not be possible to have sub-device 1 with a footprint of 3 and sub-device 2 with a footprint of 6. This limitation exists in RDM to save bandwidth. If it were not true the controller would need to interrogate every sub-device to find its settings.

Sub-devices are used to provide a neater description of a responder. Consider a dimmer rack with pluggable dimmer modules. The dimmer rack could be the root device and the modules be the sub devices. Do remember that this is not mandated by the standard; it is the product designer's decision.

A total of 512 sub-devices are allowed in RDM. These number from 1-512 allowing the '0' to be used to reference the root device. A special code of 0xffff (which means all 16 bits set to 1) is used as the broadcast address for sub-devices. When this value is used in this field, all sub-devices (but not the root device) will accept the command.

We have now discussed two broadcast concepts in RDM. To summarise:
- The UID broadcast address is used to communicate with all responders.
- The sub-device broadcast address is used to communicate with all sub-devices within the responder.

It follows from this that if a command is sent to the broadcast UID and the broadcast sub-device then all sub-devices of all responders will accept the command. This fact can be used to save very significant amounts of bandwidth.

The following table shows some examples to clarify the concept. I refer to the responder with a UID of '0x414c:01020304' as Responder A. Note that we can tell this is a product manufactured by Artistic Licence by looking for the first two hexadecimal digits in Appendix C.

Destination UID (Slots 3-8)	Sub-Device (Slots 18-19)	Accepted By
0x414c:01020304	0	Root of Responder A
0x414c:01020304	1	Sub-device 1 of Responder A
0x414c:01020304	0xffff	All Sub-devices of Responder A
0x414c:ffffffff	0	Root of all Artistic Licence responders
0x414c:ffffffff	1	Sub-device 1 of all Artistic Licence responders
0x414c:ffffffff	0xffff	All Sub-devices of all Artistic Licence responders
0xffff:ffffffff	0	Root of all responders
0xffff:ffffffff	1	Sub-device 1 of all responders
0xffff:ffffffff	0xffff	All Sub-devices of all responders

Command-Class

The command class tells us two pieces of information:

1. Whether this packet is a command or a response.
2. Whether the command is a question, an instruction or related to discovery.

This information is compacted into a single field as it makes it simpler for the responder to 'decide' whether it should respond.

The following table shows the values that are allowed:

Command Class	Value	Description	Direction	Response *
GET_COMMAND	0x20	Controller requesting a value of a parameter from responder.	Controller >>> Responder	Yes
GET_COMMAND_ RESPONSE	0x21	Responder supplying requested value.	Responder >>> Controller	No
SET_COMMAND	0x30	Controller setting the value of a parameter in responder.	Controller >>> Responder	Yes
SET_COMMAND_ RESPONSE	0x31	Responder acknowledging receipt of parameter value.	Responder >>> Controller	No
DISCOVERY_COMMAND	0x10	Controller attempting to discover the existence of responders.	Controller >>> Responder	Yes
DISCOVERY_COMMAND_ RESPONSE	0x11	Responder replying to discovery command.	Responder >>> Controller	No

As can be seen from the table, there are three categories of message from controller to responder and three from responder to controller. (*) The Response column of the table shows whether a responder should reply when it receives this message. Be aware that this assumes that the controller is communicating directly with the responder and not using broadcast. Responders do not reply to broadcast messages as this would cause a collision.

We have also introduced two new RDM terms: Get and Set. A 'GET' means that the controller is trying to retrieve data from the responder. A SET means the controller is attempting to change or set a parameter in the responder.

Parameter ID

Finally we get to the purpose of the message! The Parameter ID or PID tells us which parameter the message is either Getting or Setting. Appendix J provides a listing of all the currently published PIDs and we discuss these in detail in the next chapter.

The PID is a 16 bit number. Currently defined PIDs are in the range 0x0000-0x7fdf. The small blocks of 0x7fco-0x7fff and 0xffc0-0xffff are officially defined as for 'future expansion of the standard'. This is slightly irrelevant as there are thousands of unused codes that can also be used for expansion of the standard!

The range of values 0x8000-0xffdf is available for manufacturer specific codes. Clearly the intent is that a manufacturer will use the RDM published PIDs whenever possible as this gives the widest compatibility between manufacturers. However when no such PID exists, a manufacturer can define their own. Note that it is not possible to send manufacturer specific PIDs using the Full Broadcast address as there is no way for the responder to know the manufacturer to which it relates. Manufacturer specific PIDs can be sent using the Manufacturer Broadcast.

Parameter Data Length (PDL)

This field tells us the number of slots (or bytes) of data that are included in the Parameter Data. Values range from 0-231 decimal.

This data is redundant as the value can be calculated from the Message Length field. However by including this field we have an additional level of error checking. The relationship is:

$$\text{Message Length} = \text{PDL} + 24$$

If this is not true when a packet is parsed then an error has occurred and the packet is discarded.

Parameter Data

This is the data associated with the PID. The length of this block is variable and can range from 0 to 231 bytes. The actual length is defined by the Command Class and the PID.

Checksum

The checksum as the name suggests is used as a sum of the data to check the data's integrity.

The logic is that the transmitter adds up the contents of the packet and transmits that value at the end of the packet. The receiver also adds up the contents of the packet then checks to see if its sum is identical to the transmitter's sum. If it is, there is a very good chance that the data is not corrupt. If they do not match, the data is definitely damaged.

I say 'very good chance' intentionally. A matching checksum is not a guarantee that the data is good. Two transmission errors could theoretically cancel each other out in such a way that the data was corrupt but the checksums did match. That said, it's very rare for this to occur.

The checksum is calculated by adding all slots from the DMX512 start code in slot 0 through to the last slot of data in the Parameter Data. This unsigned 16 bit sum is then inserted in the packet following the Parameter Data.

The table below shows a controller generated packet. The packet is a Get Command for the PID DEVICE_INFO and contains no data.

Slot Number	Description	Values
0	RDM Start Code	0xcc (204)
1	Sub-Start Code	0x01 (1)
2	Message Length	0x18 (24)
3-8	Destination UID	0x414c:01020304
9-14	Source UID	0x414c:00000000
15	Transaction Number	0x01 (1)
16	Port ID / Response Type	0x01 (1)
17	Message Count	0x00 (0)
18-19	Sub-Device	0x00 (0)
20	Command Class	0x20 (32)
21-22	Parameter ID (PID)	0x0060 (96)
23	Parameter Data Length (PDL)	0 (0)
24	Checksum high byte	??
25	Checksum low byte	??

To calculate the checksum, we must add each slot value. As some of our fields are bigger than one slot in width, we must redraw this packet as individual slots to see the process:

Slot Number	Description	Hexadecimal Values	Decimal Values
0	RDM Start Code	0xcc	204
1	Sub-Start Code	0x1	1
2	Message Length	0x18	24
3	Destination UID	0x41	65
4		0x4c	76
5		0x01	1
6		0x02	2
7		0x03	3
8		0x04	4
9	Source UID	0x41	65
10		0x4c	76
11		0x00	0
12		0x00	0
13		0x00	0
14		0x00	0
15	Transaction Number	0x01	1
16	Port ID / Response Type	0x01	1
17	Message Count	0x00	0
18	Sub-Device	0x00	0
19		0x00	0
20	Command Class	0x20	32
21	Parameter ID (PID)	0x00	0
22		0x60	96
23	Parameter Data Length (PDL)	0x00	0
Total		0x028b	651

The important part of the table is the hexadecimal total of 0x028b. This means the most significant or high byte of the checksum is 0x02 and the least significant part is 0x8b.

We can now insert these figures to produce the finished packet ready for transmission:

Slot Number	Description	Values
0	RDM Start Code	0xcc (204)
1	Sub-Start Code	0x01 (1)
2	Message Length	0x18 (24)
3-8	Destination UID	0x414c:01020304
9-14	Source UID	0x414c:00000000
15	Transaction Number	0x01 (1)
16	Port ID / Response Type	0x01 (1)
17	Message Count	0x00 (0)
18-19	Sub-Device	0x00 (0)
20	Command Class	0x20 (32)
21-22	Parameter ID (PID)	0x0060 (96)
23	Parameter Data Length (PDL)	0x00 (0)
24	Checksum high byte	0x02 (2)
25	Checksum low byte	0x8b (139)

Happily these calculations are done by the microprocessors in the product! It is worth noting that it is important to make the addition of each individual slot value. Attempting to sum the numbers in each field and then convert to hexadecimal would produce a different and incorrect number.

Chapter 11 Discovery Commands

Discovery Messages

In Chapter 10 we discussed the concept and process of discovery. Let's now look at the actual packets used to achieve this. To recap: Discovery is the process by which a controller detects the UIDs of the attached responders.

There are three packets used in the process:

- DISC_MUTE
- DISC_UN_MUTE
- DISC_UNIQUE_BRANCH

The Mute Flag

The 'Mute Flag' is key to the concept of discovery. All responders have a mute flag. When the mute flag is set, the responder is said to be muted. A muted responder does not reply to DISC_UNIQUE_BRANCH messages as it has already been discovered by the controller.

The mute flag is set and reset by the commands DISC_MUTE and DISC_UN_MUTE respectively. The RDM standard requires that the mute flag is also reset (that is un-muted) in the following conditions:

- Power on.
- Hardware reset
- Software reset

In addition to these, it makes sense for a responder to un-mute if it detects that the controller to which it is attached has changed. A responder can achieve this by keeping track of the Source UID field. This helps avoid loss of discovery of a responder when it is moved from one DMX512 universe to another.

It is worth pointing out that the mute flag is not intended to have any other effect on the responder's normal operation. Specifically it should not be interpreted as any kind of reset.

DISC_MUTE

The DISC_MUTE command is used to mute (set the mute flag) a responder. This is done once the controller has discovered the responder and ensures that the responder will not reply to further DISC_UNIQUE_BRANCH messages.

The packet format is shown in the table below. For clarity I am only showing the packet slots that are of significance to the PID we are discussing. I shall use this convention for all PID descriptions.

Slot Number	Description	Values
3-8	Destination UID	Full Broadcast Manufacturer Broadcast Unicast
16	Port ID	1-255
18-19	Sub-Device	0
20	Command Class	DISCOVERY_COMMAND
21-22	Parameter ID (PID)	DISC_MUTE
23	Parameter Data Length (PDL)	0
	No Parameter Data	

The responder replies as shown in the following table:

Slot Number	Description	Values
3-8	Destination UID	Controller's UID
16	Response Type	ACK
18-19	Sub Device	0
20	Command Class	DISCOVERY_COMMAND_RESPONSE
21-22	Parameter ID (PID)	DISC_MUTE
23	Parameter Data Length (PDL)	2 or 8
24-26 or 31	Parameter Data	
	Control Field (16 bit)	
	Optional Binding UID (48 bit)	

Note that the Response Type must be ACK; no other values are allowed in discovery.

The Control Field is a sequence of bits that the responder uses to report critical configuration data at the discovery stage.

Managed Proxy Flag (Bit 0)

This flag is set if the responder is a managed proxy. A managed proxy is a device which responds on behalf of other devices. This could be an advanced RDM splitter or an Ethernet to DMX512 converter. A managed proxy implements an additional set of proxy management PIDs which allow the controller to interrogate the managed proxy for a list of the UIDs which it represents.

The concept of a managed proxy provides a number of theoretical benefits but adds significant complexity to RDM implementations. For this reason it is not mandatory that a proxy publish itself as such. It is perfectly valid for a proxy to clear this flag and simply emulate all RDM traffic on behalf of the responders that it represents. Indeed initial RDM product launches suggest this is most likely the implementation that will become preferred and that the proxy command set will see little use.

Proxied Device Flag (Bit 3)

This flag is only ever set if the Managed Proxy Flag is also set. The Proxied Device Flag indicates that the message is on behalf of another responder.

The following table shows the relationship between the two flags related to Proxy.

Managed Proxy Flag (B0)	Proxied Device Flag (B3)	Description
0	0	The responder is not a Proxy
0	1	Not Allowed
1	0	The responder is a Managed Proxy and this message is from the Managed Proxy.
1	1	The responder is a Managed Proxy and this message is from a device that is managed by the Proxy.

Sub Device Flag (Bit 1)

This flag is set if the responder supports sub-devices. This allows the controller to prepare to interrogate the responder for sub-device information.

Boot Loader Flag (Bit 2)

This flag is set if the responder is running in Boot Loader mode. This mode implied that the responder has a very limited RDM implementation and will not be fully functional until it has received a firmware upload. This allows the controller to immediately flag the situation to the operator.

The unused bits are all set to zero.

Binding UID

The Binding UID is optional and only sent if the responder has multiple DMX512 ports. The Binding UID is the UID of the primary port of the responder. This is intended to allow the controller to build a picture of the physical relationship between devices that it discovers.

DISC_UN_MUTE

The DISC_UN_MUTE command is used to un-mute (clear the mute flag) a responder. This is done prior to discovery and ensures that the responder will reply to DISC_UNIQUE_BRANCH messages.

The packet format is shown in the table below.

Slot Number	Description	Values
3-8	Destination UID	Full Broadcast Manufacturer Broadcast Unicast
16	Port ID	1-255
18-19	Sub-Device	0
20	Command Class	DISCOVERY_COMMAND
21-22	Parameter ID (PID)	DISC_UN_MUTE
23	Parameter Data Length (PDL)	0
	No Parameter Data	

The response to this command is identical in format to that of DISC_MUTE.

DISC_UNIQUE_BRANCH

The DISC_UNIQUE_BRANCH is the key command in discovery. It can be considered as a 'probing message' to detect responders.

The packet format is shown in the table below.

Slot Number	Description		Values
3-8	Destination UID		Full Broadcast
16	Port ID		1-255
18-19	Sub-Device		0
20	Command Class		DISCOVERY_COMMAND
21-22	Parameter ID (PID)		DISC_UNIQUE_BRANCH
23	Parameter Data Length (PDL)		12
24-35	Parameter Data		Two consecutive 48 bit words.
	Lower Boundary 48 bit	Upper Boundary 48 bit	

Note that this command is only ever sent to the full broadcast address as it must be processed by all responders. A responder will send a reply to this command if it is un-muted and its UID is greater than or equal to the lower boundary and less than or equal to the higher boundary.

The Discovery Response

The discovery response was the single most complex part of the standard for the RDM team to design. The discovery process is based on the concept of collisions to detect when multiple responders exist within a given range of UIDs.

The problem is that a collision is actually a 'fault condition' where two or more responders are transmitting at the same time. There is no concern about the driver electronics because RS485 driver chips are designed to withstand such faults. The problem is that what actually happens to the DMX512 wires in this situation is difficult to define as all driver chips are slightly different.

At an early stage in the design of RDM, the discovery response was specified as a standard RDM packet with Break – MaB etc. A number of manufacturers involved in the design of RDM tested with this and discovered some occasional odd effects on legacy DMX512 products. (Legacy meaning they were designed before the advent of DMX512-A or RDM). When RDM discovery happened, some legacy products would occasionally flicker. The problem turned out to be that when multiple responders cause a collision the result could occasionally look like a good zero start code packet. The drawing below shows how this can occur:

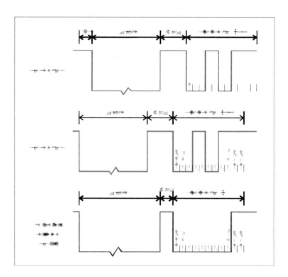

The blue and green waveforms show two responders sending a Break – MaB – RDM Start code sequence. Responder 1 happens to start its transmission 8uS or 2 bit times later.

If the DMX512 driver chips in these two responders deal with the fault condition in such a way that the lowest level wins, the red waveform results. The red waveform has a slightly longer Break and shorter MaB than the responder's transmission. Unfortunately both Break & MaB are within the DMX512 limits and the data in slot 0 is a perfectly formatted '0'. Any devices connected to this DMX512 cable will accept this as lighting level data – the result will be flicker.

The RDM development team experimented with numerous 'fixes' to the problem before concluding that the only solution was that the discovery response message needed to be a special case that did not contain a break.

Unfortunately, the problems with collision did not stop there! The next idea we tried was that just a single byte of data should be sent in response to a discovery message – surely that couldn't do any harm?

In the example above, a low level on the collision won. Sadly that is not the case on all driver chips, sometimes the high level wins. The drawing below shows the problem:

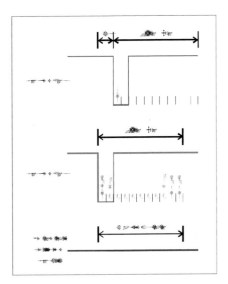

The two responders send a single byte of value 0xfe. One starts transmitting between 8uS and 36uS later than the other. The result can be that the DMX512 wire stays in a marking state. If this were to happen, the controller would think there are no responders below a particular decision point and move on. Discovery would at best be unreliable and at worst simply not work!

The solution

The reason for explaining the development history is because at first glance the discovery response looks unnecessarily complex. Its not; every part of it is there for good reason. To work reliably in all situations, the discovery response needs to achieve the following:

1. Ensure that a collision cannot appear to be a valid DMX512 packet.
2. Ensure that the collision will be seen by the controller in the event that the lowest collision level wins on the wire.
3. Ensure that the collision will be seen by the controller in the event that the highest collision level wins on the wire.
4. Ensure that splitters and other in-line electronics cannot compromise the discovery process.

Below is the discovery response packet. Let's look at how it achieves these goals:

Byte Sequence	Value	Data Type	Name	Include in Checksum
1	0xfe	Preamble	Preamble 1	No
2	0xfe		Preamble 2	
3	0xfe		Preamble 3	
4	0xfe		Preamble 4	
5	0xfe		Preamble 5	
6	0xfe		Preamble 6	
7	0xfe		Preamble 7	
8	0xaa	Header	Header	Yes
9	UID High Byte 5 OR 0xaa	Encoded UID 'EUID'	EUID 11	
10	UID High Byte 5 OR 0x55		EUID 10	
11	UID Byte 4 OR 0xaa		EUID 9	
12	UID Byte 4 OR 0x55		EUID 8	
13	UID Byte 3 OR 0xaa		EUID 7	
14	UID Byte 3 OR 0x55		EUID 6	
15	UID Byte 2 OR 0xaa		EUID 5	
16	UID Byte 2 OR 0x55		EUID 4	
17	UID Byte 1 OR 0xaa		EUID 3	
18	UID Byte 1 OR 0x55		EUID 2	
19	UID Low Byte 0 OR 0xaa		EUID 1	
20	UID Low Byte 0 OR 0x55		EUID 10	
21	Checksum Hi Byte OR 0xaa	Checksum	ECS 3	
22	Checksum Hi Byte OR 0x55		ECS 2	
23	Checksum Low Byte OR 0xaa		ECS 1	
24	Checksum Low Byte OR 0x55		ECS 0	

We now have a new concept of the EUID or 'Encoded UID'. A UID is 48 bits or 6 bytes wide. The EUID is 96 bits or 6 bytes wide. Each byte of the UID is encoded into two bytes of the EUID. The reason for doing this is to guarantee the state of each alternate bit. The values of the UID are sequentially OR'ed with 0xaa then 0x55.

The significance of these two values is that they represent alternating bit patterns and are also the inverse (or complement) of each other. The following table shows this:

Value	D7	D6	D5	D4	D3	D2	D1	D0
0xaa	1	0	1	0	1	0	1	0
0x55	0	1	0	1	0	1	0	1

Remembering that a single Bit of DMX512 data is 4uS and that the minimum Break length valid at a receiver is 88uS, a total of 22 consecutive low bits could 'look like' a valid break. The use of the EUID with alternating bit positions virtually guarantees that a collision cannot be interpreted as a valid break. This resolves item 1 of our goal list.

In fact it resolves items 2 & 3 as well. As the data is OR'ed with alternating bit positions it is virtually impossible for a collision to result in the wire staying in a marking position.

The fourth goal is resolved by the Preamble. We will discuss the detail of RDM splitters in a later chapter, but consider this:

The minimum break time for the RDM transmitter is significantly longer than that required by pure DMX512. The reason for this is that RDM splitters may slightly shorten the break of the RDM response due to the time taken for the splitter to reverse direction. If there is a Break at the front of the packet - no problem. However, the discovery response packet does not have a break. This means that the splitter could damage the first byte of the packet when it is switching direction.

The Preamble provides the solution. These are seven bytes of data that provide protection to the front of the packet. RDM allows splitters to sacrifice these bytes so that the real data is protected. Each splitter is allowed to sacrifice only one byte. In theory this means that up to seven cascaded splitters could remove the entire Preamble.

The reality is that with modern fast processors and good design splitters are unlikely to do this. That said, keep in mind that RDM theoretically limits the number of cascaded splitters to seven.

Chapter 12 Using RDM Commands

We will now look at some of the available RDM commands of PIDs. It is not my intention to detail every PID as that information is available in the RDM standard. Here I will focus on PIDs that are either of greatest interest to most users or difficult to understand. In the examples below, a green background denotes a packet sent by the controller and a yellow background is the response.

Appendix J contains a full listing of all PIDs including a cross reference of the valid Parameter Data Lengths for each Command Class.

DMX_START_ADDRESS

Getting and setting a fixture's start address is probably the most important feature of RDM.

The tables below show a controller requesting a device's root start address. The responder has a UID of 0x414c:01020304.

Slot	Description	Values	Comments
0	RDM Start Code	0xcc	
1	Sub-Start Code	0x01	
2	Message Length	0x18	
3-8	Destination UID	0x414c:01020304	
9-14	Source UID	0x414c:00000000	
15	Transaction Number	0x01	
16	Port ID	0x01	
17	Message Count	0x00	
18-19	Sub-Device	0x00	Root device
20	Command Class	0x20	GET Command
21-22	Parameter ID (PID)	0x00f0	DMX_START_ADDRESS
23	Parameter Data Length (PDL)	0	
24	Checksum high byte		
25	Checksum low byte		

A response follows of:

Slot	Description	Values	Comments
0	RDM Start Code	0xcc	
1	Sub-Start Code	0x01	
2	Message Length	0x1a	
3-8	Destination UID	0x414c:00000000	Note these are swapped
9-14	Source UID	0x414c:01020304	Compared to sender
15	Transaction Number	0x01	
16	Response Type	0x00	Ack
17	Message Count	0x00	
18-19	Sub-Device	0x00	Root device
20	Command Class	0x21	GET Command Response
21-22	Parameter ID (PID)	0x00f0	DMX_START_ADDRESS
23	Parameter Data Length (PDL)	0x02	The response is 2 bytes
24-25	Parameter Data	0x0001	This is the start Address
26	Checksum high byte		
27	Checksum low byte		

The response tells us that the responder has a root start address of '1'. There are a few points to note in this example:

Firstly the response packet has the source and destination UIDs swapped compared to the controller packet. This is because when the responder replies, it is the controller that is the destination.

Also note the change in the Command Class field. The controller packet contained 0x20 which defines the packet as a 'GET' command. The response contains 0x21 which defines the packet as a 'GET RESPONSE'.

In the response packet slot 16 has a different meaning. It is the 'Response Type'. The value of zero represent 'ACK' meaning that the packet contains the requested data.

Having retrieved the start address, the controller now sets it to a new value:

Slot	Description	Values	Comments
0	RDM Start Code	0xcc	
1	Sub-Start Code	0x01	
2	Message Length	0x1a	
3-8	Destination UID	0x414c:01020304	
9-14	Source UID	0x414c:00000000	
15	Transaction Number	0x01	
16	Port ID	0x01	
17	Message Count	0x00	
18-19	Sub-Device	0x00	Root device
20	Command Class	0x30	SET Command
21-22	Parameter ID (PID)	0x00f0	DMX_START_ADDRESS
23	Parameter Data Length (PDL)	0x02	
24-25	Parameter Data	0x0005	
26	Checksum high byte		
27	Checksum low byte		

A response follows of:

Slot	Description	Values	Comments
0	RDM Start Code	0xcc	
1	Sub-Start Code	0x01	
2	Message Length	0x18	
3-8	Destination UID	0x414c:00000000	Note these are swapped
9-14	Source UID	0x414c:01020304	Compared to sender
15	Transaction Number	0x01	
16	Response Type	0x00	Ack
17	Message Count	0x00	
18-19	Sub-Device	0x00	Root device
20	Command Class	0x31	SET Command Response
21-22	Parameter ID (PID)	0x00f0	DMX_START_ADDRESS
23	Parameter Data Length (PDL)	0x00	
24	Checksum high byte		
25	Checksum low byte		

Note that the Command Class in these transactions has changed to 0x30 and 0x31. These represent a 'SET' command followed by a 'SET RESPONSE'. The Response Type field contains 0x00 which represents ACK. This means that the responder has accepted the controller's request to set its start address to a value of 5.

QUEUED_MESSAGES

Once a controller has finished initial discovery, it regularly polls the responders it has discovered in order to:

1. Check they are still connected.
2. Find out if they have any message traffic.

RDM allows the controller's design to decide how best to implement this procedure. However the most efficient method is to use the QUEUED_MESSAGE command.

The QUEUED_MESSAGE command is the one exception to the RDM rule that the response packet will contain the same PID as the request packet. The concept of a queued message is needed because a responder may not be able to retrieve the requested data within the strict time limits of an RDM response. For example, the data may be stored in serial flash memory with a slow access time.

The example below shows a transaction in which the responder cannot reply with its start address.

Slot	Description	Values	Comments
0	RDM Start Code	0xcc	
1	Sub-Start Code	0x01	
2	Message Length	0x18	
3-8	Destination UID	0x414c:01020304	
9-14	Source UID	0x414c:00000000	
15	Transaction Number	0x01	
16	Port ID	0x01	
17	Message Count	0x00	
18-19	Sub-Device	0x00	Root device
20	Command Class	0x20	GET Command
21-22	Parameter ID (PID)	0x00f0	DMX_START_ADDRESS
23	Parameter Data Length (PDL)	0	
24	Checksum high byte		
25	Checksum low byte		

A response follows of:

Slot	Description	Values	Comments
0	RDM Start Code	0xcc	
1	Sub-Start Code	0x01	
2	Message Length	0x1a	
3-8	Destination UID	0x414c:00000000	Note these are swapped
9-14	Source UID	0x414c:01020304	Compared to sender
15	Transaction Number	0x01	
16	Response Type	0x01	ACK_TIMER
17	Message Count	0x00	
18-19	Sub-Device	0x00	Root device
20	Command Class	0x21	GET Command Response
21-22	Parameter ID (PID)	0x00f0	DMX_START_ADDRESS
23	Parameter Data Length (PDL)	0x02	The response is 2 bytes
24-25	Parameter Data	0x000a	This is the estimated delay
26	Checksum high byte		
27	Checksum low byte		

The response contains a Response Type of ACK_TIMER. This tells us that the responder could not answer the question. It also tells us that the information will be available in approximately one second. The Data field contains the value of 0x000a or 10 in decimal.

This value is multiplied by 100mS to give an approximate indication of how long the controller should wait before asking again.

However, the controller does not need to explicitly ask the question again. This is because the responder will add the information to its list of queued messaged. The controller needs only to request the queued messages to get the answer.

The transaction below shows this process:

Slot	Description	Values	Comments
0	RDM Start Code	0xcc	
1	Sub-Start Code	0x01	
2	Message Length	0x19	
3-8	Destination UID	0x414c:01020304	
9-14	Source UID	0x414c:00000000	
15	Transaction Number	0x01	
16	Port ID	0x01	
17	Message Count	0x00	
18-19	Sub-Device	0x00	Root device
20	Command Class	0x20	GET Command
21-22	Parameter ID (PID)	0x0020	QUEUED_MESSAGES
23	Parameter Data Length (PDL)	0x01	
24	Parameter Data	0x04	
25	Checksum high byte		
26	Checksum low byte		

A response follows of:

Slot	Description	Values	Comments
0	RDM Start Code	0xcc	
1	Sub-Start Code	0x01	
2	Message Length	0x1a	
3-8	Destination UID	0x414c:00000000	Note these are swapped
9-14	Source UID	0x414c:01020304	Compared to sender
15	Transaction Number	0x01	
16	Response Type	0x00	Ack
17	Message Count	0x01	
18-19	Sub-Device	0x00	Root device
20	Command Class	0x21	GET Command Response
21-22	Parameter ID (PID)	0x00f0	DMX_START_ADDRESS
23	Parameter Data Length (PDL)	0x02	The response is 2 bytes
24-25	Parameter Data	0x0005	This is the start Address
26	Checksum high byte		
27	Checksum low byte		

So the controller sends a GET: QUEUED_MESSAGES and receives a GET_RESPONSE: DMX_START_ADDRESS.

Looking at slot 17 of the response, we see that Message Count is set to 1. This tells us that there is one more message queued at the responder. The controller issues a second GET: QUEUED_MESSAGES.

Slot	Description	Values	Comments
0	RDM Start Code	0xcc	
1	Sub-Start Code	0x01	
2	Message Length	0x19	
3-8	Destination UID	0x414c:01020304	

Slot	Description	Values	Comments
9-14	Source UID	0x414c:00000000	
15	Transaction Number	0x01	
16	Port ID	0x01	
17	Message Count	0x00	
18-19	Sub-Device	0x00	Root device
20	Command Class	0x20	GET Command
21-22	Parameter ID (PID)	0x0020	QUEUED_MESSAGES
23	Parameter Data Length (PDL)	0x01	
24	Parameter Data	0x04	
25	Checksum high byte		
26	Checksum low byte		

A response follows of:

Slot	Description	Values	Comments
0	RDM Start Code	0xcc	
1	Sub-Start Code	0x01	
2	Message Length	0x1a	
3-8	Destination UID	0x414c:00000000	Note these are swapped
9-14	Source UID	0x414c:01020304	Compared to sender
15	Transaction Number	0x01	
16	Response Type	0x00	Ack
17	Message Count	0x00	
18-19	Sub-Device	0x00	Root device
20	Command Class	0x21	GET Command Response
21-22	Parameter ID (PID)	0x00e0	DMX_PERSONALITY
23	Parameter Data Length (PDL)	0x02	The response is 2 bytes
24-25	Parameter Data	0x0102	This is the personality
26	Checksum high byte		
27	Checksum low byte		

The second queued message was the fixture personality and tells us that it is set to personality 1 of possible values 1 or 2. Note that a possible reason this message was queued by the responder is that someone has manually changed the personality setting at the fixture.

Looking at slot 17 of the response, we see that Message Count is set to 0. This tells us that there are no further queued messages. In this situation, the responder will reply to further GET: QUEUED_MESSAGES with a GET_RESPONSE:STATUS_MESSAGE.

The following example shows this:

Slot	Description	Values	Comments
0	RDM Start Code	0xcc	
1	Sub-Start Code	0x01	
2	Message Length	0x19	
3-8	Destination UID	0x414c:01020304	
9-14	Source UID	0x414c:00000000	
15	Transaction Number	0x01	
16	Port ID	0x01	
17	Message Count	0x00	
18-19	Sub-Device	0x00	Root device
20	Command Class	0x20	GET Command
21-22	Parameter ID (PID)	0x0020	QUEUED_MESSAGES
23	Parameter Data Length (PDL)	0x01	
24	Parameter Data	0x04	Errors only
25	Checksum high byte		
26	Checksum low byte		

A response follows of:

Slot	Description	Values	Comments
0	RDM Start Code	0xcc	
1	Sub-Start Code	0x01	
2	Message Length	0x21	
3-8	Destination UID	0x414c:00000000	Note these are swapped
9-14	Source UID	0x414c:01020304	Compared to sender
15	Transaction Number	0x01	
16	Response Type	0x00	Ack
17	Message Count	0x00	
18-19	Sub-Device	0x00	Root device
20	Command Class	0x21	GET Command Response
21-22	Parameter ID (PID)	0x00e0	STATUS_MESSAGES
23	Parameter Data Length (PDL)	0x09	The response is 2 bytes
24-25	PD – Sub Device	0x0000	Message from root
26	PD – Status Type	0x04	Message is an error
27-28	PD – Status Message ID	0x0022	Sensor under temp error
29-30	PD – Data Value 1	0x0000	Sensor number 0
31-32	PD – Data Value 2	0x0002	Temperature is 2°C
33	Checksum high byte		
34	Checksum low byte		

In previous examples, when there were queued messages, the value of the parameter data in GET: QUEUED_MESSAGES was not used. In this example it is important as it tells the responder what type of status messages to send. The value of 0x04 tells the responder that the controller is only interested in errors.

The GET_RESPONSE: STATUS_MESSAGE contains a packed list of status messages, each of which is 9 bytes long. The maximum number of status messages in one packet is 25.

In the example above, the controller would display the following information to the operator: "Sensor 0 has an under-temperature fault at 2°C". Clearly a more intelligent controller may interrogate the controller for a description of sensor zero in order to display a more user friendly: "Pan motor sensor has an under- temperature fault at 2°C".

Chapter 13 The RDM Physical Layer

There are a number of additional constraints, that RDM places on both the electronics and the signal timing, compared to DMX512-A.

The Electronics

The key difference between DMX512-A and RDM is that RDM requires bidirectional line drivers in all devices. This simple statement does have some repercussions: At some stages in an RDM transaction, neither the controller nor the responder is driving the line. This would leave the line (cable) in an indeterminate state. It is for this reason that RDM mandates that the controller bias the line. This is achieved by adding resistors which pull up the data signal and pull down the complement signal. See Figure below.

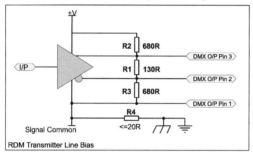

The RDM standard specifies the biasing in terms of the voltage (245mV) that must be achieved when driving a terminated line. The standard further provides a test circuit that can be used to confirm that a given biasing circuit works correctly.

When operating with 5VDC line drivers, the values shown above work correctly. R1 is the transmit termination resistor. R2 pulls the data signal towards 5V. R3 pulls the complement signal towards Signal-Common.

Packet Timing

RDM places stronger timing requirements on a number of parameters. The following table summarises the RDM timing requirements:

Controller Timing

Item	Transmitting		Receiving	
	Min	Max	Min	Max
Packet Time	1,204uS	61,924uS[1]	1,196uS	N/A
Break	176uS	352uS	88uS	352uS
MaB	12uS	88uS	8uS	88uS
Data Bit	3.92uS	4.08uS	3.92uS	4.08uS
Slot	43.12uS	44.88uS	43.12uS	44.88uS
Inter-Byte Delay	0uS	2mS	0uS	2.1mS
Average Inter-Byte Delay	0uS	76uS	0uS	76uS

Note 1: Assuming all 512 data slots transmitted.

Responder Timing

Item	Receiving		Transmitting	
	Min	Max	Min	Max
Packet Time	1,196uS	1.25S	1,204uS	61,924uS[1]
Break	88uS	≤1S[2]	176uS	352uS
MaB	8uS	≤1S[2]	12uS	88uS
Data Bit	3.92uS	4.08uS	3.92uS	4.08uS
Slot	43.12uS	44.88uS	43.12uS	44.88uS
Inter-Byte Delay	0uS	2.1mS[3]	0uS	2.0mS
Average Inter-Byte Delay	0	76uS[3]	0uS	76uS

Note 1: Assuming all 512 data slots transmitted.
Note 2: These maximum times must be set such that the Packet Time does not exceed 1S.
Note 3: This relates only to a responder receiving an RDM packet.

Break

The RDM minimum Break length has been increased to 176uS. The reason is that inline devices such as splitters can reduce the length of a responder's break. This can occur because the splitter must detect the Break and then change the bus direction. The standard allows each splitter to reduce the Break by a maximum of 22uS. This means that four cascaded splitters (with worst case Break length reduction) will result is a Break length that is 88uS and therefore still conform to DMX512

MaB Mark after Break

The MaB has been increased to 12uS for RDM packets. There is no particularly good reason for this, other than to cut the microprocessors a little slack as they are very busy around the reset sequence time.

MbB Mark before Break

The MbB for RDM is set to a minimum of 176uS. This is to allow a dead time for switching the line direction.

IBD Inter-Byte Delay

The Inter-Byte Delay is also called the Inter-Slot Time (IST). RDM limits this in two ways. Firstly the maximum IBD between any two slots is limited to 2mS. However the more stringent limitation is that of the average IBD. This is limited to 76uS and as a result limits the maximum packet length. RDM needs to do this because it must be possible for devices to calculate when to time out a non-response.

Take for example a situation where the controller sends a Get command to a responder. If the packet timing was purely based on DMX512, the responder could legitimately take one second to send its response. This would lead to an unusable system, hence the new limits of RDM.

The maximum length of a packet is defined by the following equation:

$$P_I = Break + MaB + Start Code + (n \times Slot Time) + ((n-1) \times Ave IBD)$$

Where n is the number of slots. Putting in the fixed numbers, we get:

$$P_I = 440uS + (n \times 44uS) + ((n-1) \times 76uS)$$

For a packet transmitting the maximum number of slots, n= 513. So:

$$P_I = 440uS + (513 \times 44uS) + ((512) \times 76uS) = 61.924mS$$

There is an error in the RDM standard when this equation is discussed. It states that 'n' is the number of data slots. This is incorrect and 'n' is the number of slots (i.e. it includes the start code).

Transaction Timing

RDM also places restrictions on the time between packets. This is to ensure that:

c)   There is enough time between packets for the bus to turnaround (change direction).
d)   That the controller will know when to timeout a non-response from a responder.

The fundamental timing constraint is a function of Mark before Break (MbB). RDM sets this at 176uS which means the minimum time between any two packets is 176uS.

| Item | Time | | Note |
	Min	Max	
End of Controller packet to start of Responder's reply	176uS	2mS	1
End of Controller packet to Controller receives start of Responder's reply	176uS	2.8mS	2
End of Controller Discovery packet to next Controller packet	5.8mS	1S	3
End of Controller packet to start of next controller packet if expected response not received.	3mS	1S	4
End of Controller packet to Controller drivers high impedance	0	88uS	5
End of Responder packet to Responder drivers high impedance	0	88uS	6

Response Packet Timing

When a controller sends an RDM Get command, the responder must start its reply within a window of 176uS to 2mS from the end of the controller's command. The minimum value is a function of the minimum time between any RDM packet (MbB) being 176uS. The maximum time of 2mS is a design decision of RDM. (Note 1).

RDM allows inline devices such as splitters to delay both commands and responses. This means that the time limit discussed above is dependent upon where you make the measurement! The 2mS maximum is measured at the responder. The total 'round trip' delay that is allowed is 704uS. This value when added to 2mS and rounded up gives us 2.8mS.

So even when the responder replies within the specified timing window of 2mS, the controller must allow 2.8mS. (Note 2).

Discovery Response Timing

After a controller sends a discovery message, it must wait a minimum of 5.8mS before it sends the next packet (of whatever type). During this time it is monitoring the line for discovery responses.

The figure of 5.8mS is based on the following calculation:

•   The discovery response is 24 bytes in length and each byte takes 44uS to send. RDM allows a maximum average IBD of 76uS. So the discovery response will take a maximum of (24 x 44us) + (23 x 76uS) = 2,804uS. So call it 2.8mS.
•   The maximum delay to the start of a response is 2mS (Note 1).
•   The round trip insertion delay is 704uS (Note 2).

Adding the above items gives us 5.5mS. As the RDM designers were cautious souls, an additional 300uS safety margin was added to allow for inline device bus turnaround and any late responders. Hence the figure of 5.8mS (Note 3).

Missing Response

The packet to packet timing limits are extended in the event that a controller does not receive an expected reply. This is designed to allow for the potential that the responder is late and to try to avoid bus contention in this error condition.

The controller must wait 3mS (Note 4) from the end of a request packet, before deciding that a response will not be forthcoming and therefore starting to send the next packet.

The figure is based on the 2.8mS (Note 1) time with an additional 200uS safety margin for inline device bus turnaround.

Line Driver Control

The standard specifies the times at which the line drivers of controllers, inline devices and responders should be enabled or disabled.

When the controller sends an RDM packet for which a response is expected, it must stop driving the line (and switch to receive mode) within 88uS of the end of packet. (Note 5).

In the same condition, inline devices must stop driving their outputs within 132uS of the end of packet. (See next section).

Finally, in the same condition, a responder must start its reply no earlier than 176uS from the end of packet. (Note 1).

These staggered time parameters provide an 88uS window during which time all the line drivers can be switched without causing a bus contention (that is having more than one line driver driving the line).

The chart below provides a summary of the key timing parameters for line driver control.

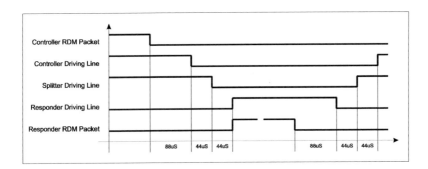

Splitter Timing

RDM Splitters must adhere to the following timing parameters:

Item	Time	
	Min	Max
End of RDM GET Packet to turnaround of output buffers	0uS	132uS
End of RDM response Packet to normal forward operation	0uS	132uS
End of RDM Discovery Message to normal forward operation	5.600uS	5.800uS
Insertion Delay	0uS	88uS
Bit Distortion	0nS	+/-75nS
Response Packet Break Shortening	0uS	22uS

Discovery Timing

In a non-discovery RDM transaction, the splitter can easily detect the start and end of a response packet. The start is a Break and the end can be calculated from the packet length field in the response packet.

Discovery response is more complicated: Firstly discovery relies on collisions which are 'intentional errors'. As such their duration is undefined. In addition there is no Break at the start of a discovery response and no packet length to decode. It is for this reason that the timing requirement for splitter turnaround during discovery is defined relative to the end of the controller's discovery command.

Insertion Delay
Insertion delay is the term used to describe the delay as data passes through the splitter. RDM sets an upper limit of 88uS and further assumes that the maximum number of cascaded inline devices will be 4.

Keeping in mind that the insertion delay will happen to packets going in both directions, the total delay this can cause is 2 x 4 x 88uS = 704uS.

In reality most splitters will have an insertion delay measured in nanoseconds and the above calculation will not limit the number of splitters that can be cascaded. The figure of 88uS was chosen based on being twice the length of time taken to transmit a slot. In principle this allows the design of inline devices that require data to be read by a microprocessor, processed and then retransmitted. An RDM capable merger is an example of such a device.

Bit Distortion
Bit Distortion describes the situation where the leading edge and the trailing edge of a data bit are delayed by different amounts. This provides two problems:

a)   The duration of the bit differs from the original.
b)   The centre of the distorted bit differs from the original.

Both problems can accumulate through multiple splitters which is the reason for the stringent limit.

Break Shortening
Splitters detect the start of the Break of an RDM response as the trigger to turnaround the line direction. As the bus turnaround takes a finite time, the Break of the response can be shortened by the splitter. RDM sets a limit of 22uS for shortening Break.

A standard DMX512 splitter is a unidirectional device. That is: it passes data in one direction, from the input to the output. As RDM is a bidirectional protocol, a special type of splitter is needed.

Numerous manufacturers produce RDM capable splitters including Artistic Licence, Doug Fleenor Design and Goddard Design Co. See Chapter 4 for examples.

The RDM standard does not define how splitters should be designed, but it does define the timing parameters to which they must adhere. Different manufacturers have taken different approaches to the electronic design, but they will all be compatible if they meet the RDM timing requirements.

Splitters can also be designed in such a way that they are also an RDM device. This has the potential benefit of allowing the control system to detect the splitters to which it is connected then both configure and monitor status. This more advanced style of splitter is often called a 'Hub'.

An understanding of how RDM splitters operate is useful both for system design and fault finding so let's look at the concepts.

RDM Splitter Operation

The figures below show a simple example of a splitter that is connected to two RDM devices. Inside the splitter arrows show the data flow direction of the input and output buffers.

Normal operation

In this instance both the input and output buffers are in the forward direction. This allows all DMX512 and RDM data to pass from the controller to the responders.

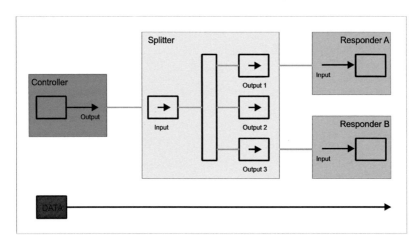

The controller now sends an RDM 'Get' command to Responder A.

RDM command just sent

Having sent the RDM Get command, the controller switches its output to receive mode (as shown by the red arrow pointing to the left). The controller is now ready to receive the response.

The splitter monitored the command sent by the controller and knows that a response is expected. It switches its output buffers to receive and starts watching all outputs to look for a Break. It also disables its input buffer.

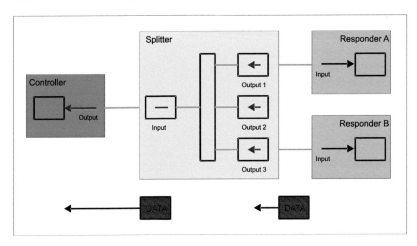

Responder starts to reply

Responder A receives the RDM command. It switches its input buffer to transmit and starts sending the Break that is the beginning of its response packet.

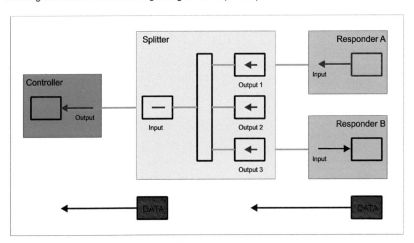

Splitter connects responder to controller

The splitter sees the transition from high to low which represents the start of the Break. It switches its input buffer to transmit thereby making a data path from Responder A to Controller.

It is worth noting that this is the reason that RDM specifies a longer minimum Break for transmitters than is required by DMX512-A. The direction switching in the splitter occurs as soon as the response Break is detected. This means that the splitter can shorten the Break. If a number of splitters are connected in series, the Break could be shortened considerably.

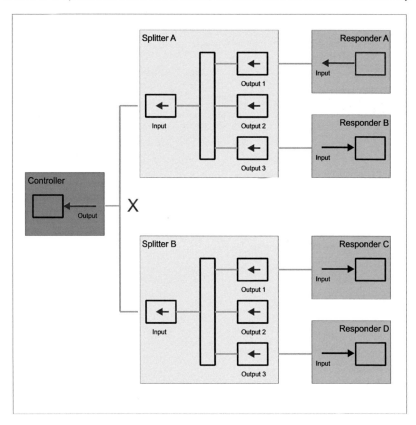

Splitter line contention

It may not be immediately obvious why these four stages are needed. Why does the splitter not simply switch direction of input and output as soon as it sees the controller's RDM command?

The drawing below explains why this cannot occur. If there was only a single splitter then it would work. However if any other splitters or responders are connected to the loop connection of the splitter, a problem would occur.

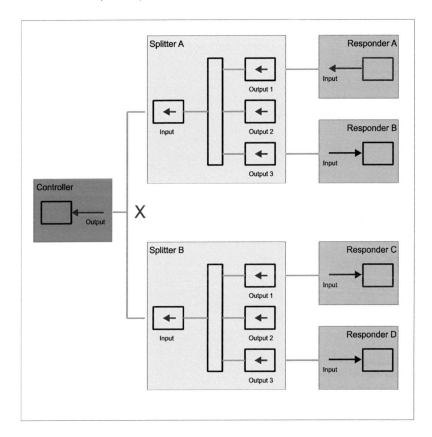

Both Splitter A and Splitter B are attempting to drive data back to the controller. This is called a Bus Contention and leads to data corruption. In fact if splitters behaved in this manner, RDM would simply not work!

RDM Splitters & Discovery

The figure below shows how splitters operate in discovery. In this example Responder B and Responder D have already been discovered and are muted.

Responder A and Responder C are both shown responding to a discovery command. The splitter is designed to recognise a discovery command and in this situation it switches to reverse data flow when it sees the first preamble byte of the discovery response.

Both splitters behave identically which means they both attempt to drive data to the controller. In this case, the contention is intentional causing the controller to see a collision.

It is worth noting that this is why there are a number of Preamble bytes at the start of the discovery response. The splitter may damage one of the preamble bytes in the process of switching direction.

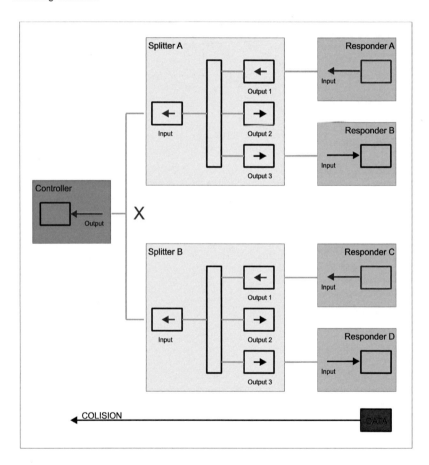

Cascading RDM Splitters

The RDM standard states that only four cascaded inline devices (splitters) can be used. In fact this is not strictly true! The number of splitters that can be cascaded depends on whether the splitter is well designed. I recently tested the Artistic Licence Rack-Split RDM and discovered that 24 can be cascaded. It may well be higher but we became bored with un-boxing the products!

There are four key factors that affect the answer to this question:

Insertion Delay

RDM allows each inline device to delay the data by a maximum of 88uS. If a splitter uses this maximum then the maximum number of splitters that can be cascaded is only four. Most splitters have an insertion delay measured in nanoseconds and this parameter is not an issue.

Break Shortening

Splitters detect the start of the Break of an RDM response as the trigger to turnaround the line direction. As the bus turnaround takes a finite time, the Break of the response can be shortened by the splitter. RDM sets a limit of 22uS for shortening Break. This is why the minimum time for a transmitted break is 176uS. Four inline devices can each shorten the break by 22uS and the Break will still be a minimum of 88uS which conforms to DMX512 receive timing requirements.

This is probably the most important factor in defining the maximum number of cascaded splitters. The actual amount by which the Break is shortened will depend on the processing power of the microprocessor in the splitter. The 22uS allowance is very high and real world splitters are unlikely to delay Break by more than a few microseconds.

Discovery Preamble Damage

The responses to discovery messages do not start with a Break. This means that an inline device may damage the leading bytes of the discovery response. That is precisely why there are Preamble bytes at the front of a discovery response. In fact there are seven Preamble bytes which means that if each splitter destroys an entire byte, six cascaded splitters will still operate correctly.

Bit Distortion

Each inline device is allowed to distort data bits by +/-75nS. The DMX512 standard states that the tolerance for bit timing is +/-80nS. Thus if a splitter does distort bits by 75nS then it would not be possible to use any cascaded splitters.

The reality is that a well designed splitter is unlikely to distort bits by more than a few nanoseconds. It is however worth noting that it is possible to design a perfectly legal RDM splitter that could not be cascaded!

Conclusion

At this point it will probably be clear that the answer to the maximum number of cascaded splitters is not a simple one! Hopefully market pressure will cause manufacturers of inline devices to declare this information in their product specification.

Chapter 15 RDM Test Equipment

Whilst RDM is a relatively new standard, numerous manufacturers are already offering sophisticated test and configuration tools. Below is an overview of the current offerings:

Artistic Licence Jump-Start

The Jump-Start is a dual function product. It can operate as a simple DMX512 'rig check' transmitter or as a sophisticated RDM test and configuration tool.

It is able to transmit the majority of available RDM commands and display the responses. It also allows key parameters such as Start Address and Lamp Personality to be set.

Jump-Start is user configured for either Draft or Standard RDM.

The product is battery powered by two 'AA' batteries.

Doug Fleenor RAD

The RAD is designed to set the Start Address of fixtures using RDM.

The product is battery powered (9V) and available in a range of garish colours!

DEALERS' CHOICE AWARD WINNER
WIDGET CATEGORY 2004

Howard Eaton Lighting RDM Lab Pack

The Lab Pack is an essential tool for anyone developing RDM products. It provides six RDM responders which can respond to pretty much every RDM command known to man.

It also provides a range of manufacturer specific PIDs that can be used to modify the response timing of the product.

Artistic Licence DMX-Workshop

DMX-Workshop is a free software package that provides detailed logging, decoding and analysis of RDM packets.

The picture shows the decoding of an RDM Get command.

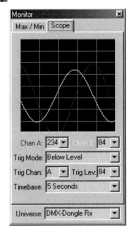

Artistic Licence Net-Lynx O/P

Net-Lynx OP is an Art-Net Ethernet to DMX

It can be used in conjunction with either DM traffic.

The product provides two independent DMX Ethernet connection.

Artistic Licence Colour-Tramp

Colour-Tramp is a full featured lighting controller that integrates RDM control and diagnostics into the user interface. The image shows the control screen from the Broadgate Finsbury Avenue Square installation in London.

The screen display can be switched from lighting control display to view RDM diagnostics and even colour coded analysis of the fixture sensor data.

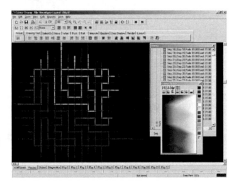

Broadgate – An RDM First

The City of London's financial district of Broadgate now boasts one of the most striking and sophisticated lighting features in the World. It consists of a large in-ground array of colour changing lamps, laid out in a semi-symmetric pattern. The array uses over 650 individually controllable light modules, each providing independent colour mixing. The set effect is a dynamic floor of colour providing effects ranging from subtle moods of colour to dynamic animation.

The concept was designed by Mark Ridler at Maurice Brill Lighting Design. Mark called in Artistic Licence to implement the concept and Artistic Licence was commissioned to develop, manufacture and install the system at Finsbury Avenue Square.

The fixture design provided numerous technical problems. The physical size of the lighting array precluded the conventional approach of centralised dimmers and 'dumb' fixtures; cable voltage drop would have led to variation in fixture brightness. The concept of an intelligent lighting fixture was the only real option. With a lighting fixture buried in the ground and only glass visible from the surface, how would we access the fixture electronics to configure the DMX address and so forth? The fixture was to be waterproof to IP68. Could we risk an access cover for the controls?

It soon became clear that a control mechanism more powerful than standard DMX512 would be required. Around that time, Artistic Licence was very heavily involved with the ESTA standards programme. A new standard called RDM or Remote Device Management was being conceived. RDM was to provide a new method of controlling intelligent fixtures and allow attributes such as DMX base address to be remotely programmed.

Even though RDM was still at the concept stage, Artistic Licence committed to using RDM for the Broadgate Project. Not only did it obviate the need for access covers, but it also provided new features such as the ability to upload software to the fixture and retrieve sensor information.

Broadgate – An RDM First

In large architectural projects such as Broadgate, fixture sensors can be a huge benefit to maintenance management. Imagine having advance warning that a fixture may need maintenance. Three sensors were implemented; for temperature, input voltage and moisture.

Use of the new RDM protocol for control had a significant impact on the entire control system and data distribution infrastructure. A new breed of DMX512 splitter was designed, allowing both DMX512 and RDM data to flow over the same cable. The Art-Net Ethernet standard was upgraded to provide a transport mechanism for the new types of control data.

The control system or lighting console was an opportunity to excel! A conventional memory console could have been used, but the task of programming the matrix of lamps on a console that understood only channel numbers was considered too great a burden. Had a conventional console been used, there would still be a requirement for a separate computer system for RDM configuration and sensor monitoring as there are not yet any production consoles that support RDM.

A number of years previously, Artistic Licence had worked with Charlie Kail at Brilliant Stages to design a control system called Lamp-Tramp. It was conceived to control two-dimensional arrays of intensity lamps and received much acclaim on the Rolling Stones Voodoo Lounge and Pink Floyd Division Bell tours. The Lamp-Tramp concept was updated to develop a new system capable of controlling colour changing fixtures. Colour-Tramp was born!

Colour-Tramp is a new breed of lighting controller that communicates via the Art-Net Ethernet standard and implements all the functionality of Remote Device Management. This allows it to operate as both a lighting controller and an installation management system. One screen can show a topographic output mimic of the lighting whilst another shows sensor status of all the fixtures.

During installation at Broadgate, the favourite function was 'Auto-Patch'. At the press of a button, all 650 fixtures are programmed such that their start address matches the patch. Imagine how many days of DIP switch setting that saved! Colour-Tramp also provides email reporting functions on the status of the fixtures. This allows concepts such as statistical analysis of fixture temperature over a period of time.The Finsbury Avenue Square project represents the very latest in lighting technology.

Statistics:
Total Fixtures: 650
Total LEDs: 100,000
Total Channels: 1,650
Total Aluminium Extrusion: 1,000 m
Total Power: 23,000 W
Control System: Colour-Tramp x 1
DMX Distribution: Iso-Split RDM x 9
Ethernet Distribution: Ether-Lynx x 2

Credits:
Client: The British Land Corporation
Lighting Design: Maurice Brill Lighting Design
Lighting Equipment Design: Artistic Licence
Executive Architect: Skidmore Owings & Merrill
Electrical Contractor: Meica Services
Development Management: M3 Consulting
Program Management: Bovis Lend Lease

AWARDS
IALD Award of Excellence 2004
LIF Exterior Lighting Category 2004
IEIJ Japan Exterior Lighting Category 2004
FX Awards Highly Commended for Best Office or Public Lighting Scheme 2005

Finsbury Avenue Square won the exterior category for what the judges called quite simply "one of the outstanding schemes of recent years", and, "a technically demanding creation".

Wybron InfoTrace

InfoTrace offers the ability to add RDM monitoring and configuration to an existing non-RDM system.

The InfoTrace product is connected between the non-RDM controller and the fixtures. It then adds RDM functionality whilst connecting to the InfoTrace PC software via an Ethernet link.

Chapter 16 Notes to RDM Product Designers

This chapter is primarily directed at designers but may also be useful to end users when tracking compatibility issues.

The 3 Second Flicker

As the first wave of RDM products went to market, I've been amazed at the number of legacy DMX512 products that do not check the start code. This usually manifests itself as a slight flicker repeating every few seconds as the device momentarily accepts an RDM packet as if it were a zero start code packet.

So the most important design issue is to check the start code!

If you hit this problem in the field, there is a workaround that is successful most of the time: Set the device's start address to values above say '50'. As most RDM packets are shorter than this the flicker is usually masked or minimised.

Many product designers are including 'RDM Disable' jumpers in their controllers to provide end users with a 'get out of jail card' when faced with this problem!

Sub-Devices

General

If a responder supports sub-devices, the designer will need to address the following:

- Set the sub-device flag in reply to the DISC_MUTE and DISC_UN_MUTE discovery commands.
- Remember that all sub-devices are identical so the reply to PIDs such as SUPPORTED_PARAMETERS must be identical independent of the sub-device.
- The standard specifically notes that the sub-device numbers need not be consecutive. So if a responder informs the controller that it has 10 sub-devices, the controller must not assume they are numbered 1-10. In my opinion this was an error of judgement in the standard that is likely to lead to compatibility issues in the future. I strongly advise designers of responders to consecutively number sub-devices starting at '1' unless there is a really strong reason to do otherwise.
- The number of sub-devices used by a responder is likely to change with personality. When a responder's personality changes, it is good design to queue a DEVICE_ INFO message so that the controller is informed of the change.

Sub-Device Footprints

When designing a responder with sub-devices there are a number of ways in which the footprint of the root and sub-devices could be published. Consider a device that has 2 sub-devices, each of which uses 3 channels or slots. The root device uses no slots directly.

One could reasonably say the root has a footprint of 0 and each sub-device has a footprint of 3. However this approach is unhelpful to the controller. A better approach is to always publish the root footprint as the total footprint of all the implemented sub devices. The result in this example would be:

- Root has a footprint of 6 and each sub-device has a footprint of 3.

Sub-Device Start Address

In some sub-device implementations the start address of the root will be distinct from the start address of the first sub device. For example: Consider a scroller power supply. Let's say the sub-devices are the individual scrollers but the root device contains one slot that is the global speed channel.

In this example there would be no interaction between getting and setting the start addresses of sub-devices and the root.

Consider a second example where the root device is just a 'holder' for the sub-devices - perhaps a dimmer rack. In this example there is no logical distinction between the start address of the root and the start address of the first sub-device.

The designer may choose to make getting and setting the start addresses of the first sub-devices and the root identical. Alternatively the root start address can be given special meaning and used as a quick method of readdressing all sub-devices consecutively from the specified start address.

A number of manufacturers implement this concept and it is proving very useful on large systems.

When to use Sub-Devices

The decision is very much subjective, but there are some issues to keep in mind:

- Modular systems are the most likely contenders for sub-devices. This would include scroller power supplies, modular dimmer racks and pixel based LED controllers.
- The user will see your implementation on screen, so try to make it helpful. If there is symmetry in the slot use of the responder, the user will find it easier to interpret if you use the root / sub-device hierarchy.
- Many controllers have the ability to auto-patch. Automated patching is more useful to the user if the controller can deal with a large quantity of small sub-devices compared to one root device with a massive footprint.

Equally there are situations where there is no benefit to using sub-devices:

- If the sub-devices do not have the ability to accept separate start addresses; the sub-devices are pointless.
- When the logical blocks of the responder have different footprints of significantly different functionality, it is difficult to implement sub-devices. Moving lamps are a good example. It would be possible to implement each attribute (pan, tilt, colour, etc) as a sub-device; however there is little benefit compared to a single root device.

Sensors

Where to put Sensors

When the responder design uses only a root device there is only one position in the hierarchy for the sensors.

If the responder has sub-devices, a decision will need to be made on whether the product's sensors are attached to the root or the sub-devices.

There are two key considerations:

- The physical position of the sensors. Consider our scroller power supply example above. Let's say each scroller has a 'motor jammed' sensor and there is also a temperature sensor in the power supply. Perhaps the most logical implementation is to attach the single temperature sensor to the root devices and each motor jammed sensor to each sub-device. The standard does not mandate this and it would be equally valid to attach all sensors to the root device.

• A number of controllers in the first wave to market do not implement sub-devices let alone sensors attached to sub-devices. So for best compatibility in the early years of RDM support, attaching all sensors to the root device may be best.

PIDs

SUPPORTED_PIDS

There are two common errors in the implementation of this command:

The first relates to the interpretation of the reply. This is one of the few packets where the amount of data may not fit in one message. The responder sends the reply in multiple response packets using ACK_OVERFLOW to indicate follow on packets. The controller continues to send Get:SUPPORTED_PIDS commands until it sees a response with ACK rather than ACK_OVERFLOW. That indicates the end of the multi-packet response.

Should the controller wish to start the sequence from the beginning, it simply needs to send any other valid PID to the responder as that will reset the multi-packet counter. The common error is to neglect to parse the Response Type field. This would lead to the controller seeing every packet as a replacement rather than addition to the list of supported PIDs.

The second relates to implementation of the message. The RDM standard requires that a responder implement the PID but does not require that a controller use the data.

This means that a controller can choose whether to use SUPPORTED_PIDs or simply send commands and learn from the response, which ones are supported. In controller design, there are times when either approach can prove beneficial. The key point is that a responder should be able to handle any PID it receives independent of whether it has published it as supported. By 'handle' I mean at the least respond with a NAK_REASON.

QUEUED_MESSAGE

The QUEUED_MESSAGE PID breaks the symmetry of all other PIDs in the sense that the response message will not contain the same PID. QUEUED_MESSAGE is interpreted by the responder as 'give me what you have'. The response may be any valid none discovery PID.

This PID is the most useful to use as a background poll to the responders. If the responders do not have a message queued, they will send a STATUS_MESSAGE instead.

Use QUEUED_MESSAGE in preference to STATUS_MESSAGE for the background polling as it is the more powerful of the two.

Text Fields

The length of a variable text field within an RDM packet is fundamentally defined by the PDL – Parameter Data Length. However, a null character may also be embedded in the text which a receiver must honour as the end of text. That said, it is incorrect to assume that there will be a null terminator in the string.

Hardware

Termination & Biasing.

RDM requires that the line is guaranteed to default to a marking state even when devices are switched off. This is achieved as follows:

- The Controller, which is located at one end of the DMX512 cable, has a 120R termination across pins 2 & 3. Note that the physical value of the termination will be higher than 120R in order to generate an effective impedance of 120R. It also has 'pull apart' resistors that force the line to mark. The value of the resistors is calculated by current. With 5V drivers a value of 560R will work. The standard defines a specific test circuit which can be used to prove that both controller and responder driver circuits are compliant.
- The end of line responder has a 120R termination across pins 2 & 3. This is usually user selected such that a responder can be placed either mid-line or at the end of line.
- Responders should be designed such that their drivers are guaranteed to power on in the high impedance state.
- Whilst not required by the standard it is good practice to include a soft 'pull apart' line bias on all responders. A value of 56K has been found to be effective.

Timing

Break Time

The RDM standard mandates that the controller transmit a break that is longer (minimum 176uS) than that required by DMX512. The reason for this is that inline devices such as splitters are allowed to shorten the break as the change direction of their buffers. An RDM responder should accept breaks down to the minimum DMX512(1990) time of 88uS.

MaB Time

The RDM standard mandates that the controller transmit a MaB that is longer (minimum 12uS).

Inter-Slot Time

The DMX512 standard did not place any specific restriction on the time between slots. The RDM standard does place restrictions on this time in order that the timeouts between packets can be defined.

There are two conditions:

- The average inter-slot time must not exceed 76uS.
- No single inter-slot time may exceed 2.0mS.

Errata

There were some minor errors in the text of the first release of the RDM standard. They are listed below. A forum for discussion of RDM matters including document errata exists at the following web address. Whilst not an ESTA sponsored site, many key members of the design team are active in the forum. http://www.rdmprotocol.org

Table 3-2 Note #3

2.804uS should be 2.804mS.

Section 3.2.1 Responder Packet Timings

The last paragraph references Table 3-2 Line 3. It should reference Table 3-3 Line 1.

Section 6.2.11 Checksum

The following text should be added to this section:

"If the checksum field in the packet does not match the calculated checksum, then the packet shall be discarded and no response sent."

Table 6-6

In the example:

Slot 1 should be 0x01.
Slot 16 should be 0x01 not 0x00
Slot 24 should be 0x04 not 0xFF.
Slot 25 should be 0x06
Slot 26 should be 0x6A

Section 6.3.3 Acknowledge Timer

The example shows an ACK_TIMER response to a GET: LAMP_STRIKES message. The example incorrectly shows a PDL of 0x04. The PDL should be 0x02. The Parameter Data (PD) section of the message should be 0x0258 rather than 0x00000258 as stated.

Section 9.2.2 Sub-Device All Call

The following text should be added to Section 9.2.2: "Broadcast GET commands sent to the SUB_DEVICE_ALL_CALL Sub-Device ID are not allowed. Any responder receiving a GET command sent to this Sub-Device ID shall respond with a NACK with a NACK Reason Code of NR_SUB_DEVICE_OUT_OF_RANGE."

All GET messages throughout Section 10 should show the show the Sub-Device GET range stopping at 0xFFFE.

Section 10. (Entire Section) Port ID

Section 6.2.7.1 states that the Port ID shall always be in the range of 1-255 for Controller generated messages.

All Get/Set message tables in Section 10 incorrectly show the Port ID range being from 0x00-0xFF. These messages should all show the allowed values for this field in the range from 0x01-0xFF.

Section 10.2.1 Get/Set Communications Status

The following sentence should be added to both the Length Mismatch and Checksum Fail paragraphs:

"Messages sent to an applicable Broadcast address shall also increment this counter."

Section 10.2.1 Communications Status

Short Message should be re-defined as the following:

"Short Message – This field shall be incremented any time the message terminates (either due to a BREAK or timeout condition occurring) before a complete Destination UID has been received."

Length Mismatch should be re-defined as the following:

"Length Mismatch - The number of slots received before a BREAK or message timeout condition occurring did not match the Message Length plus the size of the Checksum. This counter shall only be incremented if the Destination UID in the packet matches the Device's UID."

Section 10.4.2 Get Parameter Description

The TYPE field in the response for this message incorrectly is associated with a Sensors related table (Table A-12). This field has no meaning and should be filled with 0x00 in the response. Controllers should ignore the contents of this field.

Section 10.7.2 Get/Set Sensor Value

When doing a SET to reset the Sensor values, the response contains the current value for that Sensor. Sending this to Sensor 0xFF is used to reset all Sensors. The response for the Sensor values is currently undefined behaviour with Sensor 0xFF.

The following text should be added:

"The Sensor Value fields in the response to a SET Command sent to Sensor 0x0FF shall be ignored by the Controller. There is no requirement on a responder to provide specific values in this response."

Section 10.7.2 Get/Set Sensor Value

Add the following sentence to: Lowest Detected Value, Highest Detected Value, and Recorded Value:

"If this value is not supported, then this field shall be set to 0x0000."

All 16-bit and 32-bit Timers/Counters

This relates to Sections:

- 10.2.1 Communications Status
- 10.8.1 Device Hours
- 10.8.2 Lamp Hours
- 10.8.3 Lamp Strikes
- 10.8.6 Device Power Cycles

All 16-bit and 32-bit timers/counters should be referenced to explicitly be unsigned values and to not roll over if their value exceeds the max value.

The following phrase should be added to these messages:

"This value for this field shall be unsigned and not roll over when maximum value is reached."

Appendix B

Add the following text to Appendix B:

" 'Slot Label Code' refers to the Slot ID in Table C-2."

Appendix D.33 Mute

The definition should state that being Muted only stops the device from responding to UNIQ_BRANCH and not any other messages. The following text should be added:

"A device that is "muted" only stops responding to the DISC_UNIQUE_BRANCH message and shall still respond to all other messages".

Q: Why can't I use Microphone cable for DMX512?

A: Microphone cable is designed for audio signals. In the audio world, the signal you want is below about 22KHz (the upper range of human hearing). Any frequencies above that are considered interference as they cannot be heard but can degrade the signal. So mic (or audio) cable is designed to not allow those high frequencies to pass down the cable.

DMX512 runs at 250KHz, over 10 times faster than audio. Also, because it is a digital signal it has frequency components that are much higher. When you try to put DMX down an audio cable, the cable filters out the high frequencies. The net effect is that all of the 'corners' of the DMX signal become rounded. When these 'rounded' DMX signals get to the destination, the electronics (in a splitter for example) try to turn them back into a digital waveform by 'un-rounding' the corners. This introduces timing errors and can cause data loss.

Q: Why can I no longer use 3 pin XLR for DMX512?

A: In fact, the 3 pin XLR has never been allowed, DMX has always required a 5 pin XLR. The new DMX512-A standard is more forceful in saying that you must not use 3 pin XLR whereas the original DMX standard just said you should use a 5 pin XLR. The main technical reason for not using a 3 pin is simply that mic cable uses a 3 pin. So by using a 5 pin, there is less chance of mixing up the cables.

Q: Can I use the spare pins of the 5 pin XLR for low voltage power?

A: No. The spare pins can only be used for EIA-485 data. Using them for power can damage other equipment.

Q: What is the maximum cable distance for DMX512?

A: 300m

Q: How many moving lights or dimmer racks can I put on one DMX cable?

A: The maximum is 32 receivers on one cable. If you need more than this, use splitters.

Q: Why do some manufacturers say that you can put more than 32 devices on a DMX cable?

A: Generally this is because they are using specialist electronics or line drivers that have a lower load on the DMX cable. However you should be careful with such statements. If a specific manufacturer says you can put 100 (for example) of their devices on a DMX cable, I dare say you can. But what would happen when you start mixing their products with those from other manufacturers? So in conclusion, sticking to the 32 limit is a tried and trusted plan!

Q: Are cables manufactured specifically for DMX512 better than standard RS485 cables?

A: In terms of their ability to transmit the data, there is rarely any significant difference. However, cables designed for DMX512 are often much more robust.

Q: Pins 4 & 5 are not used by DMX512. Is there any need to connect them?

A: The DMX512-A standard suggests that the spare pins should be connected. However I am of the view that it is safest to leave them unconnected in the cable. The reason is that over the years different manufacturers have used pins 4&5 for a range of incompatible functions.

Q: Should the metal shell of the 5 pin XLR be connected to the screen?

A: No. The screen of the cable should connect to pin 1 and not the screen.

Q: What is the difference between ground and earth?

A: It is mainly a linguistic difference between English and American terminology.

The English use is as follows: Earth means the safety mains earth connection on a piece of equipment or the mains supply. Ground means the 0V power supply connection.

The American use is as follows: Ground means the safety mains earth connection on a piece of equipment or the mains supply.

In order to reduce the potential for total confusion, DMX512 uses the term 'Earth-Ground'. Unfortunately the DMX512 standard is not totally consistent in this use. So Europeans beware! When the standard talks of 'Grounded Transmitters' it means 'Earthed Transmitters'.

Q: What is a Ground Referenced Transmitter?

A: A DMX512 output that has a low resistance electrical connection between pin 1 of the XLR and Earth-Ground (mains earth). This is now considered the preferred arrangement.

Q: What is an Isolated Transmitter?

A: A DMX512 output that has no electrical connection between the pins of the XLR and Earth-Ground (mains earth).

Q: What is a Grounded Receiver?

A: A DMX512 input that has a direct connection between pin 1 of the XLR and Earth-Ground (mains earth). This is allowed by DMX512 but requires the manufacturer to mark the connector with a warning symbol.

Q: What is an Isolated Receiver?

A: A DMX512 input that has no electrical connection between the pins of the XLR and Earth-Ground (mains earth).

Q: What is an Non-isolated Receiver?

A: A DMX512 input that has a minimum 100R resistive connection between pin 1 of the XLR and Earth-Ground (mains earth).

Q: What is a Y-Cord?

A: A passive splitter cable that attempts to connect two DMX512 receivers to one transmitter. Y-Cords cause major problems with DMX512 and must not be used.

Q: What is a Legacy Device?

A: This is a term used to describe products that were designed to comply with DMX512 (1990) and not DMX512-A.

Q: What is a Footprint?

A: This is a new term introduced in DMX512-A. It means the number of channels used by a DMX receiving device

Q: Is it OK to use Ethernet cable such as Cat5 for DMX512?

A: The DMX512 standard says yes subject to certain conditions: You should either used STP (screened twisted pair) or if you use UTP (unshielded twisted pair) the cable must be in Earth-Grounded trunking or conduit. I consider this requirement to be somewhat excessive. I have extensively tested UTP transmission of DMX512 up to 300m in an electrically noisy environment. It performs just as well as RS485 cable.

Q: Can I use an RJ45 to connect DMX512?

A: Yes but only in control rooms and patching bays.

Q: What is the difference between a Slot and a Data Slot?

A: There are 512 Data Slots and 513 Slots in a DMX512 packet. The Start Code is not a Data Slot.

Q: What's a SIP?

A: System Information Packet. It can be interleaved with 'normal' DMX data to provide advanced features such as checksums. It is not widely supported by manufacturers.

Q: What's RDM?

A: Remote Device Management. It's a system that works with DMX512-A to allow the data to flow in either direction on the DMX cable. This allows advanced features such as remotely setting the start address.

Q: Should I discard packets with a MaB of less than 8uS?

A: Generally the answer is no – there is no purpose. A short MaB is not indicative of a corrupted packet. Also remember that DMX512(1986) was a MaB of 4uS.

Q: Should I discard packets with a Break of less than 88uS?

A: Generally the answer is yes – a shorter break could be a zero data byte with corrupted stop bits. So a short break is quite likely to indicate data corruption. In reality very few receiver manufacturers do check for a short break.

Q: What is the difference between a Framing Error and a Break?

A: A framing error occurs when the receiver sees a byte of data that is missing its start or stop bits. A Break is a special type of framing error that has all data bits set to zero.

Q: Why does RDM specify a MbB when DMX512 does not?

A: RDM switches direction of the DMX512 cable to allow bidirectional communication. This switching occurs at the end of a DMX512 frame. The purpose of the minimum 176uS MbB (Mark before Break) is to allow a 'dead period' in which the switching can occur.

Q: Why does RDM specify a longer minimum Break time than DMX512?

A: Splitters that support RDM may need to slightly shorten the Break length of each packet they pass. There exists the potential for cascaded RDM splitters to shorten the Break so much that the packet would then violate the DMX512 timing. The increased Break time requirement of RDM ensures this cannot happen.

Q: Why does the RDM Discovery Reply message not have a Break?

A: By design, RDM Discovery Reply packets can collide which will cause errors on the DMX512 cable. If these packets had a Break at the start, it is possible that older non-RDM products could interpret the collision data as a good packet. This would result in flicker.

Appendix B ESTA Start Codes

Dec	Hex	Registered To	Description
0	0x00	USITT	Default Null Start Code for Dimmers per DMX512 & DMX512/1990
1	0x01	T-Recursive	Most significant Byte of double precision transmission
2	0x02	T-Recursive	Following packet is 256 16-Bi words in Lo byte/Hi byte order
3	0x03	R.A. Gray	Undisclosed
4	0x04	T-Recursive	Checksum Message
5	0x05	T-Recursive	Answerback Query
6	0x06	T-Recursive	16 bit Lo byte
7	0x07	T-Recursive	Compressed data
8	0x08	T-Recursive	Compressed 16-bit data
9	0x09	Entertainment Technology	Undisclosed
10	0x0A	Mode Lighting	Second universe of 512 channels on one data link.
11	0x0B	Goddard Design Co.	
12	0x0C	S G M Elettronica Srl.	
13	0x0D	Engineering Arts	
14	0x0E	C.I.Tronics Lighting Designers Ltda	Minimum packet length: 4 bytes Maximum packet length: 513 bytes Description: We would use our own alternative start code to send configuration informations to our devices. Also, we would like to use the possibility of two-way communication to get the status of these devices.
15	0x0F	Morpheus Lights	
16	0x10	ADB	Undisclosed
17	0x11	Tokyo Broadcast Systems Inc.	Undisclosed
18	0x12	BJA Electronics	For updating the firmware in my equipment and to control it (Reset). My packet size will between the 3 and 256 bytes.
19	0x13	Zero 88	
20	0x14	Soundsculpture Incorporated	We are implementing a message-based protocol that is optimized for safe and secure motor control, embedded with lighting control. A unique Start Code is the ideal way to identify this alternative data type on the DMX network, while keeping packets as short as possible.
21	0x15	CDCA Ltd.	Firmware update and configuration info
22	0x16	Peradise	We build specialFx and moving set parts. The startcode will be used to identify data that is used for tacticle feedback from devices (Position, status, errors, etc).
23	0x17	Artistic Licence (UK) Ltd.	Text Packet (matches use in ANSI E1.11)

Dec	Hex	Registered To	Description
23	0x17	E1	ANSI E1.11 Text Packet
24	0x18	Artistic Licence (UK) Ltd.	Product synchronisation
25	0x19	Hubbell Entertainment, Inc.	
26	0x1a	Integrated Theatre, Inc.	Second pair data synchronisation.
27	0x1B	Espace Concept	Programme selection.
28	0x1C	KLH Electronics PLC	Triple precision data (either 20 or 24 bit).
33	0x21	ELETTROLAB S.r.l.	unknown
38	0x26	High End Systems	Undisclosed Configuration
48	0x30	Pr-Lighting Ltd.	Firmware updates.
51	0x33	TESI Elettronica srl	Manufacturer specific commands and firmware updates.
55	0x37	TIR Systems Ltd.	Code used to specify various operating parameters for DMX512 network and standalone operation. Min.frames: 15; Max frames: 40 (current), 512 (reserved for future expansion)
60	0x3C	AVAB	AVAB Internal Functions
61	0x3D	AVAB	Smart 16 Bit Format
62	0x3E	AVAB America	Manufacturer-specific configuration data.
63	0x3F	SAND Network Systems, Inc.	Manufacturer-specific configuration data.
65	0x41	Microlite	Undisclosed
66	0x42	LSC Lighting Systems (Aust) Pty. Ltd.	Proprietary remote peripheral control
67	0x43	City Theatrical, Inc.	Firmware updates and product configuration
68	0x44	Coemar Spa	
72	0x48	Enfis Ltd.	ASC is used for passing proprietary data for applications such as factory test, configuration, and software update.
76	0x4C	Phoenix Service	4Ch is the START Code used for OpenDMX messages, a protocol developed for use on LUX Italia products, and published by them for royalty-free use by anyone. Visit the LUX Italia website (http://www.luxitalia.eu) for a copy of the specification.
77	0x4D	Avolites Ltd.	Proprietary function with ART2000 products
79	0x4F	Oscar Lighting AB	Backup States - Undisclosed
80	0x50	LightProcessor Ltd	
85	0x55	E1	Test Packet
87	0x57	Wybron, Inc.	
131	0x83	Anytronics Ltd.	To synchronise both the memory contents and the internal clocks of lighting control equipment. Min packet length 24 bytes. Max 512.
144	0x90	E1	Reserved for future expansion

Dec	Hex	Registered To	Description
145	0x91	E1	91h followed by a 2 byte Manufacturer ID field is reserved for Manufacturer/Organization specific use
146-169	0x92-0xa9	E1	Reserved for Future Expansion of the DMX512 Standard
170	0xAA	SUN	Undisclosed - bi-directional data transfer
171-203	ABh-CBh	E1	Reserved for Future Expansion of the DMX512 Standard
204	0xCC	E1	E1.20 (RDM) start code
205	0xCD	E1	Reserved for Future Expansion of the DMX512 Standard
206	0xCE	E1	Reserved for Future Expansion of the DMX512 Standard
207	0xCF	E1	ANSI E1.11 System Information Packet
208	0xD0	eldoLED Ltd.	Configuration, firmware updates and standalone configuration. Framelength to vary from 12 to 512 bytes.
221	0xDD	Electronic Theatre Controls	Alternative start code DD is for use in transmitting per channel priority for use in merging streams in multi-source DMX applications. Priorities will range from 0 at the low end, which means do not use the data in the corresponding slot, to 200, which means use this data over any slot data supplied with a priority between 0 and 199. Values above 200 are reserved for future use.
223	0xDF	Doug Fleenor Design, Inc.	Undisclosed
224	0xE0	NSI/Colortran	ENR Mode Control
225	0xE1	NSI/Colortran	Dim/Non-Dim Control
239	0xEF	Electronics Diversified, Inc.	Download Dimmer Information - Undisclosed
240	0xF0	E1	ESTA RDM Draft - prototyping
241-247	0xF1-0xF7	E1	Prototyping/experimental use Only while the manufacturer/organization is waiting for their registered Alternative START Code to be assigned
255	0xFF	Avolites	Dimmer Curve Select

Appendix C DMX 512 Start Code Conflicts

Dec	Hex	Unregistered User	Conflict
1	0x01	Soundlight	Conflicts with registered T-Recursive code.
1	0x01	Mode Lighting	Conflicts with registered T-Recursive code.
139	0x8B	Martin Professional	Conflicts with ESTA reserved codes
187	0xBB	Martin Professional	Conflicts with area reserved for Future Expansion of the DMX512 Standard.
203	0xCB	Martin Professional	Conflicts with area reserved for Future Expansion of the DMX512 Standard.
222	0xDE	Martin Professional	Conflicts with area reserved for Future Expansion of the DMX512 Standard.
223	0xDF	Martin Professional	Conflicts with previously registered Doug Fleenor Design code.
224	0xE0	Martin Professional	Conflicts with registered NSI/Colortran ENR Mode Control.
239	0xEF	Martin Professional	Conflicts with registered Electronics Diversified, Inc.

Appendix D ESTA Manufacturer Codes

Dec First	Dec Second	Hex First	Hex Second	ASCII First	ASCII Second	Company
0	0	0x00	0x00			ESTA
5	10	0x05	0x0A			ChamSys Ltd.
5	115	0x05	0x73		s	JIAXING XINHUALI LIGHTING & SOUNDING CO., LTD.
6	11	0x06	0x0B			LED Effects, Inc.
8	8	0x08	0x08			Zero 88 Lighting Ltd.
9	22	0x09	0x16		▯	ACTOR-MATE CO., LTD.
18	52	0x12	0x34	▯	4	ESTA
24	136	0x18	0x88	▯	^	GUANZHOU KAVON STAGE EQUIPMENT CO., LTD.
41	153	0x29	0x99	)	™	ALL-DO INTERNATIONAL CO., LTD.
51	136	0x33	0x88	3	^	Macostar International Ltd.
56	5	0x38	0x05	8		Yifeng Lighting Co., Ltd.
56	6	0x38	0x06	8		ACME EFFECTS LTD.
56	104	0x38	0x68	8	h	LanBolight Technology Co., LTD.
56	136	0x38	0x88	8	^	Fly Dragon Lighting Equipment Co.,ltd
56	138	0x38	0x8A	8	Š	Guangzhou Yajiang (Yagang - Silver Star) Photoelectric Equipment Ltd.
64	81	0x40	0x51	@	Q	SAN JACK ANALOG HOUSE CO., LTD.
65	49	0x41	0x31	A	1	Altman Stage Lighting
65	65	0x41	0x41	A	A	AVAB America, Inc.
65	68	0x41	0x44	A	D	ADB - TTV Technologies nv
65	73	0x41	0x49	A	I	ANIDEA ENGINEERING, INC.
65	76	0x41	0x4C	A	L	Artistic Licence (UK) Ltd.
65	78	0x41	0x4E	A	N	Anytronics Ltd.
65	80	0x41	0x50	A	P	Apogee Lighting
65	83	0x41	0x53	A	S	Audio Scene
65	84	0x41	0x54	A	T	Arnold Tang Productions
65	86	0x41	0x56	A	V	Audio Visual Devices P/L
65	108	0x41	0x6C	A	l	Alenco BV
66	67	0x42	0x43	B	C	Bill Coghill Company : Bill Coghill Design
66	79	0x42	0x4F	B	O	BOTEX
67	68	0x43	0x44	C	D	CDCA Ltd.
67	73	0x43	0x49	C	I	C.I.Tronics Lighting Designers Ltda
67	77	0x43	0x4D	C	M	Coemar Spa
67	83	0x43	0x53	C	S	Capricorn Software
67	84	0x43	0x54	C	T	City Theatrical, Inc.
67	105	0x43	0x69	C	i	Cinetix Medien u. Interface GmbH
68	65	0x44	0x41	D	A	DIGITAL ART SYSTEM
68	66	0x44	0x42	D	B	ELETTROLAB S.r.l.
68	68	0x44	0x44	D	D	D.O.M. Datenverarbeitung GmbH
68	70	0x44	0x46	D	F	Doug Fleenor Design, Inc.
68	76	0x44	0x4C	D	L	Dove Lighting Systems, Inc.
68	77	0x44	0x4D	D	M	Digimedia Multimedia Lighting Solutions

Dec First	Dec Second	Hex First	Hex Second	ASCII First	ASCII Second	Company
69	65	0x45	0x41	E	A	Engineering Arts
69	68	0x45	0x44	E	D	Electronics Diversified Inc.
69	76	0x45	0x4C	E	L	Ingenieurbuero fuer Nachrichtentechnik in der Studio und Veranstaltungstechnik
69	78	0x45	0x4E	E	N	ENTTEC Pty Ltd
69	84	0x45	0x54	E	T	Entertainment Technology
70	76	0x46	0x4C	F	L	Flashlight/Ampco Holding
71	68	0x47	0x44	G	D	Goddard Design Co.
71	76	0x47	0x4C	G	L	G-LEC Europe GmbH
71	80	0x47	0x50	G	P	DES
72	67	0x48	0x43	H	C	Horizon Control Inc.
72	68	0x48	0x44	H	D	HxDx
72	69	0x48	0x45	H	E	Howard Eaton Lighting Ltd.
72	86	0x48	0x56	H	V	Enfis Ltd
72	129	0x48	0x81	H	□	Rena Electronica B.V.
73	66	0x49	0x42	I	B	IBEX UK Limited
73	69	0x49	0x45	I	E	Insta Elektro GmbH; Abteilung TEL
73	72	0x49	0x48	I	H	Ice House Productions
73	78	0x49	0x4E	I	N	Interactive Technologies, Inc.
73	80	0x49	0x50	I	P	Interesting Products, Inc.
73	82	0x49	0x52	I	R	Invisible Rival Incorporated
73	83	0x49	0x53	I	S	Integrated System Technologies Ltd.
73	84	0x49	0x54	I	T	Integrated Theatre, Inc.
74	65	0x4A	0x41	J	A	JANUS srl
74	66	0x4A	0x42	J	B	JB-lighting GmbH
74	76	0x4A	0x4C	J	L	Johnsson Lighting Technologies AB
74	83	0x4A	0x53	J	S	JSC "MFG"
74	84	0x4A	0x54	J	T	James Thomas Engineering
75	66	0x4B	0x42	K	B	KissBox
75	70	0x4B	0x46	K	F	Kino Flo, Inc.
75	76	0x4B	0x4C	K	L	KLH Electronics PLC
75	77	0x4B	0x4D	K	M	KMX Inc.
75	85	0x4B	0x55	K	U	kuwatec, Inc.
76	69	0x4C	0x45	L	E	Leviton Manufacturing Co., Inc.
76	76	0x4C	0x4C	L	L	LUMINEX Lighting Control Equipment bvba
76	77	0x4C	0x4D	L	M	Le Maitre Special Effects Inc
76	80	0x4C	0x50	L	P	LightProcessor Ltd
76	82	0x4C	0x52	L	R	High End Systems Inc.
76	83	0x4C	0x53	L	S	Licht-, Steuer- und Schaltanlagenbau GmbH (LSS GmbH)
76	84	0x4C	0x54	L	T	Licht-Technik
76	88	0x4C	0x58	L	X	Lex Products Corp.
76	100	0x4C	0x64	L	d	LED Team
76	101	0x4C	0x65	L	e	Legargeant and Associates
76	105	0x4C	0x69	L	i	LIGHTOLIER
77	65	0x4D	0x41	M	A	MA Lighting Technology GmbH
77	68	0x4D	0x44	M	D	Les Générateurs de brouillard MDG Fog Generators Ltd.
77	76	0x4D	0x4C	M	L	Mode Lighting (UK) Ltd.

Dec First	Dec Second	Hex First	Hex Second	ASCII First	ASCII Second	Company
77	80	0x4D	0x50	M	P	Martin Professional A/S
77	86	0x4D	0x56	M	V	Avolites Ltd.
78	65	0x4E	0x41	N	A	Company NA
78	74	0x4E	0x4A	N	J	NJD Electronics
78	87	0x4E	0x57	N	W	AIM Northwest
80	67	0x50	0x43	P	C	Pathway Connectivity Inc.
80	76	0x50	0x4C	P	L	Peperoni Lighting-Solutions
80	82	0x50	0x52	P	R	Production Resource Group
80	101	0x50	0x65	P	e	Peradise
80	104	0x50	0x68	P	h	Philips Lighting BV
80	117	0x50	0x75	P	u	Pulsar Light of Cambridge Ltd.
81	83	0x51	0x53	Q	S	QuickSilver Controls, Inc.
82	76	0x52	0x4C	R	L	Radical Lighting Ltd.
82	82	0x52	0x52	R	R	RoscoLab Ltd
82	83	0x52	0x53	R	S	Robe Show Lighting s.r.o.
83	66	0x53	0x42	S	B	Industrias Sola Basic S.A. de C.V.
83	67	0x53	0x43	S	C	Ocean Optics Inc.
83	68	0x53	0x44	S	D	Stardraw.com Ltd.
83	69	0x53	0x45	S	E	Selador
83	71	0x53	0x47	S	G	SGM Technology For Lighting SPA
83	73	0x53	0x49	S	I	Soundsculpture Incorporated
83	76	0x53	0x4C	S	L	SOUNDLIGHT
83	78	0x53	0x4E	S	N	Sand Network Systems
83	84	0x53	0x54	S	T	Stagetronics Ltda
83	99	0x53	0x63	S	c	SpaceCannon vH
83	104	0x53	0x68	S	h	ShowCAD Control Systems Ltd.
83	112	0x53	0x70	S	p	Spectrum Manufacturing Inc.
84	68	0x54	0x44	T	D	Technographic Displays Ltd.
84	69	0x54	0x45	T	E	TESI Elettronica srl
84	76	0x54	0x4C	T	L	Tempest Lighting Inc.
84	84	0x54	0x54	T	T	TamaTech Labo Company Ltd,
86	76	0x56	0x4C	V	L	Vari-Lite, Inc.
86	81	0x56	0x51	V	Q	Vision Quest Lighting Inc.
86	86	0x56	0x53	V	S	Viso Systems Aps
87	83	0x57	0x53	W	S	Wireless Solution Sweden AB
87	89	0x57	0x59	W	Y	Wybron, Inc.
88	136	0x58	0x88	X	ˆ	Plsao Optoelectronics Technology Co., Ltd.
97	100	0x61	0x64	a	d	Apollo Design Technology, Inc
97	108	0x61	0x6C	a	l	Advanced Lighting Systems
99	100	0x63	0x64	c	d	CDS advanced technology bv
101	71	0x65	0x47	e	G	euroGenie
101	108	0x65	0x6C	e	l	ELC lighting
101	116	0x65	0x74	e	t	Electronic Theatre Controls, Inc.
101	118	0x65	0x76	e	v	eventa Aktiengesellschaft
104	101	0x68	0x65	h	e	Hubbell Entertainment, Inc.
105	76	0x69	0x4C	i	L	iLight Technologies Inc
112	104	0x70	0x68	p	h	Pharos Architectural Controls
112	114	0x70	0x72	p	r	Pr-Lighting Ltd.
112	120	0x70	0x78	p	x	PixelRange Inc.
115	99	0x73	0x63	s	c	Sean Christopher FX

Dec First	Dec Second	Hex First	Hex Second	ASCII First	ASCII Second	Company
115	108	0x73	0x6C	s	l	Strand Lighting Ltd.
122	112	0x7A	0x70	z	p	ZP Technologies
255	255	0xFF	0xFF	ÿ	ÿ	ESTA

Appendix E Decimal,Hexadecimal & Binary Conversion

Decimal	Hexadecimal	Binary	Percent	Scale
0	0x00	0000 0000	0.00	0
1	0x01	0000 0001	0.39	0
2	0x02	0000 0010	0.78	1
3	0x03	0000 0011	1.18	1
4	0x04	0000 0100	1.57	2
5	0x05	0000 0101	1.96	2
6	0x06	0000 0110	2.35	2
7	0x07	0000 0111	2.75	3
8	0x08	0000 1000	3.14	3
9	0x09	0000 1001	3.53	4
10	0x0a	0000 1010	3.92	4
11	0x0b	0000 1011	4.31	4
12	0x0c	0000 1100	4.71	5
13	0x0d	0000 1101	5.10	5
14	0x0e	0000 1110	5.49	5
15	0x0f	0000 1111	5.88	6
16	0x10	0001 0000	6.27	6
17	0x11	0001 0001	6.67	7
18	0x12	0001 0010	7.06	7
19	0x13	0001 0011	7.45	7
20	0x14	0001 0100	7.84	8
21	0x15	0001 0101	8.24	8
22	0x16	0001 0110	8.63	9
23	0x17	0001 0111	9.02	9
24	0x18	0001 1000	9.41	9
25	0x19	0001 1001	9.80	10
26	0x1a	0001 1010	10.20	10
27	0x1b	0001 1011	10.59	11
28	0x1c	0001 1100	10.98	11
29	0x1d	0001 1101	11.37	11
30	0x1e	0001 1110	11.76	12
31	0x1f	0001 1111	12.16	12
32	0x20	0010 0000	12.55	13
33	0x21	0010 0001	12.94	13
34	0x22	0010 0010	13.33	13
35	0x23	0010 0011	13.73	14
36	0x24	0010 0100	14.12	14
37	0x25	0010 0101	14.51	15
38	0x26	0010 0110	14.90	15
39	0x27	0010 0111	15.29	15
40	0x28	0010 1000	15.69	16
41	0x29	0010 1001	16.08	16
42	0x2a	0010 1010	16.47	16
43	0x2b	0010 1011	16.86	17
44	0x2c	0010 1100	17.25	17
45	0x2d	0010 1101	17.65	18
46	0x2e	0010 1110	18.04	18
47	0x2f	0010 1111	18.43	18
48	0x30	0011 0000	18.82	19
49	0x31	0011 0001	19.22	19
50	0x32	0011 0010	19.61	20
51	0x33	0011 0011	20.00	20
52	0x34	0011 0100	20.39	20
53	0x35	0011 0101	20.78	21
54	0x36	0011 0110	21.18	21
55	0x37	0011 0111	21.57	22
56	0x38	0011 1000	21.96	22
57	0x39	0011 1001	22.35	22
58	0x3a	0011 1010	22.75	23
59	0x3b	0011 1011	23.14	23
60	0x3c	0011 1100	23.53	24
61	0x3d	0011 1101	23.92	24
62	0x3e	0011 1110	24.31	24
63	0x3f	0011 1111	24.71	25
64	0x40	0100 0000	25.10	25
65	0x41	0100 0001	25.49	25
66	0x42	0100 0010	25.88	26
67	0x43	0100 0011	26.27	26
68	0x44	0100 0100	26.67	27
69	0x45	0100 0101	27.06	27
70	0x46	0100 0110	27.45	27
71	0x47	0100 0111	27.84	28
72	0x48	0100 1000	28.24	28
73	0x49	0100 1001	28.63	29
74	0x4a	0100 1010	29.02	29
75	0x4b	0100 1011	29.41	29
76	0x4c	0100 1100	29.80	30
77	0x4d	0100 1101	30.20	30
78	0x4e	0100 1110	30.59	31
79	0x4f	0100 1111	30.98	31
80	0x50	0101 0000	31.37	31
81	0x51	0101 0001	31.76	32
82	0x52	0101 0010	32.16	32
83	0x53	0101 0011	32.55	33

Decimal	Hexadecimal	Binary	Percent	Scale
84	0x54	0101 0100	32.94	33
85	0x55	0101 0101	33.33	33
86	0x56	0101 0110	33.73	34
87	0x57	0101 0111	34.12	34
88	0x58	0101 1000	34.51	35
89	0x59	0101 1001	34.90	35
90	0x5a	0101 1010	35.29	35
91	0x5b	0101 1011	35.69	36
92	0x5c	0101 1100	36.08	36
93	0x5d	0101 1101	36.47	36
94	0x5e	0101 1110	36.86	37
95	0x5f	0101 1111	37.25	37
96	0x60	0110 0000	37.65	38
97	0x61	0110 0001	38.04	38
98	0x62	0110 0010	38.43	38
99	0x63	0110 0011	38.82	39
100	0x64	0110 0100	39.22	39
101	0x65	0110 0101	39.61	40
102	0x66	0110 0110	40.00	40
103	0x67	0110 0111	40.39	40
104	0x68	0110 1000	40.78	41
105	0x69	0110 1001	41.18	41
106	0x6a	0110 1010	41.57	42
107	0x6b	0110 1011	41.96	42
108	0x6c	0110 1100	42.35	42
109	0x6d	0110 1101	42.75	43
110	0x6e	0110 1110	43.14	43
111	0x6f	0110 1111	43.53	44
112	0x70	0111 0000	43.92	44
113	0x71	0111 0001	44.31	44
114	0x72	0111 0010	44.71	45
115	0x73	0111 0011	45.10	45
116	0x74	0111 0100	45.49	45
117	0x75	0111 0101	45.88	46
118	0x76	0111 0110	46.27	46
119	0x77	0111 0111	46.67	47
120	0x78	0111 1000	47.06	47
121	0x79	0111 1001	47.45	47
122	0x7a	0111 1010	47.84	48
123	0x7b	0111 1011	48.24	48
124	0x7c	0111 1100	48.63	49
125	0x7d	0111 1101	49.02	49
126	0x7e	0111 1110	49.41	49
127	0x7f	0111 1111	49.80	50
128	0x80	1000 0000	50.20	50
129	0x81	1000 0001	50.59	51
130	0x82	1000 0010	50.98	51
131	0x83	1000 0011	51.37	51
132	0x84	1000 0100	51.76	52
133	0x85	1000 0101	52.16	52
134	0x86	1000 0110	52.55	53
135	0x87	1000 0111	52.94	53
136	0x88	1000 1000	53.33	53
137	0x89	1000 1001	53.73	54
138	0x8a	1000 1010	54.12	54
139	0x8b	1000 1011	54.51	55
140	0x8c	1000 1100	54.90	55
141	0x8d	1000 1101	55.29	55
142	0x8e	1000 1110	55.69	56
143	0x8f	1000 1111	56.08	56
144	0x90	1001 0000	56.47	56
145	0x91	1001 0001	56.86	57
146	0x92	1001 0010	57.25	57
147	0x93	1001 0011	57.65	58
148	0x94	1001 0100	58.04	58
149	0x95	1001 0101	58.43	58
150	0x96	1001 0110	58.82	59
151	0x97	1001 0111	59.22	59
152	0x98	1001 1000	59.61	60
153	0x99	1001 1001	60.00	60
154	0x9a	1001 1010	60.39	60
155	0x9b	1001 1011	60.78	61
156	0x9c	1001 1100	61.18	61
157	0x9d	1001 1101	61.57	62
158	0x9e	1001 1110	61.96	62
159	0x9f	1001 1111	62.35	62
160	0xa0	1010 0000	62.75	63
161	0xa1	1010 0001	63.14	63
162	0xa2	1010 0010	63.53	64
163	0xa3	1010 0011	63.92	64
164	0xa4	1010 0100	64.31	64
165	0xa5	1010 0101	64.71	65
166	0xa6	1010 0110	65.10	65
167	0xa7	1010 0111	65.49	65
168	0xa8	1010 1000	65.88	66
169	0xa9	1010 1001	66.27	66
170	0xaa	1010 1010	66.67	67
171	0xab	1010 1011	67.06	67
172	0xac	1010 1100	67.45	67
173	0xad	1010 1101	67.84	68
174	0xae	1010 1110	68.24	68
175	0xaf	1010 1111	68.63	69
176	0xb0	1011 0000	69.02	69

Decimal	Hexadecimal	Binary	Percent	Scal
177	0xb1	1011 0001	69.41	69
178	0xb2	1011 0010	69.80	70
179	0xb3	1011 0011	70.20	70
180	0xb4	1011 0100	70.59	71
181	0xb5	1011 0101	70.98	71
182	0xb6	1011 0110	71.37	71
183	0xb7	1011 0111	71.76	72
184	0xb8	1011 1000	72.16	72
185	0xb9	1011 1001	72.55	73
186	0xba	1011 1010	72.94	73
187	0xbb	1011 1011	73.33	73
188	0xbc	1011 1100	73.73	74
189	0xbd	1011 1101	74.12	74
190	0xbe	1011 1110	74.51	75
191	0xbf	1011 1111	74.90	75
192	0xc0	1100 0000	75.29	75
193	0xc1	1100 0001	75.69	76
194	0xc2	1100 0010	76.08	76
195	0xc3	1100 0011	76.47	76
196	0xc4	1100 0100	76.86	77
197	0xc5	1100 0101	77.25	77
198	0xc6	1100 0110	77.65	78
199	0xc7	1100 0111	78.04	78
200	0xc8	1100 1000	78.43	78
201	0xc9	1100 1001	78.82	79
202	0xca	1100 1010	79.22	79
203	0xcb	1100 1011	79.61	80
204	0xcc	1100 1100	80.00	80
205	0xcd	1100 1101	80.39	80
206	0xce	1100 1110	80.78	81
207	0xcf	1100 1111	81.18	81
208	0xd0	1101 0000	81.57	82
209	0xd1	1101 0001	81.96	82
210	0xd2	1101 0010	82.35	82
211	0xd3	1101 0011	82.75	83
212	0xd4	1101 0100	83.14	83
213	0xd5	1101 0101	83.53	84
214	0xd6	1101 0110	83.92	84
215	0xd7	1101 0111	84.31	84
216	0xd8	1101 1000	84.71	85
217	0xd9	1101 1001	85.10	85
218	0xda	1101 1010	85.49	85
219	0xdb	1101 1011	85.88	86
220	0xdc	1101 1100	86.27	86
221	0xdd	1101 1101	86.67	87
222	0xde	1101 1110	87.06	87
223	0xdf	1101 1111	87.45	87
224	0xe0	1110 0000	87.84	88
225	0xe1	1110 0001	88.24	88
226	0xe2	1110 0010	88.63	89
227	0xe3	1110 0011	89.02	89
228	0xe4	1110 0100	89.41	89
229	0xe5	1110 0101	89.80	90
230	0xe6	1110 0110	90.20	90
231	0xe7	1110 0111	90.59	91
232	0xe8	1110 1000	90.98	91
233	0xe9	1110 1001	91.37	91
234	0xea	1110 1010	91.76	92
235	0xeb	1110 1011	92.16	92
236	0xec	1110 1100	92.55	93
237	0xed	1110 1101	92.94	93
238	0xee	1110 1110	93.33	93
239	0xef	1110 1111	93.73	94
240	0xf0	1111 0000	94.12	94
241	0xf1	1111 0001	94.51	95
242	0xf2	1111 0010	94.90	95
243	0xf3	1111 0011	95.29	95
244	0xf4	1111 0100	95.69	96
245	0xf5	1111 0101	96.08	96
246	0xf6	1111 0110	96.47	96
247	0xf7	1111 0111	96.86	97
248	0xf8	1111 1000	97.25	97
249	0xf9	1111 1001	97.65	98
250	0xfa	1111 1010	98.04	98
251	0xfb	1111 1011	98.43	98
252	0xfc	1111 1100	98.82	99
253	0xfd	1111 1101	99.22	99
254	0xfe	1111 1110	99.61	100
255	0xff	1111 1111	100.00	100

Appendix F Start Address Offsets by Universe

Start Address									Universe										
1	2	3	4	5	6	7	8	9	10	11	12	13	14	15	16	17	18	19	20
1	513	1,025	1,537	2,049	2,561	3,073	3,585	4,097	4,609	5,121	5,633	6,145	6,657	7,169	7,681	8,193	8,705	9,217	9,729
2	514	1,026	1,538	2,050	2,562	3,074	3,586	4,098	4,610	5,122	5,634	6,146	6,658	7,170	7,682	8,194	8,706	9,218	9,730
3	515	1,027	1,539	2,051	2,563	3,075	3,587	4,099	4,611	5,123	5,635	6,147	6,659	7,171	7,683	8,195	8,707	9,219	9,731
4	516	1,028	1,540	2,052	2,564	3,076	3,588	4,100	4,612	5,124	5,636	6,148	6,660	7,172	7,684	8,196	8,708	9,220	9,732
5	517	1,029	1,541	2,053	2,565	3,077	3,589	4,101	4,613	5,125	5,637	6,149	6,661	7,173	7,685	8,197	8,709	9,221	9,733
6	518	1,030	1,542	2,054	2,566	3,078	3,590	4,102	4,614	5,126	5,638	6,150	6,662	7,174	7,686	8,198	8,710	9,222	9,734
7	519	1,031	1,543	2,055	2,567	3,079	3,591	4,103	4,615	5,127	5,639	6,151	6,663	7,175	7,687	8,199	8,711	9,223	9,735
8	520	1,032	1,544	2,056	2,568	3,080	3,592	4,104	4,616	5,128	5,640	6,152	6,664	7,176	7,688	8,200	8,712	9,224	9,736
9	521	1,033	1,545	2,057	2,569	3,081	3,593	4,105	4,617	5,129	5,641	6,153	6,665	7,177	7,689	8,201	8,713	9,225	9,737
10	522	1,034	1,546	2,058	2,570	3,082	3,594	4,106	4,618	5,130	5,642	6,154	6,666	7,178	7,690	8,202	8,714	9,226	9,738
11	523	1,035	1,547	2,059	2,571	3,083	3,595	4,107	4,619	5,131	5,643	6,155	6,667	7,179	7,691	8,203	8,715	9,227	9,739
12	524	1,036	1,548	2,060	2,572	3,084	3,596	4,108	4,620	5,132	5,644	6,156	6,668	7,180	7,692	8,204	8,716	9,228	9,740
13	525	1,037	1,549	2,061	2,573	3,085	3,597	4,109	4,621	5,133	5,645	6,157	6,669	7,181	7,693	8,205	8,717	9,229	9,741
14	526	1,038	1,550	2,062	2,574	3,086	3,598	4,110	4,622	5,134	5,646	6,158	6,670	7,182	7,694	8,206	8,718	9,230	9,742
15	527	1,039	1,551	2,063	2,575	3,087	3,599	4,111	4,623	5,135	5,647	6,159	6,671	7,183	7,695	8,207	8,719	9,231	9,743
16	528	1,040	1,552	2,064	2,576	3,088	3,600	4,112	4,624	5,136	5,648	6,160	6,672	7,184	7,696	8,208	8,720	9,232	9,744
17	529	1,041	1,553	2,065	2,577	3,089	3,601	4,113	4,625	5,137	5,649	6,161	6,673	7,185	7,697	8,209	8,721	9,233	9,745
18	530	1,042	1,554	2,066	2,578	3,090	3,602	4,114	4,626	5,138	5,650	6,162	6,674	7,186	7,698	8,210	8,722	9,234	9,746
19	531	1,043	1,555	2,067	2,579	3,091	3,603	4,115	4,627	5,139	5,651	6,163	6,675	7,187	7,699	8,211	8,723	9,235	9,747
20	532	1,044	1,556	2,068	2,580	3,092	3,604	4,116	4,628	5,140	5,652	6,164	6,676	7,188	7,700	8,212	8,724	9,236	9,748
21	533	1,045	1,557	2,069	2,581	3,093	3,605	4,117	4,629	5,141	5,653	6,165	6,677	7,189	7,701	8,213	8,725	9,237	9,749
22	534	1,046	1,558	2,070	2,582	3,094	3,606	4,118	4,630	5,142	5,654	6,166	6,678	7,190	7,702	8,214	8,726	9,238	9,750
23	535	1,047	1,559	2,071	2,583	3,095	3,607	4,119	4,631	5,143	5,655	6,167	6,679	7,191	7,703	8,215	8,727	9,239	9,751
24	536	1,048	1,560	2,072	2,584	3,096	3,608	4,120	4,632	5,144	5,656	6,168	6,680	7,192	7,704	8,216	8,728	9,240	9,752
25	537	1,049	1,561	2,073	2,585	3,097	3,609	4,121	4,633	5,145	5,657	6,169	6,681	7,193	7,705	8,217	8,729	9,241	9,753
26	538	1,050	1,562	2,074	2,586	3,098	3,610	4,122	4,634	5,146	5,658	6,170	6,682	7,194	7,706	8,218	8,730	9,242	9,754
27	539	1,051	1,563	2,075	2,587	3,099	3,611	4,123	4,635	5,147	5,659	6,171	6,683	7,195	7,707	8,219	8,731	9,243	9,755
28	540	1,052	1,564	2,076	2,588	3,100	3,612	4,124	4,636	5,148	5,660	6,172	6,684	7,196	7,708	8,220	8,732	9,244	9,756
29	541	1,053	1,565	2,077	2,589	3,101	3,613	4,125	4,637	5,149	5,661	6,173	6,685	7,197	7,709	8,221	8,733	9,245	9,757
30	542	1,054	1,566	2,078	2,590	3,102	3,614	4,126	4,638	5,150	5,662	6,174	6,686	7,198	7,710	8,222	8,734	9,246	9,758
31	543	1,055	1,567	2,079	2,591	3,103	3,615	4,127	4,639	5,151	5,663	6,175	6,687	7,199	7,711	8,223	8,735	9,247	9,759
32	544	1,056	1,568	2,080	2,592	3,104	3,616	4,128	4,640	5,152	5,664	6,176	6,688	7,200	7,712	8,224	8,736	9,248	9,760
33	545	1,057	1,569	2,081	2,593	3,105	3,617	4,129	4,641	5,153	5,665	6,177	6,689	7,201	7,713	8,225	8,737	9,249	9,761
34	546	1,058	1,570	2,082	2,594	3,106	3,618	4,130	4,642	5,154	5,666	6,178	6,690	7,202	7,714	8,226	8,738	9,250	9,762
35	547	1,059	1,571	2,083	2,595	3,107	3,619	4,131	4,643	5,155	5,667	6,179	6,691	7,203	7,715	8,227	8,739	9,251	9,763
36	548	1,060	1,572	2,084	2,596	3,108	3,620	4,132	4,644	5,156	5,668	6,180	6,692	7,204	7,716	8,228	8,740	9,252	9,764
37	549	1,061	1,573	2,085	2,597	3,109	3,621	4,133	4,645	5,157	5,669	6,181	6,693	7,205	7,717	8,229	8,741	9,253	9,765
38	550	1,062	1,574	2,086	2,598	3,110	3,622	4,134	4,646	5,158	5,670	6,182	6,694	7,206	7,718	8,230	8,742	9,254	9,766
39	551	1,063	1,575	2,087	2,599	3,111	3,623	4,135	4,647	5,159	5,671	6,183	6,695	7,207	7,719	8,231	8,743	9,255	9,767
40	552	1,064	1,576	2,088	2,600	3,112	3,624	4,136	4,648	5,160	5,672	6,184	6,696	7,208	7,720	8,232	8,744	9,256	9,768
41	553	1,065	1,577	2,089	2,601	3,113	3,625	4,137	4,649	5,161	5,673	6,185	6,697	7,209	7,721	8,233	8,745	9,257	9,769
42	554	1,066	1,578	2,090	2,602	3,114	3,626	4,138	4,650	5,162	5,674	6,186	6,698	7,210	7,722	8,234	8,746	9,258	9,770
43	555	1,067	1,579	2,091	2,603	3,115	3,627	4,139	4,651	5,163	5,675	6,187	6,699	7,211	7,723	8,235	8,747	9,259	9,771
44	556	1,068	1,580	2,092	2,604	3,116	3,628	4,140	4,652	5,164	5,676	6,188	6,700	7,212	7,724	8,236	8,748	9,260	9,772
45	557	1,069	1,581	2,093	2,605	3,117	3,629	4,141	4,653	5,165	5,677	6,189	6,701	7,213	7,725	8,237	8,749	9,261	9,773
46	558	1,070	1,582	2,094	2,606	3,118	3,630	4,142	4,654	5,166	5,678	6,190	6,702	7,214	7,726	8,238	8,750	9,262	9,774
47	559	1,071	1,583	2,095	2,607	3,119	3,631	4,143	4,655	5,167	5,679	6,191	6,703	7,215	7,727	8,239	8,751	9,263	9,775
48	560	1,072	1,584	2,096	2,608	3,120	3,632	4,144	4,656	5,168	5,680	6,192	6,704	7,216	7,728	8,240	8,752	9,264	9,776
49	561	1,073	1,585	2,097	2,609	3,121	3,633	4,145	4,657	5,169	5,681	6,193	6,705	7,217	7,729	8,241	8,753	9,265	9,777
50	562	1,074	1,586	2,098	2,610	3,122	3,634	4,146	4,658	5,170	5,682	6,194	6,706	7,218	7,730	8,242	8,754	9,266	9,778
51	563	1,075	1,587	2,099	2,611	3,123	3,635	4,147	4,659	5,171	5,683	6,195	6,707	7,219	7,731	8,243	8,755	9,267	9,779
52	564	1,076	1,588	2,100	2,612	3,124	3,636	4,148	4,660	5,172	5,684	6,196	6,708	7,220	7,732	8,244	8,756	9,268	9,780
53	565	1,077	1,589	2,101	2,613	3,125	3,637	4,149	4,661	5,173	5,685	6,197	6,709	7,221	7,733	8,245	8,757	9,269	9,781
54	566	1,078	1,590	2,102	2,614	3,126	3,638	4,150	4,662	5,174	5,686	6,198	6,710	7,222	7,734	8,246	8,758	9,270	9,782
55	567	1,079	1,591	2,103	2,615	3,127	3,639	4,151	4,663	5,175	5,687	6,199	6,711	7,223	7,735	8,247	8,759	9,271	9,783
56	568	1,080	1,592	2,104	2,616	3,128	3,640	4,152	4,664	5,176	5,688	6,200	6,712	7,224	7,736	8,248	8,760	9,272	9,784
57	569	1,081	1,593	2,105	2,617	3,129	3,641	4,153	4,665	5,177	5,689	6,201	6,713	7,225	7,737	8,249	8,761	9,273	9,785
58	570	1,082	1,594	2,106	2,618	3,130	3,642	4,154	4,666	5,178	5,690	6,202	6,714	7,226	7,738	8,250	8,762	9,274	9,786
59	571	1,083	1,595	2,107	2,619	3,131	3,643	4,155	4,667	5,179	5,691	6,203	6,715	7,227	7,739	8,251	8,763	9,275	9,787
60	572	1,084	1,596	2,108	2,620	3,132	3,644	4,156	4,668	5,180	5,692	6,204	6,716	7,228	7,740	8,252	8,764	9,276	9,788
61	573	1,085	1,597	2,109	2,621	3,133	3,645	4,157	4,669	5,181	5,693	6,205	6,717	7,229	7,741	8,253	8,765	9,277	9,789
62	574	1,086	1,598	2,110	2,622	3,134	3,646	4,158	4,670	5,182	5,694	6,206	6,718	7,230	7,742	8,254	8,766	9,278	9,790
63	575	1,087	1,599	2,111	2,623	3,135	3,647	4,159	4,671	5,183	5,695	6,207	6,719	7,231	7,743	8,255	8,767	9,279	9,791
64	576	1,088	1,600	2,112	2,624	3,136	3,648	4,160	4,672	5,184	5,696	6,208	6,720	7,232	7,744	8,256	8,768	9,280	9,792
65	577	1,089	1,601	2,113	2,625	3,137	3,649	4,161	4,673	5,185	5,697	6,209	6,721	7,233	7,745	8,257	8,769	9,281	9,793
66	578	1,090	1,602	2,114	2,626	3,138	3,650	4,162	4,674	5,186	5,698	6,210	6,722	7,234	7,746	8,258	8,770	9,282	9,794
67	579	1,091	1,603	2,115	2,627	3,139	3,651	4,163	4,675	5,187	5,699	6,211	6,723	7,235	7,747	8,259	8,771	9,283	9,795
68	580	1,092	1,604	2,116	2,628	3,140	3,652	4,164	4,676	5,188	5,700	6,212	6,724	7,236	7,748	8,260	8,772	9,284	9,796
69	581	1,093	1,605	2,117	2,629	3,141	3,653	4,165	4,677	5,189	5,701	6,213	6,725	7,237	7,749	8,261	8,773	9,285	9,797
70	582	1,094	1,606	2,118	2,630	3,142	3,654	4,166	4,678	5,190	5,702	6,214	6,726	7,238	7,750	8,262	8,774	9,286	9,798
71	583	1,095	1,607	2,119	2,631	3,143	3,655	4,167	4,679	5,191	5,703	6,215	6,727	7,239	7,751	8,263	8,775	9,287	9,799
72	584	1,096	1,608	2,120	2,632	3,144	3,656	4,168	4,680	5,192	5,704	6,216	6,728	7,240	7,752	8,264	8,776	9,288	9,800
73	585	1,097	1,609	2,121	2,633	3,145	3,657	4,169	4,681	5,193	5,705	6,217	6,729	7,241	7,753	8,265	8,777	9,289	9,801
74	586	1,098	1,610	2,122	2,634	3,146	3,658	4,170	4,682	5,194	5,706	6,218	6,730	7,242	7,754	8,266	8,778	9,290	9,802
75	587	1,099	1,611	2,123	2,635	3,147	3,659	4,171	4,683	5,195	5,707	6,219	6,731	7,243	7,755	8,267	8,779	9,291	9,803
76	588	1,100	1,612	2,124	2,636	3,148	3,660	4,172	4,684	5,196	5,708	6,220	6,732	7,244	7,756	8,268	8,780	9,292	9,804
77	589	1,101	1,613	2,125	2,637	3,149	3,661	4,173	4,685	5,197	5,709	6,221	6,733	7,245	7,757	8,269	8,781	9,293	9,805
78	590	1,102	1,614	2,126	2,638	3,150	3,662	4,174	4,686	5,198	5,710	6,222	6,734	7,246	7,758	8,270	8,782	9,294	9,806
79	591	1,103	1,615	2,127	2,639	3,151	3,663	4,175	4,687	5,199	5,711	6,223	6,735	7,247	7,759	8,271	8,783	9,295	9,807
80	592	1,104	1,616	2,128	2,640	3,152	3,664	4,176	4,688	5,200	5,712	6,224	6,736	7,248	7,760	8,272	8,784	9,296	9,808
81	593	1,105	1,617	2,129	2,641	3,153	3,665	4,177	4,689	5,201	5,713	6,225	6,737	7,249	7,761	8,273	8,785	9,297	9,809
82	594	1,106	1,618	2,130	2,642	3,154	3,666	4,178	4,690	5,202	5,714	6,226	6,738	7,250	7,762	8,274	8,786	9,298	9,810
83	595	1,107	1,619	2,131	2,643	3,155	3,667	4,179	4,691	5,203	5,715	6,227	6,739	7,251	7,763	8,275	8,787	9,299	9,811
84	596	1,108	1,620	2,132	2,644	3,156	3,668	4,180	4,692	5,204	5,716	6,228	6,740	7,252	7,764	8,276	8,788	9,300	9,812
85	597	1,109	1,621	2,133	2,645	3,157	3,669	4,181	4,693	5,205	5,717	6,229	6,741	7,253	7,765	8,277	8,789	9,301	9,813

Start Address										Universe									
1	2	3	4	5	6	7	8	9	10	11	12	13	14	15	16	17	18	19	20
86	598	1,110	1,622	2,134	2,646	3,158	3,670	4,182	4,694	5,206	5,718	6,230	6,742	7,254	7,766	8,278	8,790	9,302	9,814
87	599	1,111	1,623	2,135	2,647	3,159	3,671	4,183	4,695	5,207	5,719	6,231	6,743	7,255	7,767	8,279	8,791	9,303	9,815
88	600	1,112	1,624	2,136	2,648	3,160	3,672	4,184	4,696	5,208	5,720	6,232	6,744	7,256	7,768	8,280	8,792	9,304	9,816
89	601	1,113	1,625	2,137	2,649	3,161	3,673	4,185	4,697	5,209	5,721	6,233	6,745	7,257	7,769	8,281	8,793	9,305	9,817
90	602	1,114	1,626	2,138	2,650	3,162	3,674	4,186	4,698	5,210	5,722	6,234	6,746	7,258	7,770	8,282	8,794	9,306	9,818
91	603	1,115	1,627	2,139	2,651	3,163	3,675	4,187	4,699	5,211	5,723	6,235	6,747	7,259	7,771	8,283	8,795	9,307	9,819
92	604	1,116	1,628	2,140	2,652	3,164	3,676	4,188	4,700	5,212	5,724	6,236	6,748	7,260	7,772	8,284	8,796	9,308	9,820
93	605	1,117	1,629	2,141	2,653	3,165	3,677	4,189	4,701	5,213	5,725	6,237	6,749	7,261	7,773	8,285	8,797	9,309	9,821
94	606	1,118	1,630	2,142	2,654	3,166	3,678	4,190	4,702	5,214	5,726	6,238	6,750	7,262	7,774	8,286	8,798	9,310	9,822
95	607	1,119	1,631	2,143	2,655	3,167	3,679	4,191	4,703	5,215	5,727	6,239	6,751	7,263	7,775	8,287	8,799	9,311	9,823
96	608	1,120	1,632	2,144	2,656	3,168	3,680	4,192	4,704	5,216	5,728	6,240	6,752	7,264	7,776	8,288	8,800	9,312	9,824
97	609	1,121	1,633	2,145	2,657	3,169	3,681	4,193	4,705	5,217	5,729	6,241	6,753	7,265	7,777	8,289	8,801	9,313	9,825
98	610	1,122	1,634	2,146	2,658	3,170	3,682	4,194	4,706	5,218	5,730	6,242	6,754	7,266	7,778	8,290	8,802	9,314	9,826
99	611	1,123	1,635	2,147	2,659	3,171	3,683	4,195	4,707	5,219	5,731	6,243	6,755	7,267	7,779	8,291	8,803	9,315	9,827
100	612	1,124	1,636	2,148	2,660	3,172	3,684	4,196	4,708	5,220	5,732	6,244	6,756	7,268	7,780	8,292	8,804	9,316	9,828
101	613	1,125	1,637	2,149	2,661	3,173	3,685	4,197	4,709	5,221	5,733	6,245	6,757	7,269	7,781	8,293	8,805	9,317	9,829
102	614	1,126	1,638	2,150	2,662	3,174	3,686	4,198	4,710	5,222	5,734	6,246	6,758	7,270	7,782	8,294	8,806	9,318	9,830
103	615	1,127	1,639	2,151	2,663	3,175	3,687	4,199	4,711	5,223	5,735	6,247	6,759	7,271	7,783	8,295	8,807	9,319	9,831
104	616	1,128	1,640	2,152	2,664	3,176	3,688	4,200	4,712	5,224	5,736	6,248	6,760	7,272	7,784	8,296	8,808	9,320	9,832
105	617	1,129	1,641	2,153	2,665	3,177	3,689	4,201	4,713	5,225	5,737	6,249	6,761	7,273	7,785	8,297	8,809	9,321	9,833
106	618	1,130	1,642	2,154	2,666	3,178	3,690	4,202	4,714	5,226	5,738	6,250	6,762	7,274	7,786	8,298	8,810	9,322	9,834
107	619	1,131	1,643	2,155	2,667	3,179	3,691	4,203	4,715	5,227	5,739	6,251	6,763	7,275	7,787	8,299	8,811	9,323	9,835
108	620	1,132	1,644	2,156	2,668	3,180	3,692	4,204	4,716	5,228	5,740	6,252	6,764	7,276	7,788	8,300	8,812	9,324	9,836
109	621	1,133	1,645	2,157	2,669	3,181	3,693	4,205	4,717	5,229	5,741	6,253	6,765	7,277	7,789	8,301	8,813	9,325	9,837
110	622	1,134	1,646	2,158	2,670	3,182	3,694	4,206	4,718	5,230	5,742	6,254	6,766	7,278	7,790	8,302	8,814	9,326	9,838
111	623	1,135	1,647	2,159	2,671	3,183	3,695	4,207	4,719	5,231	5,743	6,255	6,767	7,279	7,791	8,303	8,815	9,327	9,839
112	624	1,136	1,648	2,160	2,672	3,184	3,696	4,208	4,720	5,232	5,744	6,256	6,768	7,280	7,792	8,304	8,816	9,328	9,840
113	625	1,137	1,649	2,161	2,673	3,185	3,697	4,209	4,721	5,233	5,745	6,257	6,769	7,281	7,793	8,305	8,817	9,329	9,841
114	626	1,138	1,650	2,162	2,674	3,186	3,698	4,210	4,722	5,234	5,746	6,258	6,770	7,282	7,794	8,306	8,818	9,330	9,842
115	627	1,139	1,651	2,163	2,675	3,187	3,699	4,211	4,723	5,235	5,747	6,259	6,771	7,283	7,795	8,307	8,819	9,331	9,843
116	628	1,140	1,652	2,164	2,676	3,188	3,700	4,212	4,724	5,236	5,748	6,260	6,772	7,284	7,796	8,308	8,820	9,332	9,844
117	629	1,141	1,653	2,165	2,677	3,189	3,701	4,213	4,725	5,237	5,749	6,261	6,773	7,285	7,797	8,309	8,821	9,333	9,845
118	630	1,142	1,654	2,166	2,678	3,190	3,702	4,214	4,726	5,238	5,750	6,262	6,774	7,286	7,798	8,310	8,822	9,334	9,846
119	631	1,143	1,655	2,167	2,679	3,191	3,703	4,215	4,727	5,239	5,751	6,263	6,775	7,287	7,799	8,311	8,823	9,335	9,847
120	632	1,144	1,656	2,168	2,680	3,192	3,704	4,216	4,728	5,240	5,752	6,264	6,776	7,288	7,800	8,312	8,824	9,336	9,848
121	633	1,145	1,657	2,169	2,681	3,193	3,705	4,217	4,729	5,241	5,753	6,265	6,777	7,289	7,801	8,313	8,825	9,337	9,849
122	634	1,146	1,658	2,170	2,682	3,194	3,706	4,218	4,730	5,242	5,754	6,266	6,778	7,290	7,802	8,314	8,826	9,338	9,850
123	635	1,147	1,659	2,171	2,683	3,195	3,707	4,219	4,731	5,243	5,755	6,267	6,779	7,291	7,803	8,315	8,827	9,339	9,851
124	636	1,148	1,660	2,172	2,684	3,196	3,708	4,220	4,732	5,244	5,756	6,268	6,780	7,292	7,804	8,316	8,828	9,340	9,852
125	637	1,149	1,661	2,173	2,685	3,197	3,709	4,221	4,733	5,245	5,757	6,269	6,781	7,293	7,805	8,317	8,829	9,341	9,853
126	638	1,150	1,662	2,174	2,686	3,198	3,710	4,222	4,734	5,246	5,758	6,270	6,782	7,294	7,806	8,318	8,830	9,342	9,854
127	639	1,151	1,663	2,175	2,687	3,199	3,711	4,223	4,735	5,247	5,759	6,271	6,783	7,295	7,807	8,319	8,831	9,343	9,855
128	640	1,152	1,664	2,176	2,688	3,200	3,712	4,224	4,736	5,248	5,760	6,272	6,784	7,296	7,808	8,320	8,832	9,344	9,856
129	641	1,153	1,665	2,177	2,689	3,201	3,713	4,225	4,737	5,249	5,761	6,273	6,785	7,297	7,809	8,321	8,833	9,345	9,857
130	642	1,154	1,666	2,178	2,690	3,202	3,714	4,226	4,738	5,250	5,762	6,274	6,786	7,298	7,810	8,322	8,834	9,346	9,858
131	643	1,155	1,667	2,179	2,691	3,203	3,715	4,227	4,739	5,251	5,763	6,275	6,787	7,299	7,811	8,323	8,835	9,347	9,859
132	644	1,156	1,668	2,180	2,692	3,204	3,716	4,228	4,740	5,252	5,764	6,276	6,788	7,300	7,812	8,324	8,836	9,348	9,860
133	645	1,157	1,669	2,181	2,693	3,205	3,717	4,229	4,741	5,253	5,765	6,277	6,789	7,301	7,813	8,325	8,837	9,349	9,861
134	646	1,158	1,670	2,182	2,694	3,206	3,718	4,230	4,742	5,254	5,766	6,278	6,790	7,302	7,814	8,326	8,838	9,350	9,862
135	647	1,159	1,671	2,183	2,695	3,207	3,719	4,231	4,743	5,255	5,767	6,279	6,791	7,303	7,815	8,327	8,839	9,351	9,863
136	648	1,160	1,672	2,184	2,696	3,208	3,720	4,232	4,744	5,256	5,768	6,280	6,792	7,304	7,816	8,328	8,840	9,352	9,864
137	649	1,161	1,673	2,185	2,697	3,209	3,721	4,233	4,745	5,257	5,769	6,281	6,793	7,305	7,817	8,329	8,841	9,353	9,865
138	650	1,162	1,674	2,186	2,698	3,210	3,722	4,234	4,746	5,258	5,770	6,282	6,794	7,306	7,818	8,330	8,842	9,354	9,866
139	651	1,163	1,675	2,187	2,699	3,211	3,723	4,235	4,747	5,259	5,771	6,283	6,795	7,307	7,819	8,331	8,843	9,355	9,867
140	652	1,164	1,676	2,188	2,700	3,212	3,724	4,236	4,748	5,260	5,772	6,284	6,796	7,308	7,820	8,332	8,844	9,356	9,868
141	653	1,165	1,677	2,189	2,701	3,213	3,725	4,237	4,749	5,261	5,773	6,285	6,797	7,309	7,821	8,333	8,845	9,357	9,869
142	654	1,166	1,678	2,190	2,702	3,214	3,726	4,238	4,750	5,262	5,774	6,286	6,798	7,310	7,822	8,334	8,846	9,358	9,870
143	655	1,167	1,679	2,191	2,703	3,215	3,727	4,239	4,751	5,263	5,775	6,287	6,799	7,311	7,823	8,335	8,847	9,359	9,871
144	656	1,168	1,680	2,192	2,704	3,216	3,728	4,240	4,752	5,264	5,776	6,288	6,800	7,312	7,824	8,336	8,848	9,360	9,872
145	657	1,169	1,681	2,193	2,705	3,217	3,729	4,241	4,753	5,265	5,777	6,289	6,801	7,313	7,825	8,337	8,849	9,361	9,873
146	658	1,170	1,682	2,194	2,706	3,218	3,730	4,242	4,754	5,266	5,778	6,290	6,802	7,314	7,826	8,338	8,850	9,362	9,874
147	659	1,171	1,683	2,195	2,707	3,219	3,731	4,243	4,755	5,267	5,779	6,291	6,803	7,315	7,827	8,339	8,851	9,363	9,875
148	660	1,172	1,684	2,196	2,708	3,220	3,732	4,244	4,756	5,268	5,780	6,292	6,804	7,316	7,828	8,340	8,852	9,364	9,876
149	661	1,173	1,685	2,197	2,709	3,221	3,733	4,245	4,757	5,269	5,781	6,293	6,805	7,317	7,829	8,341	8,853	9,365	9,877
150	662	1,174	1,686	2,198	2,710	3,222	3,734	4,246	4,758	5,270	5,782	6,294	6,806	7,318	7,830	8,342	8,854	9,366	9,878
151	663	1,175	1,687	2,199	2,711	3,223	3,735	4,247	4,759	5,271	5,783	6,295	6,807	7,319	7,831	8,343	8,855	9,367	9,879
152	664	1,176	1,688	2,200	2,712	3,224	3,736	4,248	4,760	5,272	5,784	6,296	6,808	7,320	7,832	8,344	8,856	9,368	9,880
153	665	1,177	1,689	2,201	2,713	3,225	3,737	4,249	4,761	5,273	5,785	6,297	6,809	7,321	7,833	8,345	8,857	9,369	9,881
154	666	1,178	1,690	2,202	2,714	3,226	3,738	4,250	4,762	5,274	5,786	6,298	6,810	7,322	7,834	8,346	8,858	9,370	9,882
155	667	1,179	1,691	2,203	2,715	3,227	3,739	4,251	4,763	5,275	5,787	6,299	6,811	7,323	7,835	8,347	8,859	9,371	9,883
156	668	1,180	1,692	2,204	2,716	3,228	3,740	4,252	4,764	5,276	5,788	6,300	6,812	7,324	7,836	8,348	8,860	9,372	9,884
157	669	1,181	1,693	2,205	2,717	3,229	3,741	4,253	4,765	5,277	5,789	6,301	6,813	7,325	7,837	8,349	8,861	9,373	9,885
158	670	1,182	1,694	2,206	2,718	3,230	3,742	4,254	4,766	5,278	5,790	6,302	6,814	7,326	7,838	8,350	8,862	9,374	9,886
159	671	1,183	1,695	2,207	2,719	3,231	3,743	4,255	4,767	5,279	5,791	6,303	6,815	7,327	7,839	8,351	8,863	9,375	9,887
160	672	1,184	1,696	2,208	2,720	3,232	3,744	4,256	4,768	5,280	5,792	6,304	6,816	7,328	7,840	8,352	8,864	9,376	9,888
161	673	1,185	1,697	2,209	2,721	3,233	3,745	4,257	4,769	5,281	5,793	6,305	6,817	7,329	7,841	8,353	8,865	9,377	9,889
162	674	1,186	1,698	2,210	2,722	3,234	3,746	4,258	4,770	5,282	5,794	6,306	6,818	7,330	7,842	8,354	8,866	9,378	9,890
163	675	1,187	1,699	2,211	2,723	3,235	3,747	4,259	4,771	5,283	5,795	6,307	6,819	7,331	7,843	8,355	8,867	9,379	9,891
164	676	1,188	1,700	2,212	2,724	3,236	3,748	4,260	4,772	5,284	5,796	6,308	6,820	7,332	7,844	8,356	8,868	9,380	9,892
165	677	1,189	1,701	2,213	2,725	3,237	3,749	4,261	4,773	5,285	5,797	6,309	6,821	7,333	7,845	8,357	8,869	9,381	9,893
166	678	1,190	1,702	2,214	2,726	3,238	3,750	4,262	4,774	5,286	5,798	6,310	6,822	7,334	7,846	8,358	8,870	9,382	9,894
167	679	1,191	1,703	2,215	2,727	3,239	3,751	4,263	4,775	5,287	5,799	6,311	6,823	7,335	7,847	8,359	8,871	9,383	9,895
168	680	1,192	1,704	2,216	2,728	3,240	3,752	4,264	4,776	5,288	5,800	6,312	6,824	7,336	7,848	8,360	8,872	9,384	9,896
169	681	1,193	1,705	2,217	2,729	3,241	3,753	4,265	4,777	5,289	5,801	6,313	6,825	7,337	7,849	8,361	8,873	9,385	9,897
170	682	1,194	1,706	2,218	2,730	3,242	3,754	4,266	4,778	5,290	5,802	6,314	6,826	7,338	7,850	8,362	8,874	9,386	9,898
171	683	1,195	1,707	2,219	2,731	3,243	3,755	4,267	4,779	5,291	5,803	6,315	6,827	7,339	7,851	8,363	8,875	9,387	9,899
172	684	1,196	1,708	2,220	2,732	3,244	3,756	4,268	4,780	5,292	5,804	6,316	6,828	7,340	7,852	8,364	8,876	9,388	9,900
173	685	1,197	1,709	2,221	2,733	3,245	3,757	4,269	4,781	5,293	5,805	6,317	6,829	7,341	7,853	8,365	8,877	9,389	9,901
174	686	1,198	1,710	2,222	2,734	3,246	3,758	4,270	4,782	5,294	5,806	6,318	6,830	7,342	7,854	8,366	8,878	9,390	9,902
175	687	1,199	1,711	2,223	2,735	3,247	3,759	4,271	4,783	5,295	5,807	6,319	6,831	7,343	7,855	8,367	8,879	9,391	9,903
176	688	1,200	1,712	2,224	2,736	3,248	3,760	4,272	4,784	5,296	5,808	6,320	6,832	7,344	7,856	8,368	8,880	9,392	9,904
177	689	1,201	1,713	2,225	2,737	3,249	3,761	4,273	4,785	5,297	5,809	6,321	6,833	7,345	7,857	8,369	8,881	9,393	9,905

Start Address	Universe																		
1	2	3	4	5	6	7	8	9	10	11	12	13	14	15	16	17	18	19	20
178	690	1,202	1,714	2,226	2,738	3,250	3,762	4,274	4,786	5,298	5,810	6,322	6,834	7,346	7,858	8,370	8,882	9,394	9,906
179	691	1,203	1,715	2,227	2,739	3,251	3,763	4,275	4,787	5,299	5,811	6,323	6,835	7,347	7,859	8,371	8,883	9,395	9,907
180	692	1,204	1,716	2,228	2,740	3,252	3,764	4,276	4,788	5,300	5,812	6,324	6,836	7,348	7,860	8,372	8,884	9,396	9,908
181	693	1,205	1,717	2,229	2,741	3,253	3,765	4,277	4,789	5,301	5,813	6,325	6,837	7,349	7,861	8,373	8,885	9,397	9,909
182	694	1,206	1,718	2,230	2,742	3,254	3,766	4,278	4,790	5,302	5,814	6,326	6,838	7,350	7,862	8,374	8,886	9,398	9,910
183	695	1,207	1,719	2,231	2,743	3,255	3,767	4,279	4,791	5,303	5,815	6,327	6,839	7,351	7,863	8,375	8,887	9,399	9,911
184	696	1,208	1,720	2,232	2,744	3,256	3,768	4,280	4,792	5,304	5,816	6,328	6,840	7,352	7,864	8,376	8,888	9,400	9,912
185	697	1,209	1,721	2,233	2,745	3,257	3,769	4,281	4,793	5,305	5,817	6,329	6,841	7,353	7,865	8,377	8,889	9,401	9,913
186	698	1,210	1,722	2,234	2,746	3,258	3,770	4,282	4,794	5,306	5,818	6,330	6,842	7,354	7,866	8,378	8,890	9,402	9,914
187	699	1,211	1,723	2,235	2,747	3,259	3,771	4,283	4,795	5,307	5,819	6,331	6,843	7,355	7,867	8,379	8,891	9,403	9,915
188	700	1,212	1,724	2,236	2,748	3,260	3,772	4,284	4,796	5,308	5,820	6,332	6,844	7,356	7,868	8,380	8,892	9,404	9,916
189	701	1,213	1,725	2,237	2,749	3,261	3,773	4,285	4,797	5,309	5,821	6,333	6,845	7,357	7,869	8,381	8,893	9,405	9,917
190	702	1,214	1,726	2,238	2,750	3,262	3,774	4,286	4,798	5,310	5,822	6,334	6,846	7,358	7,870	8,382	8,894	9,406	9,918
191	703	1,215	1,727	2,239	2,751	3,263	3,775	4,287	4,799	5,311	5,823	6,335	6,847	7,359	7,871	8,383	8,895	9,407	9,919
192	704	1,216	1,728	2,240	2,752	3,264	3,776	4,288	4,800	5,312	5,824	6,336	6,848	7,360	7,872	8,384	8,896	9,408	9,920
193	705	1,217	1,729	2,241	2,753	3,265	3,777	4,289	4,801	5,313	5,825	6,337	6,849	7,361	7,873	8,385	8,897	9,409	9,921
194	706	1,218	1,730	2,242	2,754	3,266	3,778	4,290	4,802	5,314	5,826	6,338	6,850	7,362	7,874	8,386	8,898	9,410	9,922
195	707	1,219	1,731	2,243	2,755	3,267	3,779	4,291	4,803	5,315	5,827	6,339	6,851	7,363	7,875	8,387	8,899	9,411	9,923
196	708	1,220	1,732	2,244	2,756	3,268	3,780	4,292	4,804	5,316	5,828	6,340	6,852	7,364	7,876	8,388	8,900	9,412	9,924
197	709	1,221	1,733	2,245	2,757	3,269	3,781	4,293	4,805	5,317	5,829	6,341	6,853	7,365	7,877	8,389	8,901	9,413	9,925
198	710	1,222	1,734	2,246	2,758	3,270	3,782	4,294	4,806	5,318	5,830	6,342	6,854	7,366	7,878	8,390	8,902	9,414	9,926
199	711	1,223	1,735	2,247	2,759	3,271	3,783	4,295	4,807	5,319	5,831	6,343	6,855	7,367	7,879	8,391	8,903	9,415	9,927
200	712	1,224	1,736	2,248	2,760	3,272	3,784	4,296	4,808	5,320	5,832	6,344	6,856	7,368	7,880	8,392	8,904	9,416	9,928
201	713	1,225	1,737	2,249	2,761	3,273	3,785	4,297	4,809	5,321	5,833	6,345	6,857	7,369	7,881	8,393	8,905	9,417	9,929
202	714	1,226	1,738	2,250	2,762	3,274	3,786	4,298	4,810	5,322	5,834	6,346	6,858	7,370	7,882	8,394	8,906	9,418	9,930
203	715	1,227	1,739	2,251	2,763	3,275	3,787	4,299	4,811	5,323	5,835	6,347	6,859	7,371	7,883	8,395	8,907	9,419	9,931
204	716	1,228	1,740	2,252	2,764	3,276	3,788	4,300	4,812	5,324	5,836	6,348	6,860	7,372	7,884	8,396	8,908	9,420	9,932
205	717	1,229	1,741	2,253	2,765	3,277	3,789	4,301	4,813	5,325	5,837	6,349	6,861	7,373	7,885	8,397	8,909	9,421	9,933
206	718	1,230	1,742	2,254	2,766	3,278	3,790	4,302	4,814	5,326	5,838	6,350	6,862	7,374	7,886	8,398	8,910	9,422	9,934
207	719	1,231	1,743	2,255	2,767	3,279	3,791	4,303	4,815	5,327	5,839	6,351	6,863	7,375	7,887	8,399	8,911	9,423	9,935
208	720	1,232	1,744	2,256	2,768	3,280	3,792	4,304	4,816	5,328	5,840	6,352	6,864	7,376	7,888	8,400	8,912	9,424	9,936
209	721	1,233	1,745	2,257	2,769	3,281	3,793	4,305	4,817	5,329	5,841	6,353	6,865	7,377	7,889	8,401	8,913	9,425	9,937
210	722	1,234	1,746	2,258	2,770	3,282	3,794	4,306	4,818	5,330	5,842	6,354	6,866	7,378	7,890	8,402	8,914	9,426	9,938
211	723	1,235	1,747	2,259	2,771	3,283	3,795	4,307	4,819	5,331	5,843	6,355	6,867	7,379	7,891	8,403	8,915	9,427	9,939
212	724	1,236	1,748	2,260	2,772	3,284	3,796	4,308	4,820	5,332	5,844	6,356	6,868	7,380	7,892	8,404	8,916	9,428	9,940
213	725	1,237	1,749	2,261	2,773	3,285	3,797	4,309	4,821	5,333	5,845	6,357	6,869	7,381	7,893	8,405	8,917	9,429	9,941
214	726	1,238	1,750	2,262	2,774	3,286	3,798	4,310	4,822	5,334	5,846	6,358	6,870	7,382	7,894	8,406	8,918	9,430	9,942
215	727	1,239	1,751	2,263	2,775	3,287	3,799	4,311	4,823	5,335	5,847	6,359	6,871	7,383	7,895	8,407	8,919	9,431	9,943
216	728	1,240	1,752	2,264	2,776	3,288	3,800	4,312	4,824	5,336	5,848	6,360	6,872	7,384	7,896	8,408	8,920	9,432	9,944
217	729	1,241	1,753	2,265	2,777	3,289	3,801	4,313	4,825	5,337	5,849	6,361	6,873	7,385	7,897	8,409	8,921	9,433	9,945
218	730	1,242	1,754	2,266	2,778	3,290	3,802	4,314	4,826	5,338	5,850	6,362	6,874	7,386	7,898	8,410	8,922	9,434	9,946
219	731	1,243	1,755	2,267	2,779	3,291	3,803	4,315	4,827	5,339	5,851	6,363	6,875	7,387	7,899	8,411	8,923	9,435	9,947
220	732	1,244	1,756	2,268	2,780	3,292	3,804	4,316	4,828	5,340	5,852	6,364	6,876	7,388	7,900	8,412	8,924	9,436	9,948
221	733	1,245	1,757	2,269	2,781	3,293	3,805	4,317	4,829	5,341	5,853	6,365	6,877	7,389	7,901	8,413	8,925	9,437	9,949
222	734	1,246	1,758	2,270	2,782	3,294	3,806	4,318	4,830	5,342	5,854	6,366	6,878	7,390	7,902	8,414	8,926	9,438	9,950
223	735	1,247	1,759	2,271	2,783	3,295	3,807	4,319	4,831	5,343	5,855	6,367	6,879	7,391	7,903	8,415	8,927	9,439	9,951
224	736	1,248	1,760	2,272	2,784	3,296	3,808	4,320	4,832	5,344	5,856	6,368	6,880	7,392	7,904	8,416	8,928	9,440	9,952
225	737	1,249	1,761	2,273	2,785	3,297	3,809	4,321	4,833	5,345	5,857	6,369	6,881	7,393	7,905	8,417	8,929	9,441	9,953
226	738	1,250	1,762	2,274	2,786	3,298	3,810	4,322	4,834	5,346	5,858	6,370	6,882	7,394	7,906	8,418	8,930	9,442	9,954
227	739	1,251	1,763	2,275	2,787	3,299	3,811	4,323	4,835	5,347	5,859	6,371	6,883	7,395	7,907	8,419	8,931	9,443	9,955
228	740	1,252	1,764	2,276	2,788	3,300	3,812	4,324	4,836	5,348	5,860	6,372	6,884	7,396	7,908	8,420	8,932	9,444	9,956
229	741	1,253	1,765	2,277	2,789	3,301	3,813	4,325	4,837	5,349	5,861	6,373	6,885	7,397	7,909	8,421	8,933	9,445	9,957
230	742	1,254	1,766	2,278	2,790	3,302	3,814	4,326	4,838	5,350	5,862	6,374	6,886	7,398	7,910	8,422	8,934	9,446	9,958
231	743	1,255	1,767	2,279	2,791	3,303	3,815	4,327	4,839	5,351	5,863	6,375	6,887	7,399	7,911	8,423	8,935	9,447	9,959
232	744	1,256	1,768	2,280	2,792	3,304	3,816	4,328	4,840	5,352	5,864	6,376	6,888	7,400	7,912	8,424	8,936	9,448	9,960
233	745	1,257	1,769	2,281	2,793	3,305	3,817	4,329	4,841	5,353	5,865	6,377	6,889	7,401	7,913	8,425	8,937	9,449	9,961
234	746	1,258	1,770	2,282	2,794	3,306	3,818	4,330	4,842	5,354	5,866	6,378	6,890	7,402	7,914	8,426	8,938	9,450	9,962
235	747	1,259	1,771	2,283	2,795	3,307	3,819	4,331	4,843	5,355	5,867	6,379	6,891	7,403	7,915	8,427	8,939	9,451	9,963
236	748	1,260	1,772	2,284	2,796	3,308	3,820	4,332	4,844	5,356	5,868	6,380	6,892	7,404	7,916	8,428	8,940	9,452	9,964
237	749	1,261	1,773	2,285	2,797	3,309	3,821	4,333	4,845	5,357	5,869	6,381	6,893	7,405	7,917	8,429	8,941	9,453	9,965
238	750	1,262	1,774	2,286	2,798	3,310	3,822	4,334	4,846	5,358	5,870	6,382	6,894	7,406	7,918	8,430	8,942	9,454	9,966
239	751	1,263	1,775	2,287	2,799	3,311	3,823	4,335	4,847	5,359	5,871	6,383	6,895	7,407	7,919	8,431	8,943	9,455	9,967
240	752	1,264	1,776	2,288	2,800	3,312	3,824	4,336	4,848	5,360	5,872	6,384	6,896	7,408	7,920	8,432	8,944	9,456	9,968
241	753	1,265	1,777	2,289	2,801	3,313	3,825	4,337	4,849	5,361	5,873	6,385	6,897	7,409	7,921	8,433	8,945	9,457	9,969
242	754	1,266	1,778	2,290	2,802	3,314	3,826	4,338	4,850	5,362	5,874	6,386	6,898	7,410	7,922	8,434	8,946	9,458	9,970
243	755	1,267	1,779	2,291	2,803	3,315	3,827	4,339	4,851	5,363	5,875	6,387	6,899	7,411	7,923	8,435	8,947	9,459	9,971
244	756	1,268	1,780	2,292	2,804	3,316	3,828	4,340	4,852	5,364	5,876	6,388	6,900	7,412	7,924	8,436	8,948	9,460	9,972
245	757	1,269	1,781	2,293	2,805	3,317	3,829	4,341	4,853	5,365	5,877	6,389	6,901	7,413	7,925	8,437	8,949	9,461	9,973
246	758	1,270	1,782	2,294	2,806	3,318	3,830	4,342	4,854	5,366	5,878	6,390	6,902	7,414	7,926	8,438	8,950	9,462	9,974
247	759	1,271	1,783	2,295	2,807	3,319	3,831	4,343	4,855	5,367	5,879	6,391	6,903	7,415	7,927	8,439	8,951	9,463	9,975
248	760	1,272	1,784	2,296	2,808	3,320	3,832	4,344	4,856	5,368	5,880	6,392	6,904	7,416	7,928	8,440	8,952	9,464	9,976
249	761	1,273	1,785	2,297	2,809	3,321	3,833	4,345	4,857	5,369	5,881	6,393	6,905	7,417	7,929	8,441	8,953	9,465	9,977
250	762	1,274	1,786	2,298	2,810	3,322	3,834	4,346	4,858	5,370	5,882	6,394	6,906	7,418	7,930	8,442	8,954	9,466	9,978
251	763	1,275	1,787	2,299	2,811	3,323	3,835	4,347	4,859	5,371	5,883	6,395	6,907	7,419	7,931	8,443	8,955	9,467	9,979
252	764	1,276	1,788	2,300	2,812	3,324	3,836	4,348	4,860	5,372	5,884	6,396	6,908	7,420	7,932	8,444	8,956	9,468	9,980
253	765	1,277	1,789	2,301	2,813	3,325	3,837	4,349	4,861	5,373	5,885	6,397	6,909	7,421	7,933	8,445	8,957	9,469	9,981
254	766	1,278	1,790	2,302	2,814	3,326	3,838	4,350	4,862	5,374	5,886	6,398	6,910	7,422	7,934	8,446	8,958	9,470	9,982
255	767	1,279	1,791	2,303	2,815	3,327	3,839	4,351	4,863	5,375	5,887	6,399	6,911	7,423	7,935	8,447	8,959	9,471	9,983
256	768	1,280	1,792	2,304	2,816	3,328	3,840	4,352	4,864	5,376	5,888	6,400	6,912	7,424	7,936	8,448	8,960	9,472	9,984
257	769	1,281	1,793	2,305	2,817	3,329	3,841	4,353	4,865	5,377	5,889	6,401	6,913	7,425	7,937	8,449	8,961	9,473	9,985
258	770	1,282	1,794	2,306	2,818	3,330	3,842	4,354	4,866	5,378	5,890	6,402	6,914	7,426	7,938	8,450	8,962	9,474	9,986
259	771	1,283	1,795	2,307	2,819	3,331	3,843	4,355	4,867	5,379	5,891	6,403	6,915	7,427	7,939	8,451	8,963	9,475	9,987
260	772	1,284	1,796	2,308	2,820	3,332	3,844	4,356	4,868	5,380	5,892	6,404	6,916	7,428	7,940	8,452	8,964	9,476	9,988
261	773	1,285	1,797	2,309	2,821	3,333	3,845	4,357	4,869	5,381	5,893	6,405	6,917	7,429	7,941	8,453	8,965	9,477	9,989
262	774	1,286	1,798	2,310	2,822	3,334	3,846	4,358	4,870	5,382	5,894	6,406	6,918	7,430	7,942	8,454	8,966	9,478	9,990
263	775	1,287	1,799	2,311	2,823	3,335	3,847	4,359	4,871	5,383	5,895	6,407	6,919	7,431	7,943	8,455	8,967	9,479	9,991
264	776	1,288	1,800	2,312	2,824	3,336	3,848	4,360	4,872	5,384	5,896	6,408	6,920	7,432	7,944	8,456	8,968	9,480	9,992
265	777	1,289	1,801	2,313	2,825	3,337	3,849	4,361	4,873	5,385	5,897	6,409	6,921	7,433	7,945	8,457	8,969	9,481	9,993
266	778	1,290	1,802	2,314	2,826	3,338	3,850	4,362	4,874	5,386	5,898	6,410	6,922	7,434	7,946	8,458	8,970	9,482	9,994
267	779	1,291	1,803	2,315	2,827	3,339	3,851	4,363	4,875	5,387	5,899	6,411	6,923	7,435	7,947	8,459	8,971	9,483	9,995
268	780	1,292	1,804	2,316	2,828	3,340	3,852	4,364	4,876	5,388	5,900	6,412	6,924	7,436	7,948	8,460	8,972	9,484	9,996
269	781	1,293	1,805	2,317	2,829	3,341	3,853	4,365	4,877	5,389	5,901	6,413	6,925	7,437	7,949	8,461	8,973	9,485	9,997

Control Freak 167

Start Address									Universe										
1	2	3	4	5	6	7	8	9	10	11	12	13	14	15	16	17	18	19	20
270	782	1,294	1,806	2,318	2,830	3,342	3,854	4,366	4,878	5,390	5,902	6,414	6,926	7,438	7,950	8,462	8,974	9,486	9,998
271	783	1,295	1,807	2,319	2,831	3,343	3,855	4,367	4,879	5,391	5,903	6,415	6,927	7,439	7,951	8,463	8,975	9,487	9,999
272	784	1,296	1,808	2,320	2,832	3,344	3,856	4,368	4,880	5,392	5,904	6,416	6,928	7,440	7,952	8,464	8,976	9,488	10,000
273	785	1,297	1,809	2,321	2,833	3,345	3,857	4,369	4,881	5,393	5,905	6,417	6,929	7,441	7,953	8,465	8,977	9,489	10,001
274	786	1,298	1,810	2,322	2,834	3,346	3,858	4,370	4,882	5,394	5,906	6,418	6,930	7,442	7,954	8,466	8,978	9,490	10,002
275	787	1,299	1,811	2,323	2,835	3,347	3,859	4,371	4,883	5,395	5,907	6,419	6,931	7,443	7,955	8,467	8,979	9,491	10,003
276	788	1,300	1,812	2,324	2,836	3,348	3,860	4,372	4,884	5,396	5,908	6,420	6,932	7,444	7,956	8,468	8,980	9,492	10,004
277	789	1,301	1,813	2,325	2,837	3,349	3,861	4,373	4,885	5,397	5,909	6,421	6,933	7,445	7,957	8,469	8,981	9,493	10,005
278	790	1,302	1,814	2,326	2,838	3,350	3,862	4,374	4,886	5,398	5,910	6,422	6,934	7,446	7,958	8,470	8,982	9,494	10,006
279	791	1,303	1,815	2,327	2,839	3,351	3,863	4,375	4,887	5,399	5,911	6,423	6,935	7,447	7,959	8,471	8,983	9,495	10,007
280	792	1,304	1,816	2,328	2,840	3,352	3,864	4,376	4,888	5,400	5,912	6,424	6,936	7,448	7,960	8,472	8,984	9,496	10,008
281	793	1,305	1,817	2,329	2,841	3,353	3,865	4,377	4,889	5,401	5,913	6,425	6,937	7,449	7,961	8,473	8,985	9,497	10,009
282	794	1,306	1,818	2,330	2,842	3,354	3,866	4,378	4,890	5,402	5,914	6,426	6,938	7,450	7,962	8,474	8,986	9,498	10,010
283	795	1,307	1,819	2,331	2,843	3,355	3,867	4,379	4,891	5,403	5,915	6,427	6,939	7,451	7,963	8,475	8,987	9,499	10,011
284	796	1,308	1,820	2,332	2,844	3,356	3,868	4,380	4,892	5,404	5,916	6,428	6,940	7,452	7,964	8,476	8,988	9,500	10,012
285	797	1,309	1,821	2,333	2,845	3,357	3,869	4,381	4,893	5,405	5,917	6,429	6,941	7,453	7,965	8,477	8,989	9,501	10,013
286	798	1,310	1,822	2,334	2,846	3,358	3,870	4,382	4,894	5,406	5,918	6,430	6,942	7,454	7,966	8,478	8,990	9,502	10,014
287	799	1,311	1,823	2,335	2,847	3,359	3,871	4,383	4,895	5,407	5,919	6,431	6,943	7,455	7,967	8,479	8,991	9,503	10,015
288	800	1,312	1,824	2,336	2,848	3,360	3,872	4,384	4,896	5,408	5,920	6,432	6,944	7,456	7,968	8,480	8,992	9,504	10,016
289	801	1,313	1,825	2,337	2,849	3,361	3,873	4,385	4,897	5,409	5,921	6,433	6,945	7,457	7,969	8,481	8,993	9,505	10,017
290	802	1,314	1,826	2,338	2,850	3,362	3,874	4,386	4,898	5,410	5,922	6,434	6,946	7,458	7,970	8,482	8,994	9,506	10,018
291	803	1,315	1,827	2,339	2,851	3,363	3,875	4,387	4,899	5,411	5,923	6,435	6,947	7,459	7,971	8,483	8,995	9,507	10,019
292	804	1,316	1,828	2,340	2,852	3,364	3,876	4,388	4,900	5,412	5,924	6,436	6,948	7,460	7,972	8,484	8,996	9,508	10,020
293	805	1,317	1,829	2,341	2,853	3,365	3,877	4,389	4,901	5,413	5,925	6,437	6,949	7,461	7,973	8,485	8,997	9,509	10,021
294	806	1,318	1,830	2,342	2,854	3,366	3,878	4,390	4,902	5,414	5,926	6,438	6,950	7,462	7,974	8,486	8,998	9,510	10,022
295	807	1,319	1,831	2,343	2,855	3,367	3,879	4,391	4,903	5,415	5,927	6,439	6,951	7,463	7,975	8,487	8,999	9,511	10,023
296	808	1,320	1,832	2,344	2,856	3,368	3,880	4,392	4,904	5,416	5,928	6,440	6,952	7,464	7,976	8,488	9,000	9,512	10,024
297	809	1,321	1,833	2,345	2,857	3,369	3,881	4,393	4,905	5,417	5,929	6,441	6,953	7,465	7,977	8,489	9,001	9,513	10,025
298	810	1,322	1,834	2,346	2,858	3,370	3,882	4,394	4,906	5,418	5,930	6,442	6,954	7,466	7,978	8,490	9,002	9,514	10,026
299	811	1,323	1,835	2,347	2,859	3,371	3,883	4,395	4,907	5,419	5,931	6,443	6,955	7,467	7,979	8,491	9,003	9,515	10,027
300	812	1,324	1,836	2,348	2,860	3,372	3,884	4,396	4,908	5,420	5,932	6,444	6,956	7,468	7,980	8,492	9,004	9,516	10,028
301	813	1,325	1,837	2,349	2,861	3,373	3,885	4,397	4,909	5,421	5,933	6,445	6,957	7,469	7,981	8,493	9,005	9,517	10,029
302	814	1,326	1,838	2,350	2,862	3,374	3,886	4,398	4,910	5,422	5,934	6,446	6,958	7,470	7,982	8,494	9,006	9,518	10,030
303	815	1,327	1,839	2,351	2,863	3,375	3,887	4,399	4,911	5,423	5,935	6,447	6,959	7,471	7,983	8,495	9,007	9,519	10,031
304	816	1,328	1,840	2,352	2,864	3,376	3,888	4,400	4,912	5,424	5,936	6,448	6,960	7,472	7,984	8,496	9,008	9,520	10,032
305	817	1,329	1,841	2,353	2,865	3,377	3,889	4,401	4,913	5,425	5,937	6,449	6,961	7,473	7,985	8,497	9,009	9,521	10,033
306	818	1,330	1,842	2,354	2,866	3,378	3,890	4,402	4,914	5,426	5,938	6,450	6,962	7,474	7,986	8,498	9,010	9,522	10,034
307	819	1,331	1,843	2,355	2,867	3,379	3,891	4,403	4,915	5,427	5,939	6,451	6,963	7,475	7,987	8,499	9,011	9,523	10,035
308	820	1,332	1,844	2,356	2,868	3,380	3,892	4,404	4,916	5,428	5,940	6,452	6,964	7,476	7,988	8,500	9,012	9,524	10,036
309	821	1,333	1,845	2,357	2,869	3,381	3,893	4,405	4,917	5,429	5,941	6,453	6,965	7,477	7,989	8,501	9,013	9,525	10,037
310	822	1,334	1,846	2,358	2,870	3,382	3,894	4,406	4,918	5,430	5,942	6,454	6,966	7,478	7,990	8,502	9,014	9,526	10,038
311	823	1,335	1,847	2,359	2,871	3,383	3,895	4,407	4,919	5,431	5,943	6,455	6,967	7,479	7,991	8,503	9,015	9,527	10,039
312	824	1,336	1,848	2,360	2,872	3,384	3,896	4,408	4,920	5,432	5,944	6,456	6,968	7,480	7,992	8,504	9,016	9,528	10,040
313	825	1,337	1,849	2,361	2,873	3,385	3,897	4,409	4,921	5,433	5,945	6,457	6,969	7,481	7,993	8,505	9,017	9,529	10,041
314	826	1,338	1,850	2,362	2,874	3,386	3,898	4,410	4,922	5,434	5,946	6,458	6,970	7,482	7,994	8,506	9,018	9,530	10,042
315	827	1,339	1,851	2,363	2,875	3,387	3,899	4,411	4,923	5,435	5,947	6,459	6,971	7,483	7,995	8,507	9,019	9,531	10,043
316	828	1,340	1,852	2,364	2,876	3,388	3,900	4,412	4,924	5,436	5,948	6,460	6,972	7,484	7,996	8,508	9,020	9,532	10,044
317	829	1,341	1,853	2,365	2,877	3,389	3,901	4,413	4,925	5,437	5,949	6,461	6,973	7,485	7,997	8,509	9,021	9,533	10,045
318	830	1,342	1,854	2,366	2,878	3,390	3,902	4,414	4,926	5,438	5,950	6,462	6,974	7,486	7,998	8,510	9,022	9,534	10,046
319	831	1,343	1,855	2,367	2,879	3,391	3,903	4,415	4,927	5,439	5,951	6,463	6,975	7,487	7,999	8,511	9,023	9,535	10,047
320	832	1,344	1,856	2,368	2,880	3,392	3,904	4,416	4,928	5,440	5,952	6,464	6,976	7,488	8,000	8,512	9,024	9,536	10,048
321	833	1,345	1,857	2,369	2,881	3,393	3,905	4,417	4,929	5,441	5,953	6,465	6,977	7,489	8,001	8,513	9,025	9,537	10,049
322	834	1,346	1,858	2,370	2,882	3,394	3,906	4,418	4,930	5,442	5,954	6,466	6,978	7,490	8,002	8,514	9,026	9,538	10,050
323	835	1,347	1,859	2,371	2,883	3,395	3,907	4,419	4,931	5,443	5,955	6,467	6,979	7,491	8,003	8,515	9,027	9,539	10,051
324	836	1,348	1,860	2,372	2,884	3,396	3,908	4,420	4,932	5,444	5,956	6,468	6,980	7,492	8,004	8,516	9,028	9,540	10,052
325	837	1,349	1,861	2,373	2,885	3,397	3,909	4,421	4,933	5,445	5,957	6,469	6,981	7,493	8,005	8,517	9,029	9,541	10,053
326	838	1,350	1,862	2,374	2,886	3,398	3,910	4,422	4,934	5,446	5,958	6,470	6,982	7,494	8,006	8,518	9,030	9,542	10,054
327	839	1,351	1,863	2,375	2,887	3,399	3,911	4,423	4,935	5,447	5,959	6,471	6,983	7,495	8,007	8,519	9,031	9,543	10,055
328	840	1,352	1,864	2,376	2,888	3,400	3,912	4,424	4,936	5,448	5,960	6,472	6,984	7,496	8,008	8,520	9,032	9,544	10,056
329	841	1,353	1,865	2,377	2,889	3,401	3,913	4,425	4,937	5,449	5,961	6,473	6,985	7,497	8,009	8,521	9,033	9,545	10,057
330	842	1,354	1,866	2,378	2,890	3,402	3,914	4,426	4,938	5,450	5,962	6,474	6,986	7,498	8,010	8,522	9,034	9,546	10,058
331	843	1,355	1,867	2,379	2,891	3,403	3,915	4,427	4,939	5,451	5,963	6,475	6,987	7,499	8,011	8,523	9,035	9,547	10,059
332	844	1,356	1,868	2,380	2,892	3,404	3,916	4,428	4,940	5,452	5,964	6,476	6,988	7,500	8,012	8,524	9,036	9,548	10,060
333	845	1,357	1,869	2,381	2,893	3,405	3,917	4,429	4,941	5,453	5,965	6,477	6,989	7,501	8,013	8,525	9,037	9,549	10,061
334	846	1,358	1,870	2,382	2,894	3,406	3,918	4,430	4,942	5,454	5,966	6,478	6,990	7,502	8,014	8,526	9,038	9,550	10,062
335	847	1,359	1,871	2,383	2,895	3,407	3,919	4,431	4,943	5,455	5,967	6,479	6,991	7,503	8,015	8,527	9,039	9,551	10,063
336	848	1,360	1,872	2,384	2,896	3,408	3,920	4,432	4,944	5,456	5,968	6,480	6,992	7,504	8,016	8,528	9,040	9,552	10,064
337	849	1,361	1,873	2,385	2,897	3,409	3,921	4,433	4,945	5,457	5,969	6,481	6,993	7,505	8,017	8,529	9,041	9,553	10,065
338	850	1,362	1,874	2,386	2,898	3,410	3,922	4,434	4,946	5,458	5,970	6,482	6,994	7,506	8,018	8,530	9,042	9,554	10,066
339	851	1,363	1,875	2,387	2,899	3,411	3,923	4,435	4,947	5,459	5,971	6,483	6,995	7,507	8,019	8,531	9,043	9,555	10,067
340	852	1,364	1,876	2,388	2,900	3,412	3,924	4,436	4,948	5,460	5,972	6,484	6,996	7,508	8,020	8,532	9,044	9,556	10,068
341	853	1,365	1,877	2,389	2,901	3,413	3,925	4,437	4,949	5,461	5,973	6,485	6,997	7,509	8,021	8,533	9,045	9,557	10,069
342	854	1,366	1,878	2,390	2,902	3,414	3,926	4,438	4,950	5,462	5,974	6,486	6,998	7,510	8,022	8,534	9,046	9,558	10,070
343	855	1,367	1,879	2,391	2,903	3,415	3,927	4,439	4,951	5,463	5,975	6,487	6,999	7,511	8,023	8,535	9,047	9,559	10,071
344	856	1,368	1,880	2,392	2,904	3,416	3,928	4,440	4,952	5,464	5,976	6,488	7,000	7,512	8,024	8,536	9,048	9,560	10,072
345	857	1,369	1,881	2,393	2,905	3,417	3,929	4,441	4,953	5,465	5,977	6,489	7,001	7,513	8,025	8,537	9,049	9,561	10,073
346	858	1,370	1,882	2,394	2,906	3,418	3,930	4,442	4,954	5,466	5,978	6,490	7,002	7,514	8,026	8,538	9,050	9,562	10,074
347	859	1,371	1,883	2,395	2,907	3,419	3,931	4,443	4,955	5,467	5,979	6,491	7,003	7,515	8,027	8,539	9,051	9,563	10,075
348	860	1,372	1,884	2,396	2,908	3,420	3,932	4,444	4,956	5,468	5,980	6,492	7,004	7,516	8,028	8,540	9,052	9,564	10,076
349	861	1,373	1,885	2,397	2,909	3,421	3,933	4,445	4,957	5,469	5,981	6,493	7,005	7,517	8,029	8,541	9,053	9,565	10,077
350	862	1,374	1,886	2,398	2,910	3,422	3,934	4,446	4,958	5,470	5,982	6,494	7,006	7,518	8,030	8,542	9,054	9,566	10,078
351	863	1,375	1,887	2,399	2,911	3,423	3,935	4,447	4,959	5,471	5,983	6,495	7,007	7,519	8,031	8,543	9,055	9,567	10,079
352	864	1,376	1,888	2,400	2,912	3,424	3,936	4,448	4,960	5,472	5,984	6,496	7,008	7,520	8,032	8,544	9,056	9,568	10,080
353	865	1,377	1,889	2,401	2,913	3,425	3,937	4,449	4,961	5,473	5,985	6,497	7,009	7,521	8,033	8,545	9,057	9,569	10,081
354	866	1,378	1,890	2,402	2,914	3,426	3,938	4,450	4,962	5,474	5,986	6,498	7,010	7,522	8,034	8,546	9,058	9,570	10,082
355	867	1,379	1,891	2,403	2,915	3,427	3,939	4,451	4,963	5,475	5,987	6,499	7,011	7,523	8,035	8,547	9,059	9,571	10,083
356	868	1,380	1,892	2,404	2,916	3,428	3,940	4,452	4,964	5,476	5,988	6,500	7,012	7,524	8,036	8,548	9,060	9,572	10,084
357	869	1,381	1,893	2,405	2,917	3,429	3,941	4,453	4,965	5,477	5,989	6,501	7,013	7,525	8,037	8,549	9,061	9,573	10,085
358	870	1,382	1,894	2,406	2,918	3,430	3,942	4,454	4,966	5,478	5,990	6,502	7,014	7,526	8,038	8,550	9,062	9,574	10,086
359	871	1,383	1,895	2,407	2,919	3,431	3,943	4,455	4,967	5,479	5,991	6,503	7,015	7,527	8,039	8,551	9,063	9,575	10,087
360	872	1,384	1,896	2,408	2,920	3,432	3,944	4,456	4,968	5,480	5,992	6,504	7,016	7,528	8,040	8,552	9,064	9,576	10,088
361	873	1,385	1,897	2,409	2,921	3,433	3,945	4,457	4,969	5,481	5,993	6,505	7,017	7,529	8,041	8,553	9,065	9,577	10,089

Start Address	Universe																		
1	2	3	4	5	6	7	8	9	10	11	12	13	14	15	16	17	18	19	20
362	874	1,386	1,898	2,410	2,922	3,434	3,946	4,458	4,970	5,482	5,994	6,506	7,018	7,530	8,042	8,554	9,066	9,578	10,090
363	875	1,387	1,899	2,411	2,923	3,435	3,947	4,459	4,971	5,483	5,995	6,507	7,019	7,531	8,043	8,555	9,067	9,579	10,091
364	876	1,388	1,900	2,412	2,924	3,436	3,948	4,460	4,972	5,484	5,996	6,508	7,020	7,532	8,044	8,556	9,068	9,580	10,092
365	877	1,389	1,901	2,413	2,925	3,437	3,949	4,461	4,973	5,485	5,997	6,509	7,021	7,533	8,045	8,557	9,069	9,581	10,093
366	878	1,390	1,902	2,414	2,926	3,438	3,950	4,462	4,974	5,486	5,998	6,510	7,022	7,534	8,046	8,558	9,070	9,582	10,094
367	879	1,391	1,903	2,415	2,927	3,439	3,951	4,463	4,975	5,487	5,999	6,511	7,023	7,535	8,047	8,559	9,071	9,583	10,095
368	880	1,392	1,904	2,416	2,928	3,440	3,952	4,464	4,976	5,488	6,000	6,512	7,024	7,536	8,048	8,560	9,072	9,584	10,096
369	881	1,393	1,905	2,417	2,929	3,441	3,953	4,465	4,977	5,489	6,001	6,513	7,025	7,537	8,049	8,561	9,073	9,585	10,097
370	882	1,394	1,906	2,418	2,930	3,442	3,954	4,466	4,978	5,490	6,002	6,514	7,026	7,538	8,050	8,562	9,074	9,586	10,098
371	883	1,395	1,907	2,419	2,931	3,443	3,955	4,467	4,979	5,491	6,003	6,515	7,027	7,539	8,051	8,563	9,075	9,587	10,099
372	884	1,396	1,908	2,420	2,932	3,444	3,956	4,468	4,980	5,492	6,004	6,516	7,028	7,540	8,052	8,564	9,076	9,588	10,100
373	885	1,397	1,909	2,421	2,933	3,445	3,957	4,469	4,981	5,493	6,005	6,517	7,029	7,541	8,053	8,565	9,077	9,589	10,101
374	886	1,398	1,910	2,422	2,934	3,446	3,958	4,470	4,982	5,494	6,006	6,518	7,030	7,542	8,054	8,566	9,078	9,590	10,102
375	887	1,399	1,911	2,423	2,935	3,447	3,959	4,471	4,983	5,495	6,007	6,519	7,031	7,543	8,055	8,567	9,079	9,591	10,103
376	888	1,400	1,912	2,424	2,936	3,448	3,960	4,472	4,984	5,496	6,008	6,520	7,032	7,544	8,056	8,568	9,080	9,592	10,104
377	889	1,401	1,913	2,425	2,937	3,449	3,961	4,473	4,985	5,497	6,009	6,521	7,033	7,545	8,057	8,569	9,081	9,593	10,105
378	890	1,402	1,914	2,426	2,938	3,450	3,962	4,474	4,986	5,498	6,010	6,522	7,034	7,546	8,058	8,570	9,082	9,594	10,106
379	891	1,403	1,915	2,427	2,939	3,451	3,963	4,475	4,987	5,499	6,011	6,523	7,035	7,547	8,059	8,571	9,083	9,595	10,107
380	892	1,404	1,916	2,428	2,940	3,452	3,964	4,476	4,988	5,500	6,012	6,524	7,036	7,548	8,060	8,572	9,084	9,596	10,108
381	893	1,405	1,917	2,429	2,941	3,453	3,965	4,477	4,989	5,501	6,013	6,525	7,037	7,549	8,061	8,573	9,085	9,597	10,109
382	894	1,406	1,918	2,430	2,942	3,454	3,966	4,478	4,990	5,502	6,014	6,526	7,038	7,550	8,062	8,574	9,086	9,598	10,110
383	895	1,407	1,919	2,431	2,943	3,455	3,967	4,479	4,991	5,503	6,015	6,527	7,039	7,551	8,063	8,575	9,087	9,599	10,111
384	896	1,408	1,920	2,432	2,944	3,456	3,968	4,480	4,992	5,504	6,016	6,528	7,040	7,552	8,064	8,576	9,088	9,600	10,112
385	897	1,409	1,921	2,433	2,945	3,457	3,969	4,481	4,993	5,505	6,017	6,529	7,041	7,553	8,065	8,577	9,089	9,601	10,113
386	898	1,410	1,922	2,434	2,946	3,458	3,970	4,482	4,994	5,506	6,018	6,530	7,042	7,554	8,066	8,578	9,090	9,602	10,114
387	899	1,411	1,923	2,435	2,947	3,459	3,971	4,483	4,995	5,507	6,019	6,531	7,043	7,555	8,067	8,579	9,091	9,603	10,115
388	900	1,412	1,924	2,436	2,948	3,460	3,972	4,484	4,996	5,508	6,020	6,532	7,044	7,556	8,068	8,580	9,092	9,604	10,116
389	901	1,413	1,925	2,437	2,949	3,461	3,973	4,485	4,997	5,509	6,021	6,533	7,045	7,557	8,069	8,581	9,093	9,605	10,117
390	902	1,414	1,926	2,438	2,950	3,462	3,974	4,486	4,998	5,510	6,022	6,534	7,046	7,558	8,070	8,582	9,094	9,606	10,118
391	903	1,415	1,927	2,439	2,951	3,463	3,975	4,487	4,999	5,511	6,023	6,535	7,047	7,559	8,071	8,583	9,095	9,607	10,119
392	904	1,416	1,928	2,440	2,952	3,464	3,976	4,488	5,000	5,512	6,024	6,536	7,048	7,560	8,072	8,584	9,096	9,608	10,120
393	905	1,417	1,929	2,441	2,953	3,465	3,977	4,489	5,001	5,513	6,025	6,537	7,049	7,561	8,073	8,585	9,097	9,609	10,121
394	906	1,418	1,930	2,442	2,954	3,466	3,978	4,490	5,002	5,514	6,026	6,538	7,050	7,562	8,074	8,586	9,098	9,610	10,122
395	907	1,419	1,931	2,443	2,955	3,467	3,979	4,491	5,003	5,515	6,027	6,539	7,051	7,563	8,075	8,587	9,099	9,611	10,123
396	908	1,420	1,932	2,444	2,956	3,468	3,980	4,492	5,004	5,516	6,028	6,540	7,052	7,564	8,076	8,588	9,100	9,612	10,124
397	909	1,421	1,933	2,445	2,957	3,469	3,981	4,493	5,005	5,517	6,029	6,541	7,053	7,565	8,077	8,589	9,101	9,613	10,125
398	910	1,422	1,934	2,446	2,958	3,470	3,982	4,494	5,006	5,518	6,030	6,542	7,054	7,566	8,078	8,590	9,102	9,614	10,126
399	911	1,423	1,935	2,447	2,959	3,471	3,983	4,495	5,007	5,519	6,031	6,543	7,055	7,567	8,079	8,591	9,103	9,615	10,127
400	912	1,424	1,936	2,448	2,960	3,472	3,984	4,496	5,008	5,520	6,032	6,544	7,056	7,568	8,080	8,592	9,104	9,616	10,128
401	913	1,425	1,937	2,449	2,961	3,473	3,985	4,497	5,009	5,521	6,033	6,545	7,057	7,569	8,081	8,593	9,105	9,617	10,129
402	914	1,426	1,938	2,450	2,962	3,474	3,986	4,498	5,010	5,522	6,034	6,546	7,058	7,570	8,082	8,594	9,106	9,618	10,130
403	915	1,427	1,939	2,451	2,963	3,475	3,987	4,499	5,011	5,523	6,035	6,547	7,059	7,571	8,083	8,595	9,107	9,619	10,131
404	916	1,428	1,940	2,452	2,964	3,476	3,988	4,500	5,012	5,524	6,036	6,548	7,060	7,572	8,084	8,596	9,108	9,620	10,132
405	917	1,429	1,941	2,453	2,965	3,477	3,989	4,501	5,013	5,525	6,037	6,549	7,061	7,573	8,085	8,597	9,109	9,621	10,133
406	918	1,430	1,942	2,454	2,966	3,478	3,990	4,502	5,014	5,526	6,038	6,550	7,062	7,574	8,086	8,598	9,110	9,622	10,134
407	919	1,431	1,943	2,455	2,967	3,479	3,991	4,503	5,015	5,527	6,039	6,551	7,063	7,575	8,087	8,599	9,111	9,623	10,135
408	920	1,432	1,944	2,456	2,968	3,480	3,992	4,504	5,016	5,528	6,040	6,552	7,064	7,576	8,088	8,600	9,112	9,624	10,136
409	921	1,433	1,945	2,457	2,969	3,481	3,993	4,505	5,017	5,529	6,041	6,553	7,065	7,577	8,089	8,601	9,113	9,625	10,137
410	922	1,434	1,946	2,458	2,970	3,482	3,994	4,506	5,018	5,530	6,042	6,554	7,066	7,578	8,090	8,602	9,114	9,626	10,138
411	923	1,435	1,947	2,459	2,971	3,483	3,995	4,507	5,019	5,531	6,043	6,555	7,067	7,579	8,091	8,603	9,115	9,627	10,139
412	924	1,436	1,948	2,460	2,972	3,484	3,996	4,508	5,020	5,532	6,044	6,556	7,068	7,580	8,092	8,604	9,116	9,628	10,140
413	925	1,437	1,949	2,461	2,973	3,485	3,997	4,509	5,021	5,533	6,045	6,557	7,069	7,581	8,093	8,605	9,117	9,629	10,141
414	926	1,438	1,950	2,462	2,974	3,486	3,998	4,510	5,022	5,534	6,046	6,558	7,070	7,582	8,094	8,606	9,118	9,630	10,142
415	927	1,439	1,951	2,463	2,975	3,487	3,999	4,511	5,023	5,535	6,047	6,559	7,071	7,583	8,095	8,607	9,119	9,631	10,143
416	928	1,440	1,952	2,464	2,976	3,488	4,000	4,512	5,024	5,536	6,048	6,560	7,072	7,584	8,096	8,608	9,120	9,632	10,144
417	929	1,441	1,953	2,465	2,977	3,489	4,001	4,513	5,025	5,537	6,049	6,561	7,073	7,585	8,097	8,609	9,121	9,633	10,145
418	930	1,442	1,954	2,466	2,978	3,490	4,002	4,514	5,026	5,538	6,050	6,562	7,074	7,586	8,098	8,610	9,122	9,634	10,146
419	931	1,443	1,955	2,467	2,979	3,491	4,003	4,515	5,027	5,539	6,051	6,563	7,075	7,587	8,099	8,611	9,123	9,635	10,147
420	932	1,444	1,956	2,468	2,980	3,492	4,004	4,516	5,028	5,540	6,052	6,564	7,076	7,588	8,100	8,612	9,124	9,636	10,148
421	933	1,445	1,957	2,469	2,981	3,493	4,005	4,517	5,029	5,541	6,053	6,565	7,077	7,589	8,101	8,613	9,125	9,637	10,149
422	934	1,446	1,958	2,470	2,982	3,494	4,006	4,518	5,030	5,542	6,054	6,566	7,078	7,590	8,102	8,614	9,126	9,638	10,150
423	935	1,447	1,959	2,471	2,983	3,495	4,007	4,519	5,031	5,543	6,055	6,567	7,079	7,591	8,103	8,615	9,127	9,639	10,151
424	936	1,448	1,960	2,472	2,984	3,496	4,008	4,520	5,032	5,544	6,056	6,568	7,080	7,592	8,104	8,616	9,128	9,640	10,152
425	937	1,449	1,961	2,473	2,985	3,497	4,009	4,521	5,033	5,545	6,057	6,569	7,081	7,593	8,105	8,617	9,129	9,641	10,153
426	938	1,450	1,962	2,474	2,986	3,498	4,010	4,522	5,034	5,546	6,058	6,570	7,082	7,594	8,106	8,618	9,130	9,642	10,154
427	939	1,451	1,963	2,475	2,987	3,499	4,011	4,523	5,035	5,547	6,059	6,571	7,083	7,595	8,107	8,619	9,131	9,643	10,155
428	940	1,452	1,964	2,476	2,988	3,500	4,012	4,524	5,036	5,548	6,060	6,572	7,084	7,596	8,108	8,620	9,132	9,644	10,156
429	941	1,453	1,965	2,477	2,989	3,501	4,013	4,525	5,037	5,549	6,061	6,573	7,085	7,597	8,109	8,621	9,133	9,645	10,157
430	942	1,454	1,966	2,478	2,990	3,502	4,014	4,526	5,038	5,550	6,062	6,574	7,086	7,598	8,110	8,622	9,134	9,646	10,158
431	943	1,455	1,967	2,479	2,991	3,503	4,015	4,527	5,039	5,551	6,063	6,575	7,087	7,599	8,111	8,623	9,135	9,647	10,159
432	944	1,456	1,968	2,480	2,992	3,504	4,016	4,528	5,040	5,552	6,064	6,576	7,088	7,600	8,112	8,624	9,136	9,648	10,160
433	945	1,457	1,969	2,481	2,993	3,505	4,017	4,529	5,041	5,553	6,065	6,577	7,089	7,601	8,113	8,625	9,137	9,649	10,161
434	946	1,458	1,970	2,482	2,994	3,506	4,018	4,530	5,042	5,554	6,066	6,578	7,090	7,602	8,114	8,626	9,138	9,650	10,162
435	947	1,459	1,971	2,483	2,995	3,507	4,019	4,531	5,043	5,555	6,067	6,579	7,091	7,603	8,115	8,627	9,139	9,651	10,163
436	948	1,460	1,972	2,484	2,996	3,508	4,020	4,532	5,044	5,556	6,068	6,580	7,092	7,604	8,116	8,628	9,140	9,652	10,164
437	949	1,461	1,973	2,485	2,997	3,509	4,021	4,533	5,045	5,557	6,069	6,581	7,093	7,605	8,117	8,629	9,141	9,653	10,165
438	950	1,462	1,974	2,486	2,998	3,510	4,022	4,534	5,046	5,558	6,070	6,582	7,094	7,606	8,118	8,630	9,142	9,654	10,166
439	951	1,463	1,975	2,487	2,999	3,511	4,023	4,535	5,047	5,559	6,071	6,583	7,095	7,607	8,119	8,631	9,143	9,655	10,167
440	952	1,464	1,976	2,488	3,000	3,512	4,024	4,536	5,048	5,560	6,072	6,584	7,096	7,608	8,120	8,632	9,144	9,656	10,168
441	953	1,465	1,977	2,489	3,001	3,513	4,025	4,537	5,049	5,561	6,073	6,585	7,097	7,609	8,121	8,633	9,145	9,657	10,169
442	954	1,466	1,978	2,490	3,002	3,514	4,026	4,538	5,050	5,562	6,074	6,586	7,098	7,610	8,122	8,634	9,146	9,658	10,170
443	955	1,467	1,979	2,491	3,003	3,515	4,027	4,539	5,051	5,563	6,075	6,587	7,099	7,611	8,123	8,635	9,147	9,659	10,171
444	956	1,468	1,980	2,492	3,004	3,516	4,028	4,540	5,052	5,564	6,076	6,588	7,100	7,612	8,124	8,636	9,148	9,660	10,172
445	957	1,469	1,981	2,493	3,005	3,517	4,029	4,541	5,053	5,565	6,077	6,589	7,101	7,613	8,125	8,637	9,149	9,661	10,173
446	958	1,470	1,982	2,494	3,006	3,518	4,030	4,542	5,054	5,566	6,078	6,590	7,102	7,614	8,126	8,638	9,150	9,662	10,174
447	959	1,471	1,983	2,495	3,007	3,519	4,031	4,543	5,055	5,567	6,079	6,591	7,103	7,615	8,127	8,639	9,151	9,663	10,175
448	960	1,472	1,984	2,496	3,008	3,520	4,032	4,544	5,056	5,568	6,080	6,592	7,104	7,616	8,128	8,640	9,152	9,664	10,176
449	961	1,473	1,985	2,497	3,009	3,521	4,033	4,545	5,057	5,569	6,081	6,593	7,105	7,617	8,129	8,641	9,153	9,665	10,177
450	962	1,474	1,986	2,498	3,010	3,522	4,034	4,546	5,058	5,570	6,082	6,594	7,106	7,618	8,130	8,642	9,154	9,666	10,178
451	963	1,475	1,987	2,499	3,011	3,523	4,035	4,547	5,059	5,571	6,083	6,595	7,107	7,619	8,131	8,643	9,155	9,667	10,179
452	964	1,476	1,988	2,500	3,012	3,524	4,036	4,548	5,060	5,572	6,084	6,596	7,108	7,620	8,132	8,644	9,156	9,668	10,180
453	965	1,477	1,989	2,501	3,013	3,525	4,037	4,549	5,061	5,573	6,085	6,597	7,109	7,621	8,133	8,645	9,157	9,669	10,181

Start Address									Universe										
1	2	3	4	5	6	7	8	9	10	11	12	13	14	15	16	17	18	19	20
454	966	1,478	1,990	2,502	3,014	3,526	4,038	4,550	5,062	5,574	6,086	6,598	7,110	7,622	8,134	8,646	9,158	9,670	10,182
455	967	1,479	1,991	2,503	3,015	3,527	4,039	4,551	5,063	5,575	6,087	6,599	7,111	7,623	8,135	8,647	9,159	9,671	10,183
456	968	1,480	1,992	2,504	3,016	3,528	4,040	4,552	5,064	5,576	6,088	6,600	7,112	7,624	8,136	8,648	9,160	9,672	10,184
457	969	1,481	1,993	2,505	3,017	3,529	4,041	4,553	5,065	5,577	6,089	6,601	7,113	7,625	8,137	8,649	9,161	9,673	10,185
458	970	1,482	1,994	2,506	3,018	3,530	4,042	4,554	5,066	5,578	6,000	6,602	7,114	7,626	8,138	8,650	0,162	0,674	10,186
459	971	1,483	1,995	2,507	3,019	3,531	4,043	4,555	5,067	5,579	6,091	6,603	7,115	7,627	8,139	8,651	9,163	9,675	10,187
460	972	1,484	1,996	2,508	3,020	3,532	4,044	4,556	5,068	5,580	6,092	6,604	7,116	7,628	8,140	8,652	9,164	9,676	10,188
461	973	1,485	1,997	2,509	3,021	3,533	4,045	4,557	5,069	5,581	6,093	6,605	7,117	7,629	8,141	8,653	9,165	9,677	10,189
462	974	1,486	1,998	2,510	3,022	3,534	4,046	4,558	5,070	5,582	6,094	6,606	7,118	7,630	8,142	8,654	9,166	9,678	10,190
463	975	1,487	1,999	2,511	3,023	3,535	4,047	4,559	5,071	5,583	6,095	6,607	7,119	7,631	8,143	8,655	9,167	9,679	10,191
464	976	1,488	2,000	2,512	3,024	3,536	4,048	4,560	5,072	5,584	6,096	6,608	7,120	7,632	8,144	8,656	9,168	9,680	10,192
465	977	1,489	2,001	2,513	3,025	3,537	4,049	4,561	5,073	5,585	6,097	6,609	7,121	7,633	8,145	8,657	9,169	9,681	10,193
466	978	1,490	2,002	2,514	3,026	3,538	4,050	4,562	5,074	5,586	6,098	6,610	7,122	7,634	8,146	8,658	9,170	9,682	10,194
467	979	1,491	2,003	2,515	3,027	3,539	4,051	4,563	5,075	5,587	6,099	6,611	7,123	7,635	8,147	8,659	9,171	9,683	10,195
468	980	1,492	2,004	2,516	3,028	3,540	4,052	4,564	5,076	5,588	6,100	6,612	7,124	7,636	8,148	8,660	9,172	9,684	10,196
469	981	1,493	2,005	2,517	3,029	3,541	4,053	4,565	5,077	5,589	6,101	6,613	7,125	7,637	8,149	8,661	9,173	9,685	10,197
470	982	1,494	2,006	2,518	3,030	3,542	4,054	4,566	5,078	5,590	6,102	6,614	7,126	7,638	8,150	8,662	9,174	9,686	10,198
471	983	1,495	2,007	2,519	3,031	3,543	4,055	4,567	5,079	5,591	6,103	6,615	7,127	7,639	8,151	8,663	9,175	9,687	10,199
472	984	1,496	2,008	2,520	3,032	3,544	4,056	4,568	5,080	5,592	6,104	6,616	7,128	7,640	8,152	8,664	9,176	9,688	10,200
473	985	1,497	2,009	2,521	3,033	3,545	4,057	4,569	5,081	5,593	6,105	6,617	7,129	7,641	8,153	8,665	9,177	9,689	10,201
474	986	1,498	2,010	2,522	3,034	3,546	4,058	4,570	5,082	5,594	6,106	6,618	7,130	7,642	8,154	8,666	9,178	9,690	10,202
475	987	1,499	2,011	2,523	3,035	3,547	4,059	4,571	5,083	5,595	6,107	6,619	7,131	7,643	8,155	8,667	9,179	9,691	10,203
476	988	1,500	2,012	2,524	3,036	3,548	4,060	4,572	5,084	5,596	6,108	6,620	7,132	7,644	8,156	8,668	9,180	9,692	10,204
477	989	1,501	2,013	2,525	3,037	3,549	4,061	4,573	5,085	5,597	6,109	6,621	7,133	7,645	8,157	8,669	9,181	9,693	10,205
478	990	1,502	2,014	2,526	3,038	3,550	4,062	4,574	5,086	5,598	6,110	6,622	7,134	7,646	8,158	8,670	9,182	9,694	10,206
479	991	1,503	2,015	2,527	3,039	3,551	4,063	4,575	5,087	5,599	6,111	6,623	7,135	7,647	8,159	8,671	9,183	9,695	10,207
480	992	1,504	2,016	2,528	3,040	3,552	4,064	4,576	5,088	5,600	6,112	6,624	7,136	7,648	8,160	8,672	9,184	9,696	10,208
481	993	1,505	2,017	2,529	3,041	3,553	4,065	4,577	5,089	5,601	6,113	6,625	7,137	7,649	8,161	8,673	9,185	9,697	10,209
482	994	1,506	2,018	2,530	3,042	3,554	4,066	4,578	5,090	5,602	6,114	6,626	7,138	7,650	8,162	8,674	9,186	9,698	10,210
483	995	1,507	2,019	2,531	3,043	3,555	4,067	4,579	5,091	5,603	6,115	6,627	7,139	7,651	8,163	8,675	9,187	9,699	10,211
484	996	1,508	2,020	2,532	3,044	3,556	4,068	4,580	5,092	5,604	6,116	6,628	7,140	7,652	8,164	8,676	9,188	9,700	10,212
485	997	1,509	2,021	2,533	3,045	3,557	4,069	4,581	5,093	5,605	6,117	6,629	7,141	7,653	8,165	8,677	9,189	9,701	10,213
486	998	1,510	2,022	2,534	3,046	3,558	4,070	4,582	5,094	5,606	6,118	6,630	7,142	7,654	8,166	8,678	9,190	9,702	10,214
487	999	1,511	2,023	2,535	3,047	3,559	4,071	4,583	5,095	5,607	6,119	6,631	7,143	7,655	8,167	8,679	9,191	9,703	10,215
488	1,000	1,512	2,024	2,536	3,048	3,560	4,072	4,584	5,096	5,608	6,120	6,632	7,144	7,656	8,168	8,680	9,192	9,704	10,216
489	1,001	1,513	2,025	2,537	3,049	3,561	4,073	4,585	5,097	5,609	6,121	6,633	7,145	7,657	8,169	8,681	9,193	9,705	10,217
490	1,002	1,514	2,026	2,538	3,050	3,562	4,074	4,586	5,098	5,610	6,122	6,634	7,146	7,658	8,170	8,682	9,194	9,706	10,218
491	1,003	1,515	2,027	2,539	3,051	3,563	4,075	4,587	5,099	5,611	6,123	6,635	7,147	7,659	8,171	8,683	9,195	9,707	10,219
492	1,004	1,516	2,028	2,540	3,052	3,564	4,076	4,588	5,100	5,612	6,124	6,636	7,148	7,660	8,172	8,684	9,196	9,708	10,220
493	1,005	1,517	2,029	2,541	3,053	3,565	4,077	4,589	5,101	5,613	6,125	6,637	7,149	7,661	8,173	8,685	9,197	9,709	10,221
494	1,006	1,518	2,030	2,542	3,054	3,566	4,078	4,590	5,102	5,614	6,126	6,638	7,150	7,662	8,174	8,686	9,198	9,710	10,222
495	1,007	1,519	2,031	2,543	3,055	3,567	4,079	4,591	5,103	5,615	6,127	6,639	7,151	7,663	8,175	8,687	9,199	9,711	10,223
496	1,008	1,520	2,032	2,544	3,056	3,568	4,080	4,592	5,104	5,616	6,128	6,640	7,152	7,664	8,176	8,688	9,200	9,712	10,224
497	1,009	1,521	2,033	2,545	3,057	3,569	4,081	4,593	5,105	5,617	6,129	6,641	7,153	7,665	8,177	8,689	9,201	9,713	10,225
498	1,010	1,522	2,034	2,546	3,058	3,570	4,082	4,594	5,106	5,618	6,130	6,642	7,154	7,666	8,178	8,690	9,202	9,714	10,226
499	1,011	1,523	2,035	2,547	3,059	3,571	4,083	4,595	5,107	5,619	6,131	6,643	7,155	7,667	8,179	8,691	9,203	9,715	10,227
500	1,012	1,524	2,036	2,548	3,060	3,572	4,084	4,596	5,108	5,620	6,132	6,644	7,156	7,668	8,180	8,692	9,204	9,716	10,228
501	1,013	1,525	2,037	2,549	3,061	3,573	4,085	4,597	5,109	5,621	6,133	6,645	7,157	7,669	8,181	8,693	9,205	9,717	10,229
502	1,014	1,526	2,038	2,550	3,062	3,574	4,086	4,598	5,110	5,622	6,134	6,646	7,158	7,670	8,182	8,694	9,206	9,718	10,230
503	1,015	1,527	2,039	2,551	3,063	3,575	4,087	4,599	5,111	5,623	6,135	6,647	7,159	7,671	8,183	8,695	9,207	9,719	10,231
504	1,016	1,528	2,040	2,552	3,064	3,576	4,088	4,600	5,112	5,624	6,136	6,648	7,160	7,672	8,184	8,696	9,208	9,720	10,232
505	1,017	1,529	2,041	2,553	3,065	3,577	4,089	4,601	5,113	5,625	6,137	6,649	7,161	7,673	8,185	8,697	9,209	9,721	10,233
506	1,018	1,530	2,042	2,554	3,066	3,578	4,090	4,602	5,114	5,626	6,138	6,650	7,162	7,674	8,186	8,698	9,210	9,722	10,234
507	1,019	1,531	2,043	2,555	3,067	3,579	4,091	4,603	5,115	5,627	6,139	6,651	7,163	7,675	8,187	8,699	9,211	9,723	10,235
508	1,020	1,532	2,044	2,556	3,068	3,580	4,092	4,604	5,116	5,628	6,140	6,652	7,164	7,676	8,188	8,700	9,212	9,724	10,236
509	1,021	1,533	2,045	2,557	3,069	3,581	4,093	4,605	5,117	5,629	6,141	6,653	7,165	7,677	8,189	8,701	9,213	9,725	10,237
510	1,022	1,534	2,046	2,558	3,070	3,582	4,094	4,606	5,118	5,630	6,142	6,654	7,166	7,678	8,190	8,702	9,214	9,726	10,238
511	1,023	1,535	2,047	2,559	3,071	3,583	4,095	4,607	5,119	5,631	6,143	6,655	7,167	7,679	8,191	8,703	9,215	9,727	10,239
512	1,024	1,536	2,048	2,560	3,072	3,584	4,096	4,608	5,120	5,632	6,144	6,656	7,168	7,680	8,192	8,704	9,216	9,728	10,240

Appendix G Start Address DIP Switches

Start Address	256	128	64	32	16	8	4	2	1
0	0	0	0	0	0	0	0	0	0
1	0	0	0	0	0	0	0	0	1
2	0	0	0	0	0	0	0	1	0
3	0	0	0	0	0	0	0	1	1
4	0	0	0	0	0	0	1	0	0
5	0	0	0	0	0	0	1	0	1
6	0	0	0	0	0	0	1	1	0
7	0	0	0	0	0	0	1	1	1
8	0	0	0	0	0	1	0	0	0
9	0	0	0	0	0	1	0	0	1
10	0	0	0	0	0	1	0	1	0
11	0	0	0	0	0	1	0	1	1
12	0	0	0	0	0	1	1	0	0
13	0	0	0	0	0	1	1	0	1
14	0	0	0	0	0	1	1	1	0
15	0	0	0	0	0	1	1	1	1
16	0	0	0	0	1	0	0	0	0
17	0	0	0	0	1	0	0	0	1
18	0	0	0	0	1	0	0	1	0
19	0	0	0	0	1	0	0	1	1
20	0	0	0	0	1	0	1	0	0
21	0	0	0	0	1	0	1	0	1
22	0	0	0	0	1	0	1	1	0
23	0	0	0	0	1	0	1	1	1
24	0	0	0	0	1	1	0	0	0
25	0	0	0	0	1	1	0	0	1
26	0	0	0	0	1	1	0	1	0
27	0	0	0	0	1	1	0	1	1
28	0	0	0	0	1	1	1	0	0
29	0	0	0	0	1	1	1	0	1
30	0	0	0	0	1	1	1	1	0
31	0	0	0	0	1	1	1	1	1
32	0	0	0	1	0	0	0	0	0
33	0	0	0	1	0	0	0	0	1
34	0	0	0	1	0	0	0	1	0
35	0	0	0	1	0	0	0	1	1
36	0	0	0	1	0	0	1	0	0
37	0	0	0	1	0	0	1	0	1
38	0	0	0	1	0	0	1	1	0
39	0	0	0	1	0	0	1	1	1
40	0	0	0	1	0	1	0	0	0
41	0	0	0	1	0	1	0	0	1
42	0	0	0	1	0	1	0	1	0
43	0	0	0	1	0	1	0	1	1
44	0	0	0	1	0	1	1	0	0
45	0	0	0	1	0	1	1	0	1
46	0	0	0	1	0	1	1	1	0
47	0	0	0	1	0	1	1	1	1
48	0	0	0	1	1	0	0	0	0
49	0	0	0	1	1	0	0	0	1
50	0	0	0	1	1	0	0	1	0
51	0	0	0	1	1	0	0	1	1
52	0	0	0	1	1	0	1	0	0
53	0	0	0	1	1	0	1	0	1
54	0	0	0	1	1	0	1	1	0
55	0	0	0	1	1	0	1	1	1
56	0	0	0	1	1	1	0	0	0
57	0	0	0	1	1	1	0	0	1
58	0	0	0	1	1	1	0	1	0
59	0	0	0	1	1	1	0	1	1
60	0	0	0	1	1	1	1	0	0
61	0	0	0	1	1	1	1	0	1
62	0	0	0	1	1	1	1	1	0
63	0	0	0	1	1	1	1	1	1
64	0	0	1	0	0	0	0	0	0
65	0	0	1	0	0	0	0	0	1
66	0	0	1	0	0	0	0	1	0
67	0	0	1	0	0	0	0	1	1
68	0	0	1	0	0	0	1	0	0
69	0	0	1	0	0	0	1	0	1
70	0	0	1	0	0	0	1	1	0
71	0	0	1	0	0	0	1	1	1
72	0	0	1	0	0	1	0	0	0
73	0	0	1	0	0	1	0	0	1
74	0	0	1	0	0	1	0	1	0
75	0	0	1	0	0	1	0	1	1
76	0	0	1	0	0	1	1	0	0
77	0	0	1	0	0	1	1	0	1
78	0	0	1	0	0	1	1	1	0
79	0	0	1	0	0	1	1	1	1

Start Address	256	128	64	32	16	8	4	2	1
80	0	0	1	0	1	0	0	0	0
81	0	0	1	0	1	0	0	0	1
82	0	0	1	0	1	0	0	1	0
83	0	0	1	0	1	0	0	1	1
84	0	0	1	0	1	0	1	0	0
85	0	0	1	0	1	0	1	0	1
86	0	0	1	0	1	0	1	1	0
87	0	0	1	0	1	0	1	1	1
88	0	0	1	0	1	1	0	0	0
89	0	0	1	0	1	1	0	0	1
90	0	0	1	0	1	1	0	1	0
91	0	0	1	0	1	1	0	1	1
92	0	0	1	0	1	1	1	0	0
93	0	0	1	0	1	1	1	0	1
94	0	0	1	0	1	1	1	1	0
95	0	0	1	0	1	1	1	1	1
96	0	0	1	1	0	0	0	0	0
97	0	0	1	1	0	0	0	0	1
98	0	0	1	1	0	0	0	1	0
99	0	0	1	1	0	0	0	1	1
100	0	0	1	1	0	0	1	0	0
101	0	0	1	1	0	0	1	0	1
102	0	0	1	1	0	0	1	1	0
103	0	0	1	1	0	0	1	1	1
104	0	0	1	1	0	1	0	0	0
105	0	0	1	1	0	1	0	0	1
106	0	0	1	1	0	1	0	1	0
107	0	0	1	1	0	1	0	1	1
108	0	0	1	1	0	1	1	0	0
109	0	0	1	1	0	1	1	0	1
110	0	0	1	1	0	1	1	1	0
111	0	0	1	1	0	1	1	1	1
112	0	0	1	1	1	0	0	0	0
113	0	0	1	1	1	0	0	0	1
114	0	0	1	1	1	0	0	1	0
115	0	0	1	1	1	0	0	1	1
116	0	0	1	1	1	0	1	0	0
117	0	0	1	1	1	0	1	0	1
118	0	0	1	1	1	0	1	1	0
119	0	0	1	1	1	0	1	1	1
120	0	0	1	1	1	1	0	0	0
121	0	0	1	1	1	1	0	0	1
122	0	0	1	1	1	1	0	1	0
123	0	0	1	1	1	1	0	1	1
124	0	0	1	1	1	1	1	0	0
125	0	0	1	1	1	1	1	0	1
126	0	0	1	1	1	1	1	1	0
127	0	0	1	1	1	1	1	1	1
128	0	1	0	0	0	0	0	0	0
129	0	1	0	0	0	0	0	0	1
130	0	1	0	0	0	0	0	1	0
131	0	1	0	0	0	0	0	1	1
132	0	1	0	0	0	0	1	0	0
133	0	1	0	0	0	0	1	0	1
134	0	1	0	0	0	0	1	1	0
135	0	1	0	0	0	0	1	1	1
136	0	1	0	0	0	1	0	0	0
137	0	1	0	0	0	1	0	0	1
138	0	1	0	0	0	1	0	1	0
139	0	1	0	0	0	1	0	1	1
140	0	1	0	0	0	1	1	0	0
141	0	1	0	0	0	1	1	0	1
142	0	1	0	0	0	1	1	1	0
143	0	1	0	0	0	1	1	1	1
144	0	1	0	0	1	0	0	0	0
145	0	1	0	0	1	0	0	0	1
146	0	1	0	0	1	0	0	1	0
147	0	1	0	0	1	0	0	1	1
148	0	1	0	0	1	0	1	0	0
149	0	1	0	0	1	0	1	0	1
150	0	1	0	0	1	0	1	1	0
151	0	1	0	0	1	0	1	1	1
152	0	1	0	0	1	1	0	0	0
153	0	1	0	0	1	1	0	0	1
154	0	1	0	0	1	1	0	1	0
155	0	1	0	0	1	1	0	1	1
156	0	1	0	0	1	1	1	0	0
157	0	1	0	0	1	1	1	0	1
158	0	1	0	0	1	1	1	1	0
159	0	1	0	0	1	1	1	1	1
160	0	1	0	1	0	0	0	0	0
161	0	1	0	1	0	0	0	0	1
162	0	1	0	1	0	0	0	1	0
163	0	1	0	1	0	0	0	1	1
164	0	1	0	1	0	0	1	0	0
165	0	1	0	1	0	0	1	0	1

Start Address	256	128	64	32	16	8	4	2	1
166	0	1	0	1	0	0	1	1	0
167	0	1	0	1	0	0	1	1	1
168	0	1	0	1	0	1	0	0	0
169	0	1	0	1	0	1	0	0	1
170	0	1	0	1	0	1	0	1	0
171	0	1	0	1	0	1	0	1	1
172	0	1	0	1	0	1	1	0	0
173	0	1	0	1	0	1	1	0	1
174	0	1	0	1	0	1	1	1	0
175	0	1	0	1	0	1	1	1	1
176	0	1	0	1	1	0	0	0	0
177	0	1	0	1	1	0	0	0	1
178	0	1	0	1	1	0	0	1	0
179	0	1	0	1	1	0	0	1	1
180	0	1	0	1	1	0	1	0	0
181	0	1	0	1	1	0	1	0	1
182	0	1	0	1	1	0	1	1	0
183	0	1	0	1	1	0	1	1	1
184	0	1	0	1	1	1	0	0	0
185	0	1	0	1	1	1	0	0	1
186	0	1	0	1	1	1	0	1	0
187	0	1	0	1	1	1	0	1	1
188	0	1	0	1	1	1	1	0	0
189	0	1	0	1	1	1	1	0	1
190	0	1	0	1	1	1	1	1	0
191	0	1	0	1	1	1	1	1	1
192	0	1	1	0	0	0	0	0	0
193	0	1	1	0	0	0	0	0	1
194	0	1	1	0	0	0	0	1	0
195	0	1	1	0	0	0	0	1	1
196	0	1	1	0	0	0	1	0	0
197	0	1	1	0	0	0	1	0	1
198	0	1	1	0	0	0	1	1	0
199	0	1	1	0	0	0	1	1	1
200	0	1	1	0	0	1	0	0	0
201	0	1	1	0	0	1	0	0	1
202	0	1	1	0	0	1	0	1	0
203	0	1	1	0	0	1	0	1	1
204	0	1	1	0	0	1	1	0	0
205	0	1	1	0	0	1	1	0	1
206	0	1	1	0	0	1	1	1	0
207	0	1	1	0	0	1	1	1	1
208	0	1	1	0	1	0	0	0	0
209	0	1	1	0	1	0	0	0	1
210	0	1	1	0	1	0	0	1	0
211	0	1	1	0	1	0	0	1	1
212	0	1	1	0	1	0	1	0	0
213	0	1	1	0	1	0	1	0	1
214	0	1	1	0	1	0	1	1	0
215	0	1	1	0	1	0	1	1	1
216	0	1	1	0	1	1	0	0	0
217	0	1	1	0	1	1	0	0	1
218	0	1	1	0	1	1	0	1	0
219	0	1	1	0	1	1	0	1	1
220	0	1	1	0	1	1	1	0	0
221	0	1	1	0	1	1	1	0	1
222	0	1	1	0	1	1	1	1	0
223	0	1	1	0	1	1	1	1	1
224	0	1	1	1	0	0	0	0	0
225	0	1	1	1	0	0	0	0	1
226	0	1	1	1	0	0	0	1	0
227	0	1	1	1	0	0	0	1	1
228	0	1	1	1	0	0	1	0	0
229	0	1	1	1	0	0	1	0	1
230	0	1	1	1	0	0	1	1	0
231	0	1	1	1	0	0	1	1	1
232	0	1	1	1	0	1	0	0	0
233	0	1	1	1	0	1	0	0	1
234	0	1	1	1	0	1	0	1	0
235	0	1	1	1	0	1	0	1	1
236	0	1	1	1	0	1	1	0	0
237	0	1	1	1	0	1	1	0	1
238	0	1	1	1	0	1	1	1	0
239	0	1	1	1	0	1	1	1	1
240	0	1	1	1	1	0	0	0	0
241	0	1	1	1	1	0	0	0	1
242	0	1	1	1	1	0	0	1	0
243	0	1	1	1	1	0	0	1	1
244	0	1	1	1	1	0	1	0	0
245	0	1	1	1	1	0	1	0	1
246	0	1	1	1	1	0	1	1	0
247	0	1	1	1	1	0	1	1	1
248	0	1	1	1	1	1	0	0	0
249	0	1	1	1	1	1	0	0	1
250	0	1	1	1	1	1	0	1	0
251	0	1	1	1	1	1	0	1	1

Start Address	256	128	64	32	16	8	4	2	1
252	0	1	1	1	1	1	1	0	0
253	0	1	1	1	1	1	1	0	1
254	0	1	1	1	1	1	1	1	0
255	0	1	1	1	1	1	1	1	1
256	1	0	0	0	0	0	0	0	0
257	1	0	0	0	0	0	0	0	1
258	1	0	0	0	0	0	0	1	0
259	1	0	0	0	0	0	0	1	1
260	1	0	0	0	0	0	1	0	0
261	1	0	0	0	0	0	1	0	1
262	1	0	0	0	0	0	1	1	0
263	1	0	0	0	0	0	1	1	1
264	1	0	0	0	0	1	0	0	0
265	1	0	0	0	0	1	0	0	1
266	1	0	0	0	0	1	0	1	0
267	1	0	0	0	0	1	0	1	1
268	1	0	0	0	0	1	1	0	0
269	1	0	0	0	0	1	1	0	1
270	1	0	0	0	0	1	1	1	0
271	1	0	0	0	0	1	1	1	1
272	1	0	0	0	1	0	0	0	0
273	1	0	0	0	1	0	0	0	1
274	1	0	0	0	1	0	0	1	0
275	1	0	0	0	1	0	0	1	1
276	1	0	0	0	1	0	1	0	0
277	1	0	0	0	1	0	1	0	1
278	1	0	0	0	1	0	1	1	0
279	1	0	0	0	1	0	1	1	1
280	1	0	0	0	1	1	0	0	0
281	1	0	0	0	1	1	0	0	1
282	1	0	0	0	1	1	0	1	0
283	1	0	0	0	1	1	0	1	1
284	1	0	0	0	1	1	1	0	0
285	1	0	0	0	1	1	1	0	1
286	1	0	0	0	1	1	1	1	0
287	1	0	0	0	1	1	1	1	1
288	1	0	0	1	0	0	0	0	0
289	1	0	0	1	0	0	0	0	1
290	1	0	0	1	0	0	0	1	0
291	1	0	0	1	0	0	0	1	1
292	1	0	0	1	0	0	1	0	0
293	1	0	0	1	0	0	1	0	1
294	1	0	0	1	0	0	1	1	0
295	1	0	0	1	0	0	1	1	1
296	1	0	0	1	0	1	0	0	0
297	1	0	0	1	0	1	0	0	1
298	1	0	0	1	0	1	0	1	0
299	1	0	0	1	0	1	0	1	1
300	1	0	0	1	0	1	1	0	0
301	1	0	0	1	0	1	1	0	1
302	1	0	0	1	0	1	1	1	0
303	1	0	0	1	0	1	1	1	1
304	1	0	0	1	1	0	0	0	0
305	1	0	0	1	1	0	0	0	1
306	1	0	0	1	1	0	0	1	0
307	1	0	0	1	1	0	0	1	1
308	1	0	0	1	1	0	1	0	0
309	1	0	0	1	1	0	1	0	1
310	1	0	0	1	1	0	1	1	0
311	1	0	0	1	1	0	1	1	1
312	1	0	0	1	1	1	0	0	0
313	1	0	0	1	1	1	0	0	1
314	1	0	0	1	1	1	0	1	0
315	1	0	0	1	1	1	0	1	1
316	1	0	0	1	1	1	1	0	0
317	1	0	0	1	1	1	1	0	1
318	1	0	0	1	1	1	1	1	0
319	1	0	0	1	1	1	1	1	1
320	1	0	1	0	0	0	0	0	0
321	1	0	1	0	0	0	0	0	1
322	1	0	1	0	0	0	0	1	0
323	1	0	1	0	0	0	0	1	1
324	1	0	1	0	0	0	1	0	0
325	1	0	1	0	0	0	1	0	1
326	1	0	1	0	0	0	1	1	0
327	1	0	1	0	0	0	1	1	1
328	1	0	1	0	0	1	0	0	0
329	1	0	1	0	0	1	0	0	1
330	1	0	1	0	0	1	0	1	0
331	1	0	1	0	0	1	0	1	1
332	1	0	1	0	0	1	1	0	0
333	1	0	1	0	0	1	1	0	1
334	1	0	1	0	0	1	1	1	0
335	1	0	1	0	0	1	1	1	1
336	1	0	1	0	1	0	0	0	0
337	1	0	1	0	1	0	0	0	1

Start Address	256	128	64	32	16	8	4	2	1
338	1	0	1	0	1	0	0	1	0
339	1	0	1	0	1	0	0	1	1
340	1	0	1	0	1	0	1	0	0
341	1	0	1	0	1	0	1	0	1
342	1	0	1	0	1	0	1	1	0
343	1	0	1	0	1	0	1	1	1
344	1	0	1	0	1	1	0	0	0
345	1	0	1	0	1	1	0	0	1
346	1	0	1	0	1	1	0	1	0
347	1	0	1	0	1	1	0	1	1
348	1	0	1	0	1	1	1	0	0
349	1	0	1	0	1	1	1	0	1
350	1	0	1	0	1	1	1	1	0
351	1	0	1	0	1	1	1	1	1
352	1	0	1	1	0	0	0	0	0
353	1	0	1	1	0	0	0	0	1
354	1	0	1	1	0	0	0	1	0
355	1	0	1	1	0	0	0	1	1
356	1	0	1	1	0	0	1	0	0
357	1	0	1	1	0	0	1	0	1
358	1	0	1	1	0	0	1	1	0
359	1	0	1	1	0	0	1	1	1
360	1	0	1	1	0	1	0	0	0
361	1	0	1	1	0	1	0	0	1
362	1	0	1	1	0	1	0	1	0
363	1	0	1	1	0	1	0	1	1
364	1	0	1	1	0	1	1	0	0
365	1	0	1	1	0	1	1	0	1
366	1	0	1	1	0	1	1	1	0
367	1	0	1	1	0	1	1	1	1
368	1	0	1	1	1	0	0	0	0
369	1	0	1	1	1	0	0	0	1
370	1	0	1	1	1	0	0	1	0
371	1	0	1	1	1	0	0	1	1
372	1	0	1	1	1	0	1	0	0
373	1	0	1	1	1	0	1	0	1
374	1	0	1	1	1	0	1	1	0
375	1	0	1	1	1	0	1	1	1
376	1	0	1	1	1	1	0	0	0
377	1	0	1	1	1	1	0	0	1
378	1	0	1	1	1	1	0	1	0
379	1	0	1	1	1	1	0	1	1
380	1	0	1	1	1	1	1	0	0
381	1	0	1	1	1	1	1	0	1
382	1	0	1	1	1	1	1	1	0
383	1	0	1	1	1	1	1	1	1
384	1	1	0	0	0	0	0	0	0
385	1	1	0	0	0	0	0	0	1
386	1	1	0	0	0	0	0	1	0
387	1	1	0	0	0	0	0	1	1
388	1	1	0	0	0	0	1	0	0
389	1	1	0	0	0	0	1	0	1
390	1	1	0	0	0	0	1	1	0
391	1	1	0	0	0	0	1	1	1
392	1	1	0	0	0	1	0	0	0
393	1	1	0	0	0	1	0	0	1
394	1	1	0	0	0	1	0	1	0
395	1	1	0	0	0	1	0	1	1
396	1	1	0	0	0	1	1	0	0
397	1	1	0	0	0	1	1	0	1
398	1	1	0	0	0	1	1	1	0
399	1	1	0	0	0	1	1	1	1
400	1	1	0	0	1	0	0	0	0
401	1	1	0	0	1	0	0	0	1
402	1	1	0	0	1	0	0	1	0
403	1	1	0	0	1	0	0	1	1
404	1	1	0	0	1	0	1	0	0
405	1	1	0	0	1	0	1	0	1
406	1	1	0	0	1	0	1	1	0
407	1	1	0	0	1	0	1	1	1
408	1	1	0	0	1	1	0	0	0
409	1	1	0	0	1	1	0	0	1
410	1	1	0	0	1	1	0	1	0
411	1	1	0	0	1	1	0	1	1
412	1	1	0	0	1	1	1	0	0
413	1	1	0	0	1	1	1	0	1
414	1	1	0	0	1	1	1	1	0
415	1	1	0	0	1	1	1	1	1
416	1	1	0	1	0	0	0	0	0
417	1	1	0	1	0	0	0	0	1
418	1	1	0	1	0	0	0	1	0
419	1	1	0	1	0	0	0	1	1
420	1	1	0	1	0	0	1	0	0
421	1	1	0	1	0	0	1	0	1
422	1	1	0	1	0	0	1	1	0
423	1	1	0	1	0	0	1	1	1

Start Address	256	128	64	32	16	8	4	2	1
424	1	1	0	1	0	1	0	0	0
425	1	1	0	1	0	1	0	0	1
426	1	1	0	1	0	1	0	1	0
427	1	1	0	1	0	1	0	1	1
428	1	1	0	1	0	1	1	0	0
429	1	1	0	1	0	1	1	0	1
430	1	1	0	1	0	1	1	1	0
431	1	1	0	1	0	1	1	1	1
432	1	1	0	1	1	0	0	0	0
433	1	1	0	1	1	0	0	0	1
434	1	1	0	1	1	0	0	1	0
435	1	1	0	1	1	0	0	1	1
436	1	1	0	1	1	0	1	0	0
437	1	1	0	1	1	0	1	0	1
438	1	1	0	1	1	0	1	1	0
439	1	1	0	1	1	0	1	1	1
440	1	1	0	1	1	1	0	0	0
441	1	1	0	1	1	1	0	0	1
442	1	1	0	1	1	1	0	1	0
443	1	1	0	1	1	1	0	1	1
444	1	1	0	1	1	1	1	0	0
445	1	1	0	1	1	1	1	0	1
446	1	1	0	1	1	1	1	1	0
447	1	1	0	1	1	1	1	1	1
448	1	1	1	0	0	0	0	0	0
449	1	1	1	0	0	0	0	0	1
450	1	1	1	0	0	0	0	1	0
451	1	1	1	0	0	0	0	1	1
452	1	1	1	0	0	0	1	0	0
453	1	1	1	0	0	0	1	0	1
454	1	1	1	0	0	0	1	1	0
455	1	1	1	0	0	0	1	1	1
456	1	1	1	0	0	1	0	0	0
457	1	1	1	0	0	1	0	0	1
458	1	1	1	0	0	1	0	1	0
459	1	1	1	0	0	1	0	1	1
460	1	1	1	0	0	1	1	0	0
461	1	1	1	0	0	1	1	0	1
462	1	1	1	0	0	1	1	1	0
463	1	1	1	0	0	1	1	1	1
464	1	1	1	0	1	0	0	0	0
465	1	1	1	0	1	0	0	0	1
466	1	1	1	0	1	0	0	1	0
467	1	1	1	0	1	0	0	1	1
468	1	1	1	0	1	0	1	0	0
469	1	1	1	0	1	0	1	0	1
470	1	1	1	0	1	0	1	1	0
471	1	1	1	0	1	0	1	1	1
472	1	1	1	0	1	1	0	0	0
473	1	1	1	0	1	1	0	0	1
474	1	1	1	0	1	1	0	1	0
475	1	1	1	0	1	1	0	1	1
476	1	1	1	0	1	1	1	0	0
477	1	1	1	0	1	1	1	0	1
478	1	1	1	0	1	1	1	1	0
479	1	1	1	0	1	1	1	1	1
480	1	1	1	1	0	0	0	0	0
481	1	1	1	1	0	0	0	0	1
482	1	1	1	1	0	0	0	1	0
483	1	1	1	1	0	0	0	1	1
484	1	1	1	1	0	0	1	0	0
485	1	1	1	1	0	0	1	0	1
486	1	1	1	1	0	0	1	1	0
487	1	1	1	1	0	0	1	1	1
488	1	1	1	1	0	1	0	0	0
489	1	1	1	1	0	1	0	0	1
490	1	1	1	1	0	1	0	1	0
491	1	1	1	1	0	1	0	1	1
492	1	1	1	1	0	1	1	0	0
493	1	1	1	1	0	1	1	0	1
494	1	1	1	1	0	1	1	1	0
495	1	1	1	1	0	1	1	1	1
496	1	1	1	1	1	0	0	0	0
497	1	1	1	1	1	0	0	0	1
498	1	1	1	1	1	0	0	1	0
499	1	1	1	1	1	0	0	1	1
500	1	1	1	1	1	0	1	0	0
501	1	1	1	1	1	0	1	0	1
502	1	1	1	1	1	0	1	1	0
503	1	1	1	1	1	0	1	1	1
504	1	1	1	1	1	1	0	0	0
505	1	1	1	1	1	1	0	0	1
506	1	1	1	1	1	1	0	1	0
507	1	1	1	1	1	1	0	1	1
508	1	1	1	1	1	1	1	0	0
509	1	1	1	1	1	1	1	0	1

Start Address	256	128	64	32	16	8	4	2	1
510	1	1	1	1	1	1	1	1	0
511	1	1	1	1	1	1	1	1	1
512	1	1	1	1	1	1	1	1	1

Appendix H World Information

A table of international voltages may seem to be unrelated to the subject of DMX512. However, when taking a DMX splitter out to Swaziland, it is useful to know what mains lead you will need!

The following information is gleaned from numerous sources including my own travels, web sites and simply phoning colleagues and asking. It is accurate at the time of printing.

Country	Connector	Voltage	Frequency
Afghanistan	Euro2, UK5, Shuko	240 V (170-280)	50 Hz
Albania	Euro2, Shuko	220 V	50 Hz
Algeria	Euro2, Shuko	230 V	50 Hz
American Samoa	US2, US3, Shuko, Australian	120 V	60 Hz
Andorra	Euro2, Shuko	220 V	50 Hz
Angola	Euro2	220 V	50 Hz
Anguilla	US2	110 V	60 Hz
Antigua	US2, US3	230 V	60 Hz
Argentina	Euro2, Australian (L / N reversed)	220 V	50 Hz
Armenia	Euro2, Shuko	220 V	50 Hz
Aruba	US2, US3, Shuko	115 V	60 Hz
Australia	Australian	230 V	50 Hz
Austria	Euro2, Shuko	230 V	50 Hz
Azerbaijan	Euro2	220 V	50 Hz
Azores	US3, Euro2, Shuko	220 V	50 Hz
Bahamas	US2, US3	120 V	60 Hz
Bahrain	UK13	230 V	50 Hz
Balearic Islands	Euro2, Shuko	220 V	50 Hz
Bangladesh	US3, Euro2, UK5, UK3, Danish	220 V	50 Hz
Barbados	US2, US3	115 V	50 Hz
Belarus	Euro2	220 V	50 Hz
Belgium	Shuko	230 V	50 Hz
Belize	US3, UK13	110/220 V	60 Hz
Benin	Shuko	220 V	50 Hz
Bermuda	US2, US3	120 V	60 Hz
Bhutan	UK5, Shuko, UK13, UK15	230 V	50 Hz
Bolivia	US2, Euro2	220/230 V Some areas 115V	50 Hz
Bosnia	Euro2, Shuko	220 V	50 Hz
Botswana	UK5, UK13, UK15	220 V	50 Hz
Brazil	US2, US3, Australian. Australian type usually 220V. US type usually 110V	110-220 V	60 Hz
Brunei	UK13	240 V	50 Hz
Bulgaria	Euro2, Shuko	230 V	50 Hz
Burkina Faso	Euro2, Shuko	220 V	50 Hz
Burundi	Euro2, Shuko	220 V	50 Hz
Cambodia	US2, Euro2, UK13	230 V	50 Hz
Cameroon	Euro2, Shuko	220 V	50 Hz
Canada	US2, US3	120 V	60 Hz
Canary Islands	Euro2, Shuko, Italian	220 V	50 Hz
Cape Verde	Euro2, Shuko	220 V	50 Hz
Cayman Islands	US2, US3	120 V	60 Hz
Central African Republic	Euro2, Shuko	220 V	50 Hz
Chad	UK5, Shuko	220 V	50 Hz
Channel Islands	Euro2, Shuko	230 V	50 Hz
Chile	Euro2, Italian	220 V	50 Hz
China (Mainland)	UK13, US2, Australian	220 V	50 Hz
Colombia	US2, US3	110 V	60 Hz
Comoros	Euro2, Shuko	220 V	50 Hz
Congo-Brazzaville	Euro2, Shuko	230 V	50 Hz
Congo-Kinshasa	Euro2, UK5	220 V	50 Hz
Cook Islands	Australian	240 V	50 Hz
Costa Rica	US2, US3	120 V	60 Hz
Côte d'Ivoire	Euro2, Shuko	230 V	50 Hz
Croatia	Euro2, Shuko	230 V	50 Hz
Cuba	US2, US3, Euro2, Italian	110 V	60 Hz
Cyprus	UK13	240 V	50 Hz
Czech Republic	Shuko	230 V	50 Hz
Denmark	Euro2, Danish	230 V	50 Hz
Djibouti	Euro2, Shuko	220 V	50 Hz
Dominica	UK5, UK13	230 V	50 Hz
Dominican Republic	US2	110 V	60 Hz
East Timor	Euro2, Shuko, Australian	220 V	50 Hz
Ecuador	US2, US3	220 V	60 Hz
Egypt	Euro2	220 V	50 Hz
El Salvador	US2, US3, Euro2, UK5, UK13, Shuko, Australian, Swiss, Italian	115 V	60 Hz
Equatorial Guinea	Euro2, Shuko	220 V	50 Hz
Eritrea	Euro2	230 V	50 Hz
Estonia	Shuko	230 V	50 Hz
Ethiopia	UK5, Swiss, Italian	220 V	50 Hz
Faeroe Islands	Euro2, Danish	220 V	50 Hz
Falkland Islands	UK13	240 V	50 Hz
Fiji	Australian	240 V	50 Hz
Finland	Euro2, Shuko	230 V	50 Hz
France	Shuko	230 V	50 Hz

Country	Connector	Voltage	Frequency
French Guyana	Euro2, UK5, Shuko	220 V	50 Hz
Gaza	Israel	230 V	50 Hz
Gabon	Euro2	220 V	50 Hz
Gambia	UK13	230 V	50 Hz
Germany	Euro2, Shuko	230 V	50 Hz
Ghana	UK13, UK5	230 V	50 Hz
Gibraltar	Euro2, UK13	240 V	50 Hz
Greece	Euro2, Shuko, UK5	220 V	50 Hz
Greenland	Euro2, Danish	220 V	50 Hz
Grenada	UK13	230 V	50 Hz
Guadeloupe	Euro2, Shuko, UK5	230 V	50 Hz
Guam	US2, US3	110 V	60 Hz
Guatemala	A, B, G, I	120 V	60 Hz
Guinea	C, F, K	220 V	50 Hz
Guinea-Bissau	C	220 V	50 Hz
Guyana	A, B, D, G	240 V	60 Hz
Haiti	US2, US3	110 V	60 Hz
Honduras	US2, US3	110 V	60 Hz
Hong Kong	UK13 (UK5 & UK15 in older buildings)	220 V	50 Hz
Hungary	Euro2, Shuko	230 V	50 Hz
Iceland	Euro2, Shuko	230 V	50 Hz
India	UK5, Euro2, UK15	230 V	50 Hz
Indonesia	Euro2, Shuko, UK3	120/230 V	50 Hz
Iran	Euro2	230 V	50 Hz
Iraq	Euro2, UK5, UK13	230 V	50 Hz
Republic of Ireland	UK13	230 V	50 Hz
Isle of Man	UK13	240 V	50 Hz
Israel	Israel, Euro2, UK5	230 V	50 Hz
Italy	Italian, Shuko	230 V	50 Hz
Jamaica	US2, US3	110 V	50 Hz
Japan	US2, US3	100 V	Eastern Japan: 50 Hz Western Japan: 60 Hz
Jordan	US3, Euro2, UK5, Shuko, UK13, Swiss	230 V	50 Hz
Kenya	UK13	240 V	50 Hz
Kazakhstan	Euro2	220 V	50 Hz
Kiribati	Australian	240 V	50 Hz
Korea, North	Euro2	220 V	50 Hz
Korea, South	Euro2, Shuko	220 V	60 Hz
Kuwait	Euro2, Shuko	240 V	50 Hz
Laos	US2, US3, Euro2, Shuko	230 V	50 Hz
Latvia	Euro2, Shuko	220 V	50 Hz
Lebanon	US2, US3, Euro2, UK5, UK13	110/200 V	50 Hz
Lesotho	UK15	220 V	50 Hz
Liberia	Guide as follows, but no guarantee! 110V: US2, US3 240V: Euro2, Shuko	120/240 V	50 Hz and 60 Hz
Libya	UK5	127/230V	50 Hz
Lithuania	Euro2, Shuko	220 V	50 Hz
Liechtenstein	Swiss	230 V	50 Hz
Luxembourg	Euro2, Shuko	220 V	50 Hz
Macau	Pre-Handover buildings: UK5, UK15, some Shuko. Post-Handover: UK13	220 V	50 Hz
Macedonia (FYROM)	Euro2, Shuko	220 V	50 Hz
Madagascar	Euro2, UK5, Shuko, Swiss, Danish	127/220 V	50 Hz
Madeira	Euro2, Shuko	220 V	50 Hz
Malawi	UK13	230 V	50 Hz
Malaysia	UK13	240 V	50 Hz
Maldives	US2, UK5, UK13, Swiss, Danish, Italian	230 V	50 Hz
Mali	Euro2, Shuko	220 V	50 Hz
Malta	UK13	240 V	50 Hz
Martinique	Euro2, UK5, Shuko	220 V	50 Hz
Mauritania	Euro2	220 V	50 Hz
Mauritius	Euro2, UK13	230 V	50 Hz
Mexico	US2	127 V Some 240V split phase power	60 Hz
Micronesia	US2, US3	120 V	60 Hz
Moldova (Rep of)	Euro2	220 V	50 Hz
Monaco	Euro2, Shuko	220 V	50 Hz
Mongolia	Euro2, Shuko	230 V	50 Hz
Montseurrat	US2, US3	230 V	60 Hz
Morocco	Euro2, Shuko	127/220 V	50 Hz
Mozambique	Euro2, Shuko, UK15. UK15 predominant near SA border and in capital Maputo.	220 V	50 Hz
Myanmar/Burma	Euro2, UK5, Shuko, UK13	230 V	50 Hz
Namibia	UK5, UK15	220 V	50 Hz
Nauru	Australian	240 V	50 Hz
Nepal	Euro2, UK5, UK15	230 V	50 Hz
Netherlands	Euro2, Shuko	230 V	50 Hz
Netherlands Antilles	US2, US3, Shuko	127/220 V	50 Hz
New Caledonia	Shuko	220 V	50 Hz
New Zealand	Australian	230 V	50 Hz
Nicaragua	US2	120 V	60 Hz
Niger	US2, US3, Euro2, UK5, Shuko	220 V	50 Hz
Nigeria	UK5, UK13	240 V	50 Hz
Norway	Euro2, Shuko	230 V	50 Hz
Okinawa	US2, US3, Australian	100 V	60 Hz
Oman	UK13, Euro2	240 V (Variable)	50 Hz
Pakistan	UK5, Euro2	230 V	50 Hz
Panama	US2, US3	110 V	60 Hz
Papua New Guinea	Australia	240 V	50 Hz
Paraguay	Euro2	220 V	50 Hz
Peru	US2, US3, Euro2	220 V	60 Hz
Philippines	US2, US3, Euro2	220 V	60 Hz

Country	Connector	Voltage	Frequency
Poland	Euro2, Shuko	230 V	50 Hz
Portugal	Euro2, Shuko	230 V	50 Hz
Puerto Rico	US2, US3	120 V	60 Hz
Qatar	UK5, UK13	240 V	50 Hz
Réunion	Shuko	220 V	50 Hz
Romania	Euro2, Shuko	230 V	50 Hz
Russian Federation	Euro2, Shuko	220 V	50 Hz
Rwanda	Euro2, Swiss	230 V	50 Hz
St. Kitts and Nevis	UK5, UK13	230 V	60 Hz
St. Lucia	UK13	240 V	50 Hz
St. Vincent	US2, Euro2, Shuko, UK13, Australian, Danish	230 V	50 Hz
Saudi Arabia	UK13, Shuko, US2, US3	127/220 V	60 Hz
Senegal	Euro2, UK5, Shuko, Danish	230 V	50 Hz
Serbia and Montenegro	Euro2, Shuko	220 V	50 Hz
Seychelles	UK13	240 V	50 Hz
Sierra Leone	UK13, UK5	230 V	50 Hz
Singapore	UK13	230 V	50 Hz
Slovakia	Shuko	230 V	50 Hz
Slovenia	Euro2, Shuko	230 V	50 Hz
Somalia	Euro2	220 V	50 Hz
South Africa	UK15	220-250 V	50 Hz
Spain	Euro2, Shuko	230 V	50 Hz
Sri Lanka	UK5, UK15	230 V	50 Hz
Sudan	UK5, Euro2	230 V	50 Hz
Surinam	Euro2, Shuko	110 V	60 Hz
Swaziland	UK15	230 V	50 Hz
Sweden	Euro2, Shuko	230 V	50 Hz
Switzerland	Swiss, Euro2	230 V	50 Hz
Syria	Euro2, Shuko, Italian	220 V	50 Hz
Tahiti	US2, US3, Shuko	110/220 V	60 Hz
Tajikistan	Euro2, Australian	220 V	50 Hz
Taiwan (ROC)	US2, US3	110 V	60 Hz
Tanzania	UK13, UK5	230 V	50 Hz
Thailand	US2, Euro2	220 V	50 Hz
Togo	Euro2	220 V	50 Hz
Tonga	Australian	240 V	50 Hz
Trinidad & Tobago	US2, US3	115 V	60 Hz
Tunisia	Euro2, Shuko	230 V	50 Hz
Turkey	Euro2, Shuko	230 V	50 Hz
Turkmenistan	US3, Shuko	220 V	50 Hz
Uganda	UK13	240 V	50 Hz
Ukraine	Euro2, Shuko	220 V	50 Hz
United Arab Emirates	Euro2, UK5, UK13	220 V	50 Hz
United Kingdom	UK13 (UK15 used in Theatre)	230 V	50 Hz
United States of America	US2 US3	120 V	60 Hz
Uruguay	Euro2, Shuko, Australian, Italian. Shuko most common. Live / Neutral reversed!	220 V	50 Hz
Uzbekistan	Euro2, Australian	220 V	50 Hz
Venezuela	US2, US3	120 V	60 Hz
Vietnam	US2, Euro2, UK13	127/220 Will standardise on 220V	50 Hz
Virgin Islands	US2, US3	110 V	60 Hz
Western Samoa	Australian	230 V	50 Hz
Yemen	US2, UK5, UK13	230 V	50 Hz
Zambia	Euro2, UK5, UK13	230 V	50 Hz
Zimbabwe	UK5, UK13	220 V	50 Hz

This section provides a quick reference for terms likely to be encountered in lighting control technology. There is always a compromise between clarity and pure definition in the description of such terms. Where necessary, I have chosen clarity, so purists please accept my apologies. Entries of particular relevance to DMX512 and RDM are highlighted in blue.

ADC
Analogue to Digital converter. A component designed to convert analogue information into digital form. Examples include translating audio into a form that can be recorded on CD.

Analogue
A continuously varying signal. Contrast to Digital. (US spelling Analog).

ANSI
American National Standards Institute.

Art-Net
Public domain Ethernet protocol for the transmission of real time Entertainment Technology data over Ethernet. Invented by Artistic Licence.

ASC
Alternative Start Code. A DMX512 term used to describe any packet that uses a start code other than zero. ASC packets are used for the RDM (Remote Device Management) protocol. This is sometimes incorrectly written as Alternate Start Code.

ASCII
American Standard Code for Information Interchange. A coding system that allows alphanumeric characters and punctuation to be represented as a 7 bit code. The predecessor to ASCII was EBCDIC.

Asynchronous Transmission
A form of data transmission whereby the transmitter and receiver are not intrinsically synchronised. The data is enclosed in markers called start and stop bits, so that it can be decoded by the receiver.
DMX512 uses Asynchronous Transmission.

Attenuation
The reduction in the amplitude (or voltage) of a signal caused by the impedance of the cable.

Attenuation Coefficient
A measure of the attenuation of a cable per unit distance. The number is usually given in dB/m or decibels per metre. A lower number equates to a 'better' cable.

Attenuation Imbalance
A measure of the difference in attenuation between two pairs of a multiple pair cable. In good quality cable, this number should be almost zero.

AWG
American Wire Gauge. An American system for defining the size of a non-ferrous wire. See also SWG.

Backplane
The bus in the back of a hub chassis that connects interface modules.

Balanced Pair

An electrical transmission line that uses two identical conductors that are symmetrical with respect to a common reference point.
The technique is designed to minimise signal interference.

Bandwidth

The data-carrying capacity of a transmission medium measured in bits per second (bps) or in cycles per second or Hertz (Hz).

Baud

Number of physical transitions per second of a communication link. Expressed in 'Baud'.
1 baud = 1 transition per second. The baud rate is not the same as the data rate which is measured in bits per second.

Bend Radius

The minimum radius to which a cable can be curved without sustaining damage.

BER

Bit Error Rate. The percentage of bits received that contain errors compared to those received that do not contain errors. A perfect transmission system will have a BER of zero.

Binary

A number system, also called Base-2, that using only two digits, 0 and 1. This compares to decimal or Base-10 which uses the ten digits 0 to 9.

Bit

Bit is an abbreviation for BInary DigiT. A bit is the smallest element of computer storage and data transmission.

Bit/s

Also written as Bits per second or BitS-1. This is the measurement of the speed of transmission of digital data.

Bluetooth

A short range radio protocol for connection between devices such as mobile phones and computers. Operates in the same radio frequency band as WiFi.

BNC

A bayonet-locking connector used for 10Base-2 Thinnet and video, coaxial cabling. BNC is an acronym for British Naval Connector.
Two types exist, 50 ohm and 75 ohm. The former is used for Ethernet and the latter for video.

Bonding

A permanent electrical connection. Commonly used in conjunction with earth wiring.

Break

A Break is a logic zero state used in DMX512 to signal the start of a packet. In DMX512 (all versions) a break is 88uS or greater. RDM tightens this specification for transmitters to the range 176uS – 352uS. The increased minimum required by RDM is designed to allow multiple cascaded splitters to shorten the break whilst remaining within the DMX512 specification.

Broadcast Full

In RDM, a Full Broadcast packet is sent to the special UID address called 'BROADCAST_ ALL_DEVICES_ID' of value 0xffff:ffffffff. All RDM responders will accept messages directed to this UID.

Broadcast Manufacturer
In RDM, a Manufacturer Broadcast packet is sent to the special UID address called 'ALL_ DEVICES_ID' of value 0xzzyy:ffffffff. All RDM responders of Manufacturer ID 0xzzyy will accept messages directed to this UID.

BSI
British Standards Institute

Bus Topology
A network architecture in which all the nodes are connected to a single cable which is terminated at each end.

Byte
A group of 8 bits that allow representation of 256 different numbers.

Cable Tray
Metal or plastic trays used to support and secure cable installation.

CAN
CAN or Controller Area Network was originally developed by Bosch for the automotive industry. The CAN protocol is now an international standard, ISO 11898.

Capacitance
A measure of the ability of two conductors to store electric charge. Unit of measurement is the Farad. Prescalars are pF (10-12), nF (10-9) and uF (10-6).

Checksum
A simple method of identifying errors in data transmission. The transmitter adds together all of the data bytes to be transmitted and sends this along with the data.
The receiver performs the same calculation and compares the result to that sent by the transmitter.
If the calculations do not match, an error has occurred. If they do match, there is a high probability that the data is intact. It does not guarantee that the data is intact as there are many different data sequences that result in identical checksums.
Both 8 and 16 bit checksums are used in different communication protocols. The 16 bit version provides a higher probability that matching checksums equate to good data.
The CRC provides a higher level solution to the same problem.

Coax
Coax is an abbreviation for Coaxial Cable. It is characterised by a central conductor, with a concentric insulating or dielectric material and an outer conducting screen.
The outer conducting screen is intended to contain the inner conductor in a Faraday Cage.

Collision
The term used when two or more RDM devices attempt to communicate at the same time. This occurs during the discovery phase of RDM.

Common Mode Conversion Ratio
A measure of the balance between the two conductors of a twisted pair, with respect to Earth-Ground.

Common Mode Voltage
A term used in the characterisation of balanced wiring systems. It is the part of the input voltages, for which the amplitude and either the phase or the polarity are the same, which exists between each of the input terminals and a reference point.

Compatible
A product that operates correctly with a standard but does not necessarily fulfil all the obligations mandated by a standard.

Compliant
A product that completely adheres to the requirements of a standard.

Conductance
The reciprocal of resistance.

Conducted Interference
Electrical interference that is propagated via electrical connection with the equipment causing the interference. Contrast with Radiated Interference.

CPWG
Control Protocols Working Group. A committee operated by ESTA and tasked with the management of standards such as DMX512-A, RDM and ACN.

CRC
Cyclical Redundancy Check. This is a mathematical calculation used to check the integrity of transmitted messages.
The transmitter performs the calculation on the data to be transmitted. The result is then sent with the transmitted data.
The receiver performs the same calculation and compares its result with the transmitter's result.
If they match, the data is intact. If they do not match, a transmission error has occurred. The receiver then requests the transmitter to resend.
A CRC requires more processing power than the simpler Checksum, but is capable of detecting more errors.

Crimper
Tool used for terminating wires into a connector without using solder.

Crossed Pair
A colloquial term meaning a pair of wires within a twisted pair cable that are accidentally cross wired. This fault is likely to cause significant signal degradation as the balanced transmission will not be able to operate.

Crosstalk
Crosstalk is a type of interference generated by running multiple twisted pairs within a single cable. The individual twisted pairs behave like the windings of a transformer, coupling a small amount of signal from one pair into the next.

Cut Off Frequency
The frequency above which no significant energy is transferred into the cable.

DAC
Digital to Analogue converter. A component designed to convert digital information into analogue information. Examples include converting digital audio back into sound.

Data Compression
A generic term meaning a technique used to reduce the bandwidth required when transmitting data.

Data Slot
This is a term used in DMX512 and DMX over Ethernet protocols. Data Slots are numbered from 1 to 512 and identify the channel information. This contrasts with the term 'Slot'.

DeciBel
A logarithmic unit that expresses the ratio between two numbers.
Abbreviation dB.

Demultiplex
Often abbreviated to DEMUX. This is the opposite of Multiplex and involves translating one signal into many. It may also include digital to analogue conversion and decompression.

Dielectric
The electrical insulator used in the fabrication of capacitors and coaxial cables.

Dielectric Loss
The attenuation of a signal caused by the extent to which the cable dielectric conducts.

Digital
A generic term meaning that a circuit or system uses binary information as opposed to continuously varying analogue information.

Distortion
Any unwanted affect of circuitry or transmission system that causes the output to differ from the input.

DMX over Ethernet
A generic term used to describe protocols such as Art-Net and ShowNet that are geared to transmitting DMX512 frames over Ethernet. This is as distinct from protocols such as ACN.

DMX512
The USITT standard for transmission of lighting control data over a balanced RS485 data link. The term DMX512 is used to generically describe all variants of the protocol.

DMX512 (1990)
The second issue of the standard was released in 1990. The only significant change was the relaxation of the Mark After Break timing from 4uS to 8uS. The difference is significant to product designers as the 4uS requirement was a significant technical burden when using microprocessors to receive the protocol.
Very little pre DMX512 (1990) equipment remains in the market. This is largely due to the significant support or the standard starting in the early 1990's.

DMX512 2000
DMX512 2000 is a colloquial name for DMX512-A. It is no longer in common use.

DMX512-A
DMX512-A is the third issue of the DMX512 standard. It was approved by the ESTA Control Protocols Working Group on 18th March 2004. DMX512-A is backwards compatible with DMX512(1990). The new standard provides a range of increased functionality, much of it aimed at simpler integration with Ethernet based networks.

Down-Lynx
An Artistic Licence product used to convert Art-Net Ethernet into two distinct universes of DMX512-A.

Duplex
A system that allows signals to travel simultaneously in two directions. The word is a compression of 'Dual Multiplex'. Contrast with Half Duplex.

Earth

UK use: Electrical connection to equipment chassis and therefore the third conductor of the electricity supply.
See also: Signal-Common, Ground & Earth-Ground.

Earth Loop (Ground Loop)

The flow of current through Signal-Common conductor caused by voltage differences between local Earth-Ground points.

Earth-Ground

ESTA sponsored international term meaning: Electrical connection to equipment chassis and therefore the third conductor of the electricity supply.
See also: Signal-Common, Earth & Ground.

Echo

See Reflection.

EEPROM

Electrically Erasable Programmable Read Only Memory. It differs from EPROM by using an electronic control rather than ultraviolet light for erasure. Largely superseded by Flash memory.

EIA/TIA 568

The wiring standard for telecommunication cable plant, including termination detail for the RJ45.

EIA/TIA

Electronic Industry Association/Telecommunications Industry Association. A body involved in the setting of various industry standards including those applicable to cabling.

Electrical Screen

An Earth-Grounded metal or conductive shield placed around electronics to isolate the circuitry from external electromagnetic fields. See Faraday Cage.

EMC

Electromagnetic Compatibility. The ability of differing electronic and electrical systems to coexist without being disrupted by electromagnet interference, or disrupting other equipment by causing interference. EMC is a major component of the CE (European) and FCC (US) regulatory standards.

EMI

Electromagnetic Interference - Unwanted "noise" created by current-producing devices such as electric motors and fluorescent lights. EMI affects the quality of the signal passing through data transmission medium.

Encoding

The conversion of data into a particular format suited to a particular purpose.

Encryption

A method of encoding data that includes a security system for security purposes.

EPROM

Erasable programmable read only memory. A type of memory that can be erased using ultra-violet light. EPROM was widely used for firmware before the invention of Flash memory.

Error Detection

A generic term used to describe various methods for detecting and or repairing transmission errors.

ESTA
Entertainment Services and Technology Association.

ETC NetII
A TCP/IP proprietary protocol used by Electronic Theatre Controls.

Ethercon
A connector developed by Neutrik. It provides an RJ45 mounted inside a latching XLR housing.

Far Field
The electromagnetic field that exists at a distance of several wavelengths from the equipment generating the field. Contrast to Near Field.

Faraday Cage
A metal enclosure designed to stop electromagnetic radiation.

Filter
A device used to remove certain frequencies from a signal. This may be to reduce bandwidth in a transmission system or for aesthetic reasons such as audio filtering.

Firestop
The filler used to restore the burn time rating of a firewall that has been penetrated by cable or other services.

Firewall
A building partition that has a specific rating of burn time, allowing occupants of the building to escape in an emergency.

Firmware
The operating software of a product. Firmware is invariably held in a chip as opposed to software, which is usually stored by magnetic media.

FLASH
A form of non-volatile memory. It is frequently used to hold the operating software of a product. It has the benefit that is can be updated for product improvements.

Frame
A well-defined block of data ready for transmission.

Frequency
The number of times that a signal repeats within one second. The unit is Hertz (Hz). The usual SI multipliers apply: 109Hz = 1GHz, 106Hz = 1MHz, 103Hz = 1KHz.

Frequency Response
The relationship between the frequency of a signal and the attenuation of the transmission medium at that frequency.

Ground
UK use: Common voltage in a circuit
US use: Electrical connection to equipment chassis and therefore the third conductor of the electricity supply.
See also: Signal-Common, Earth & Earth-Ground.

Ground Loop
See Earth Loop

Half Duplex
A system that allows a signal to travel in one direction at any given time. Contrast with Duplex.

Harmonic
A waveform that is an integral wavelength multiple of the original. See Overtone.

Harmonic Distortion
A type of distortion caused by the interaction between a signal and harmonics of that signal.

ID
Inner Diameter. The internal diameter of a tube.

IEA
Electronic Industries Association – A professional organisation that formulates computer and communications standards in the U.S.

IEEE
Institute of Electrical and Electronics Engineers – A professional organisation that formulates computer and communications standards in the U.S. and works with other standards-setting bodies including the International Standards Organization (ISO).

Inductance
The property of a conductor whereby a current is induced as a result of the voltage changing. The unit is Henry, symbol H.

Insertion Delay
The signal delay caused by the insertion of a component in a transmission system. Insertion delay is usually expressed in time, i.e. nS.

Insertion Loss
The reduction in amplitude of a signal caused by the insertion of a component into a transmission network. The insertion loss is usually expressed as a percentage of output voltage to input voltage such that no insertion loss is represented as zero percent.

ISO
International Standards Organization - An internationally recognized standards body.

Inter-slot Time
The time between the end of the second stop bit of slot x and the beginning of the start bit of slot x+1. In RDM the average Inter-slot Time must not exceed 76uS and any specific Inter-slot time must not exceed 2.0mS (subject to the overall packet length being less than 1S).

Jabber
An error condition whereby RDM devices transmit on the DMX cable without being requested to do so.

Jacket
The outer plastic or rubber protective cover of a cable.
See Screen & Shield.

Krone
UK manufacturer of Ethernet termination connectors. Often used as a generic term. See Punch Down (US term)

MaB (Mark after Break)
This is the time period between the end of a DMX512 Break and the beginning of the start bit of the Start Code. In DMX512 this value must be 8uS or greater. RDM tightens this parameter to 12uS or greater.

MbB (Mark before Break)
This is the time period between the end of the second stop bit of the last slot and the beginning of the next DMX512 Break.

MIDI
Music Industry Digital Interface. A serial communication protocol developed to allow interconnection of musical equipment. It is also commonly used for remote control between lighting equipment.

Mismatch Loss
Loss of power developed into a load caused by connection to transmission medium with non-matching impedance.

Multiplex
Often abbreviated to MUX. Multiplex is a technique for converting many signals into one, usually for transmission by cable. Multiplex systems may include both analogue to digital conversion and compression.

Near Field
The electromagnetic radiation field that exists within one wave length of the source.

NEC
National Electrical Code. US standard for electrical safety in building installation.

Net-Lynx
Artistic Licence product used to convert DMX512 to or from Art-Net Ethernet.

Nibble
Nibble is one half of a byte or four bits. A byte has an upper and a lower nibble. See US spelling Nybble.

Non-volatile RAM
Memory which holds its information even when main power is turned off. Usually, non-volatile RAM is backed up via a battery.

NVP
Nominal Velocity of Propagation. The speed of a signal in cable expressed as a ratio to the speed of light.
The NVP for Cat5 cable is approximately 75%. That means that the signal travels at around 2.3×10^8 ms-1, or passes 1m every 4.3nS.

Nybble
See Nibble. (US spelling)

OD
Outer Diameter. The external diameter of a cable.

Overtone
A waveform that is an integral wavelength multiple of the original. See Harmonic

Patch Bay
A cable termination area where DMX cables connect between equipment.

PLASA
Professional Light & Sound Association. The UK trade organisation for the entertainment technology industry.

Plenum
The air-carrying portion of a heating of air conditioning system that can be used for carrying communication cable.

Plenum Cable

A cable conforming to local wiring regulations for installation into a Plenum Area.

Plenum Rated

See Plenum Cable.

PROM

Programmable Read Only Memory.

PROPAGATION DELAY

The time taken for a signal to pass along a transmission line.

Propagation Velocity

The speed at which a signal travels within a specific media.

Protocol

A standardised set of rules specifying the packet format, timing, sequencing and/or error checking for data transmission.

Radiated Interference

Electrical interference that is propagated by electromagnetic radiation from the equipment causing the interference. Contrast with Conducted Interference.

RAM

Random Access Memory.

RDM

Remote Device Management. The colloquial name for ESTA Standard E1.20. RDM provides bi-directional data transmission over the primary DMX512 data pair.

Reflection

A wave that has been reflected from one or more points in a transmission system. Reflections are typically caused by an impedance mismatch at the cable end. If reflected waves are of significant amplitude, partial or complete loss of data can occur. This is caused by the destructive superposition of the transmitted and reflected waves causing zero amplitude.

RFI

Radio Frequency Interference – Unwanted "noise" created by current-producing devices such as electric motors and fluorescent lights. RFI affects the quality of the signal passing through some data transmission medium.

RJ Lynx

A robust and waterproof version of the RJ45.

RJ45

An 8 pin connector primarily used for ethernet connections, although increasingly used for DMX512.

ROM

Read Only Memory.

RP

Recommended Practice. A document that generally augments a standard. It usually contains real world examples of how the standard writers felt the standard should be implemented.

RS232

An IEA standard definition for the 25-pin interface linking DTEs and DCEs. RS232-C is suitable for both synchronous and asynchronous communications.

RS422
An IEA recommended standard definition for extending an RS232C interface beyond the 50 foot limit.

RS485
Similar to RS422 but is used in multi-point application where up to 64 network devices may be interconnected. RS485 is the electrical specification for DMX512.

Screen
UK use: Identical to Shield
US use: Identical to Jacket.

Shall
In 'standards speak', the word 'shall' means that an item is not optional, i.e. you are not compliant with the standard if you do not implement this item. 'Shall' sits above 'may' and 'should' in priority.

Shield
Outer metallic conductor in a cable. Intended to produce a faraday cage.
See Screen & Jacket.

Should
In 'standards speak', the word 'should' means that an item is theoretically optional, but the standards writers feel you would need a very good reason to ignore the item. 'Should' sits between 'may' and 'shall' in priority.

ShowNet
A DMX over Ethernet protocol developed by Strand Lighting. The protocol is based on broadcast UDP packets and uses a simple form of run Length Encoding (RLE).

Signal-Common
The common voltage in a circuit.
See also: Earth, Ground & Earth-Ground.

Signal to Noise Ratio
The ratio between the electrical noise and the actual signal measured as a logarithmic ration and expressed in decibels (dB).

Simplex
A transmission system that allows data to travel in one direction only. Contrast to Duplex and Half-Duplex. DMX512 (1990) is Simplex. RDM is half-Duplex.

SIP
System Information Packet. The SIP is a new feature of DMX512-A. SIP's use Alternative Start Code 207 and provide a range of system level data such as checksums, firmware revision numbers and data originator's identification.

Skin Effect
The tendency for electrical signals of high frequency to flow near the surface of a conductor.

Slot
This is a term used in DMX512 and DMX over Ethernet protocols. Slots are numbered from 0 to 512. Slot zero is the DMX512 Start Code. Slots 1 to 512 identify the channel information. This contrasts with the term 'Data Slot'.

Splitter
A device used to buffer and optionally isolate multiple connections to a transmission network.

STP

Shielded Twisted Pair or Screened Twisted Pair. A version of UTP cable with an additional coaxial metal screen used to shield the twisted pairs from electromagnetic interference.

SWG

Standard Wire Gauge. The UK standard for describing the diameter of conductors in a cable. Smaller gauge numbers represent thicker diameter cable.
In Europe the cross sectional area of the conductor is widely used. For example, the term 7/0.2 is understood to mean 7 strands of wire, each of cross sectional area 0.2mm2.
See also: AWG.

Synchronous Transmission

A method of transmitting data whereby the transmitter and receiver operate in synchronism with a prearranged message structure and arbitration system.

Task Group

A committee involved in the development of standards.

TDR

Time Domain Reflectometry. See Time Domain Reflectometer.

TEXT DMX

One of the new data types added to DMX512-A. It allows human readable text to be sent over a DMX cable using a non-zero start code. It is primarily intended for retrieving configuration and status information from devices that do not have a physical user interface.

Time Domain Reflectometer

A device for measuring cable length or finding faults in cables. This is achieved by measuring the propagation time of a signal in the cable.

TLA

Three Letter Abbreviation.

Transceiver

Transceiver is an abbreviation for Transmitter – Receiver.

Twisted Pair

A transmission line in which two insulated conductors are twisted together to form a pair.

Unicast - Networking

Unicast is the term used to describe communication where a piece of information is sent from one point to another point. In this case there is just one sender, and one receiver.
Unicast transmission, in which a packet is sent from a single source to a specified destination, is the predominant form of transmission on LANs and the Internet. All LANs support the Unicast transfer mode.

Unicast - RDM

In RDM, Unicast transmission of a packet means that the packet is sent to a specific UID address and not either of the Broadcast addresses.

Universe

A term describing a block of 512 channels of lighting information. In DMX512 this refers to all of the data on one cable. In streaming protocols such as Art-Net, it is a logical group of 512 channels.

Up-Lynx
Artistic Licence product used to convert two distinct DMX512 universes to Art-Net Ethernet data.

UTP
Unshielded Twisted Pair - Cabling without an electrical covering to protect it from EMI and RFI. The cable consists of at least two conductors twisted together six twists per inch to minimise the effects of electromagnetic radiation.

Vapourware
Software that has been specified but not yet written (!)

VHF
Very High Frequency. A range of frequencies from 30 to 300MHz.

WiFi
Wireless Fidelity, a term used to describe IEEE802.11b devices that have been tested and approved by WECA.

Wireless
Communication via a radio link.

XLR
A connector developed by ITT Cannon. The original had three pins and was used for audio, hence the name which describes the function of each pin:
X = Screen
L = Live or signal
R = Return or complement
The connector range now provides a selection of pin counts and more recently, the Ethercon,

Appendix J Other Interfaces

OVERVIEW

I have attempted to cover the subjects of DMX512 and RDM in some detail. There are of course numerous other types of interface and many are used in the Entertainment Technology industry.

This chapter seeks to describe the bulk of these other interfaces. I do not intend to provide any significant detail, purely a description.

The Web Links chapter provides a range of on-line information.

Bluetooth

Bluetooth is an international standard for communication over a radio link. It uses the same radio frequency band (2.4GHz) as WiFi, however the differing modulation techniques mean that Bluetooth and WiFi do not conflict.

Bluetooth is named after Harald Blåtand ("Bluetooth"), King of Denmark from 940 to 981, who was responsible for uniting Denmark and Norway.

The technology is primarily designed for short range communication between mobile computers, PDA's and mobile phones. In many ways it supersedes IrDA.

Bluetooth offers a data rate of 1Mbs and can carry three simultaneous voice channels.

Bluetooth supports both point to point and point to multipoint connections.

Key features:

- Adhoc network topology
- Advanced power management designed for battery operated products
- Limited number of nodes can be connected
- Operates in 2.4GHz band

Relevance to Entertainment Technology:

Given the limited number of nodes that can connect to a network, it is likely that ZigBee will be the preferred radio solution in Entertainment Technology.

IrDA

IrDA is a standard defined by the IrDA consortium and stands for the Infrared Data Association

It specifies a method to wirelessly transfer data via infrared radiation. The IrDA specifications include standards for both the physical devices and the protocols they use to communicate with each other.

The IrDA standards have arisen from the need to connect various mobile devices together. The primary use is connecting mobile computers, PDA's and communication devices such as mobile phones. IrDA is also seeing use in more sophisticated applications such as remote configuration programmes and remote control.

IrDA devices communicate using infrared LED's of a wavelength of 875 nm and operate over a distance of approximately 1m.

The available transmission speed ranges from 2400 to 115200 kbps. The data format is asynchronous serial with pulse modulation.

A packet consists of two start words followed by target address (IrDA devices are assigned numbers by the means of IrDA protocol, so they are able to unambiguously identify themselves), data, CRC-16 and a stop word. The whole packet or frame including the CRC-16 is generated by an IrDA compatible chipset.

Key features:

- Standard method for Infrared communication.
- Variable and high data rates
- Very limited distance
- Chipsets available 'off-the-shelf'

Relevance to Entertainment Technology:

The transmission distance fundamentally limits the potential applications in Entertainment Technology. The only significant applications include PDA software for programming products that lack a user interface and very short range data links.

MIDI

MIDI stands for the Musical Instrument Digital Interface. Although designed for communication between musical instruments, the protocol has been widely used for remote control and synchronisation in the entertainment technology industry.

MIDI is a bi-directional protocol that transfers data over an inexpensive current loop interface. The connector used is a 5-pin DIN. Cable distance is limited to 15m, however RS485 converters can be used to extend cables to several hundred metres.

MIDI is a point to point interface and cannot 'loop through'. For this reason, most MIDI equipment is designed with Input, Output and Through connectors.

Data is transferred as asynchronous serial information at a baud rate of 31.25 Kbaud. (Note that data rate and baud rate are identical for MIDI. It is therefore valid to express the transmission speed in either baud or bits per second). Most MIDI messages consist of two or three characters. This means that it takes approximately 1mS to send a message. This is usually too slow for real time lighting control but is fine for triggering.

A MIDI message starts with a Status byte followed by one or more Data bytes. The status byte is identified by the most significant bit being set to one. This means that status bytes can take the range 128 to 255 whilst data bytes are limited to the range 0 to 127.

MIDI implements sixteen logical channels. This allows devices on a MIDI network to be individually addressed. Two types of message class exist. The Channel Messages (such as Note On) are sent to a specific MIDI channel. System Messages are sent to all devices connected to the network.

Channel Messages:

Channel Messages encode the destination address or MIDI Channel in the low nibble of the status byte. The bits of the status byte are divided as follows:

1cccnnnn

The nnnn part takes a value in the range 0 to 15 and is the MIDI Channel.

The ccc part defines the actual MIDI message

The following table defines these commands:

Message	Hex	Decimal	Data byte count
Note off	8n	128+n	2
Note on	9n	144+n	2
Polyphonic key pressure	An	160+n	2
Control/Mode change	Bn	176+n	2
Program change	Cn	192+n	1
Monophonic channel pressure	Dn	208+n	1
Pitch bend change	En	224+n	2

System Messages:

System Messages do not include a MIDI Channel, they 'broadcast' to all connected devices. There are three types of System Message:

Common:

System Common messages are intended for all connected devices. They include messages such as Song Select, Tune Request and MIDI Timecode.

Real Time:

System Real Time messages include items such as timing clock and song start / stop. Real Time messages can be inserted inside other multiple character messages.

Exclusive:

System Exclusive (SysEx) messages are used to transfer manufacturer specific information and data files between products.

Message	Hex	Decimal	Data byte count
System Exclusive			
System exclusive status	F0	240	variable
System Common			
MIDI Time Code (MTC)	F1	241	1
Song position pointer	F2	242	2
Song select	F3	243	1
(Undefined)	F4	244	0
(Undefined)	F5	245	1
Tune request	F6	246	0
End of exclusive (EOX)	F7	247	0
System Real Time			
Timing clock	F8	248	0
(Undefined)	F9	249	0

Start	FA	250	0
Continue	FB	251	0
Stop	FC	252	0
(Undefined)	FD	253	0
Active sense	FE	254	0
System reset	FF	255	0

Key features:

- Low cost
- Widely supported
- Simple to implement
- Relevance to Entertainment Technology:

MIDI is widely used in entertainment technology applications, both for its original purpose of musical instrument communication and also as a remote control mechanism.

Firewire

Firewire was originally developed by Apple Computer Inc as a high speed serial bus for peripherals. Initial support for the standard was to say the least lukewarm. Firewire was in danger of becoming a historical footnote when Sony launched their range of digital video products in 1995. The high speed nature of Firewire was perfect for this type of data intensive application.

Firewire became a defacto standard and was later accepted by the IEEE and is now called IEEE 1394.

Adoption of Firewire, or more properly the IEEE 1394 High Performance Serial Bus, has been widespread. It is supported by the Digital VCR consortium, which includes such heavyweights as Sony and Matsushita. It has also bee adopted by the European Digital Video Broadcast consortium for use in set top boxes.

Firewire suffers the same cable length limitation as USB. The maximum cable length is 4.5m. However, with a maximum data rate of 400MBS, this is a minor inconvenience for its intended application.

Firewire 2 is due out soon, which amongst other enhancements will double the data rate to 800MBs. Future versions of Firewire are expected to attain data rates of 1.GBs.

The Firewire cable is officially six wires. Two cores are used for power, whilst the other 4 conductors are made from two cross wired pairs. This allows all Firewire devices to have the same transmit and receive wiring irrelevant of whether they are a data sending or consuming device.

Perhaps surprisingly, the remote power option is not implemented on many Firewire products. This has led to both 6 pin and 4 pin versions of the interface. Connection between the two schemes is a simple wiring adapter that ignores the power pins.

When available, the power is in the range 8 to 40V and limited to 1.5A maximum.

Key features:

- **Support**. Protocol support for IEEE 1394 built in to the latest versions of Windows and Apple operating systems.
- **Hot pluggable**. It is possible to connect or disconnect an IEEE 1394 device at any time.

- **Peripherals**. A total of 63 devices can be connected to a single bus. The standard also allows any computers connected to the bus to communicate at the maximum speed. It can therefore be used as a very fast form of built in networking.
- **Power**. The IEEE 1394 bus can supply up to 1.5A for remote powered devices.

Relevance to Entertainment Technology:

The Firewire standard is largely over specified for Entertainment Technology applications other than video and audio streaming devices. It is unlikely to have any significant impact upon control protocol based networks.

CAN

CAN or Controller Area Network was originally developed by Bosch for the automotive industry. The similarities with Entertainment Technology are notable. The industry was using a range of multiwire interfaces with little standardisation. The growth of technology, such as ABS and traction control, that required communication between disparate parts of the vehicle was the catalyst for CAN.

The key requirements were: low cost, high noise immunity and point to point communications without the need for a central controller.

The widespread adoption of CAN suggests that it achieved these goals.

The CAN protocol is now an international standard, ISO 11898.

CAN is probably the most efficient and elegant protocol in use today. The most significant part of any protocol design is that of addressing. CAN introduces the concept of context based addressing. Any CAN device on the network can be the transmitter. When data is sent, instead of including a source or destination address in the data packet, CAN includes a unique identifier that describes not only the message content but the priority.

This is of huge benefit in bus arbitration. As there is no concept of receiver address, it is very easy to add receivers without network reconfiguration.

The context sensitive addressing scheme also implicitly supports multiple reception in either broadcast or multicast modes. All CAN receivers will 'see' a message, but can easily parse the data based on content and priority. This allows the simple integration of multiple processors requiring access to a common sensor. For example, both traction control and ABS would require data from the tyre pressure sensors.

Key features:

- Support. Numerous semiconductor manufacturers now offer silicon level support for the protocol.
- Low Cost. Quantity use in the automotive industry has pushed prices to a very low level.
- Immunity. The protocol is designed to operate in the harsh automotive environment.

Relevance to Entertainment Technology:

The similar requirements of automotive and Entertainment Technology suggest that CAN should see significant application in entertainment technology.

This has not, to date, been seen. The key reason for this is that CAN has significant distance limitations. This is not surprising as it was designed for use inside a vehicle.

USB

Universal Serial Bus – USB was developed by a group of telecom and computer companies including Compaq, DEC, IBM, Intel, Microsoft and NEC.

The standard is intended to allow a range of peripherals to be connected to a PC without the annoyance of removing the computer's case. USB has largely supplanted the parallel and serial interface connectors that were used previously. Perhaps the key feature in this success was the ability to power the peripheral via the USB cable. It is exactly this issue that created a need for the IEEE802.3af powered Ethernet standard.

USB has been a great success to date, but does suffer from some significant limitations. The major limitation is cable length, which is limited to 5m. Whilst this is fine for the mouse or a printer on the same desk, it can become a problem for even the smallest home office.

It will be interesting to see the extent to which newer technologies such as powered Ethernet or Bluetooth, supplant USB.

Two major revisions to the standard exist. Most devices in production today (early 2002) use the V1.1 protocol. This allows two speeds of operation. The slower rate of 1.5MBS is mainly used for input devices such as mice and keyboards. The higher rate of up to 12MBS is used for devices such as storage and audio – video capture.

A revised standard, V2.0, is now finished. This allows communication at up to 480MBs. There does not yet seem to be massive product support for this version. Perhaps because manufacturers are currently snowed under with the range of platforms and communication standards requiring support!

Key features:

- **Support**. Protocol support for USB is built in to the latest versions of Windows and Apple operating systems.
- **Hot pluggable.** It is in theory possible to connect or disconnect an USB device at any time. It would be great if someone could inform my USB printer of that!
- **Peripherals.** A total of 127 devices can be connected to a single USB bus. This can be extended with USB Hubs.
- **Power.** USB devices such as Hubs typically supply up to 500mA to downstream devices. Originating devices such as a portable PC may limit this to around 100mA.

Relevance to Entertainment Technology:

The short cable distance limits the relevance of USB for ET applications. Some products, such as USB to DMX512 adapters exist. It is likely that Powered Ethernet will in time replace these products.

ZigBee

ZigBee is the name of an alliance of companies formed around the IEEE 802.15.4 specification. The specification was approved in May 2003.

IEEE 802.15.4 is a specification for data distribution at low data rates in the Industrial, Scientific and Medical (ISM) radio bands. The data rate is limited to 250Kbs. That is the same as DMX512 and one quarter the speed of Bluetooth.

The ZigBee protocol promises to provide longer battery life (months or even years on a single battery charge) and to be a lower-cost alternative to Bluetooth for wireless sensing and control applications

The ZigBee alliance, which includes such companies as Invensys, Honeywell, Mitsubishi Electric, Motorola, and Philips, takes its name from the zig-zag path of bees that form mesh networks between flowers. ZigBee proponents believe that mesh networking is the key to unattended wireless systems in the home, business, or industry. Mesh networking provides redundancy by allowing data to flow through multiple paths and around failed nodes.

The IEEE 802.15.4 wireless standard was developed specifically for remote monitoring and control.

The IEEE standard defines the transmission and reception of data using the physical radio channel (PHY), the channel access of the personal area network (PAN) and the reliable data transport (RDT).

ZigBee defines the topology management, MAC management, routing, discovery protocol, and security management, and includes the 802.15.4 portions.

ZigBee is designed to operate in two radio bands: The 868-928 MHz band or the 2.4 GHz ISM band.

ZigBee's bandwidth is lower than Bluetooth, but the range is greater and the number of nodes is much greater. Up to 255 nodes can be connected to a ZigBee network (compared to 8 for a Bluetooth network). The relatively high number of nodes per network opens the possibility of using ZigBee for lighting automation, such as networked office lighting control.

Key features:

- **Low Bandwidth**. Although classed as low bandwidth in networking terms, it runs at the DMX512 data rate and is suited to lighting control.
- **Multiband.** It is designed to work in two radio bands, this allows product designers to opt out of the crowded 2.4GHz band.
- **Nodes.** A total of 255 devices can be connected to a single network. This makes it viable for networked lighting control.
- **Redundancy.** The multiple path or 'Zig-Zag' data paths improve reliability relative to other technologies.

Relevance to Entertainment Technology:

ZigBee is likely to make serious inroads into Entertainment Technology.

It is far superior to Bluetooth in this environment and significantly lower cost than WiFi.

Appendix K RDM PIDs

| Parameter ID | Value | Description | PDL / Allowed | | | | | | Must be Supported |
			DISCOVERY	DISC_RESPONSE	GET	GET_RESPONSE	SET	SET_RESPONSE	
Network Management									
DISC_UNIQUE_ BRANCH	0x0001	Controller transmits to discover the existence of responders.	12	24	x	x	x	x	✓
DISC_MUTE	0x0002	Mutes the responder such that it no longer replies to discovery messages.	0	2/8	x	x	x	x	✓
DISC_UN_ MUTE	0x0003	Un-mutes the responder such that it will respond to discovery messages.	0	2/8	x	x	x	x	✓
PROXIED_ DEVICES	0x0010	Controller requests packed list of UIDs for which this responder is a proxy.	x	x	0	0-228	x	x	
PROXIED_ DEVICE_ COUNT	0x0011	Controller requests quantity of UIDs for which this responder is a proxy	x	x	0	3	x	x	
COMMS_ STATUS	0x0015	Requests information from responder regarding any communication errors that may have occurred.	x	x	0	6	0	0	
Status									
QUEUED_ MESSAGE	0x0020	Controller retrieves messages that responder has queued. Responder replies with STATUS_MESSAGES if it has an empty message queue.	x	x	1	Var	x	x	
STATUS_ MESSAGES	0x0030	Controller requests responder's list of packed status messages.	x	x	1	0-225	x	x	
STATUS_ID_ DESCRIPTION	0x0031	Controller requests a txt string describing the specified status code.	x	x	2	0-32	x	x	
CLEAR_ STATUS_ID	0x0032	Controller clears the responder's status message queue.	x	x	x	x	0	0	
SUB_DEVICE_ STATUS_ REPORT_THR	0x0033	Controller instructs responder regarding the severity of status	x	x	0	1	1	0	

					PDL / Allowed				
Parameter ID	Value	Description	DISCOVERY	DISC_RESPONSE	GET	GET_RESPONSE	SET	SET_RESPONSE	Must be Supported
ESHOLD		messages it wishes to receive.							

RDM Information

Parameter ID	Value	Description	DISCOVERY	DISC_RESPONSE	GET	GET_RESPONSE	SET	SET_RESPONSE	Must be Supported
SUPPORTED_ PARAMETERS	0x0050	Controller requests the list of PIDs supported by this responder, including manufacturer specific PIDs. Note: Support of this PID only mandatory if responder supports greater than minimum set of PIDs.	✗	✗	0	0-230	✗	✗	✓
PARAMETER_ DESCRIPTION	0x0051	Controller requests text string describing a specified PID. Note: Support of this PID only mandatory if responder publishes manufacturer specific PIDs in SUPPORTED_PARAM ETERS.	✗	✗	2	20-52	✗	✗	✓

Product Information

Parameter ID	Value	Description	DISCOVERY	DISC_RESPONSE	GET	GET_RESPONSE	SET	SET_RESPONSE	Must be Supported
DEVICE_INFO	0x0060	Controller requests general information block from responder which includes start address, footprint, sub-device count etc.	✗	✗	0	19	✗	✗	✓
PRODUCT_ DETAIL_ ID_LIST	0x0070	Controller requests a packed list of up to 6 categories to further define the responder's functionality.	✗	✗	0	2-12	✗	✗	
DEVICE_ MODEL_ DESCRIPTION	0x0080	Controller requests text string describing the model of the responder.	✗	✗	0	0-32	✗	✗	
MANU FACTURER_ LABEL	0x0081	Controller requests text string describing the name of the responder's manufacturer.	✗	✗	0	0-32	✗	✗	
DEVICE_LABEL	0x0082	Controller gets or sets a descriptive text string for this responder.	✗	✗	0	0-32	0-32	0	
FACTORY_ DEFAULTS	0x0090	Controller resets responder to factory defaults or queries whether it is in a factory default state.	✗	✗	0	1	0	0	

Parameter ID	Value	Description	DISCOVERY	DISC_RESPONSE	GET	GET_RESPONSE	SET	SET_RESPONSE	Must be Supported
						PDL / Allowed			
LANGUAGE_CAPABILITIES	0x00A0	Controller queries which languages the responder supports.	x	x	0	0-230	x	x	
LANGUAGE	0x00B0	Controller instructs responder to operate in a specified language or queries which language is currently selected.	x	x	0	2	2	0	
SOFTWARE_ VERSION_ LABEL	0x00C0	Controller requests a text string describing the software version of the responder.	x	x	0	0-32	x	x	✓
BOOT_ SOFTWARE_ VERSION_ID	0x00C1	Controller requests a 32 bit code describing the boot loader software version of the responder.	x	x	0	4	x	x	
BOOT_ SOFTWARE_ VERSION_ LABEL	0x00C2	Controller requests a text string describing the boot loader software version of the responder.	x	x	0	0-32	x	x	
DMX512 Setup									
DMX_ PERSONALITY	0x00E0	Controller gets or sets the current personality of the responder.	x	x	0	2	1	0	
DMX_ PERSONALITY DESCRIPTION	0x00E1	Controller requests a text string describing the specified personality.	x	x	1	3-35	x	x	
DMX_START_ ADDRESS	0x00F0	Controller gets or sets the responder's start address.	x	x	0	2	2	0	✓
SLOT_INFO	0x0120	Controller requests a pack list which describes the functionality of each slot consumed by the responder's footprint.	x	x	0	0-230	x	x	
SLOT_ DESCRIPTION	0x0121	Controller requests a text string that describes the functionality of the specified slot information code.	x	x	2	2-34	x	x	
DEFAULT_ SLOT_VALUE	0x0122	Controller requests a pack list of slot offsets and their associated default values for this responder.	x	x	0	0-231	x	x	
Sensors									

Parameter ID	Value	Description	DISCOVERY	DISC_RESPONSE	GET	GET_RESPONSE	SET	SET_RESPONSE	Must be Supported
					PDL / Allowed				
SENSOR_DEFINITION	0x0200	Controller requests information describing the specified sensor number.	✗	✗	1	13-45	✗	✗	
SENSOR_VALUE	0x0201	Controller requests an information block describing the current and historical values of this sensor.	✗	✗	1	9	1	9	
RECORD_SENSORS	0x0202	Controller instructs responder to record its current sensor values for later retrieval.	✗	✗	✗	✗	1	0	
Power & Lamp Settings									
DEVICE_HOURS	0x0400	Controller requests the total number of hours that the responder has been energised.	✗	✗	0	4	4	0	
LAMP_HOURS	0x0401	Controller requests the total number of hours that the responder's lamp has been energised.	✗	✗	0	4	4	0	
LAMP_STRIKES	0x0402	Controller requests the total number of times the responder's lamp has been struck.	✗	✗	0	4	4	0	
LAMP_STATE	0x0403	Controller requests the current lamp state (on, off, blown, striking etc) of the responder.	✗	✗	0	1	1	0	
LAMP_ON_MODE	0x0404	Controller requests information on how to strike the responder's lamp.	✗	✗	0	1	1	0	
DEVICE_POWER_CYCLES	0x0405	Controller requests the total number of times the responder has been power cycled.	✗	✗	0	4	4	0	
Display Settings									
DISPLAY_INVERT	0x0500	Controller instructs responder to invert user interface display or queries same.	✗	✗	0	1	1	0	

Parameter ID	Value	Description	DISCOVERY	DISC_RESPONSE	GET	GET_RESPONSE	SET	SET_RESPONSE	Must be Supported
DISPLAY_ LEVEL	0x0501	Controller instructs responder regarding brightness of user interface display or queries same.	✗	✗	0	1	1	0	
Configuration									
PAN_INVERT	0x0600	Controller instructs responder to invert pan axis or queries same.	✗	✗	0	1	1	0	
TILT_INVERT	0x0601	Controller instructs responder to invert tilt axis or queries same.	✗	✗	0	1	1	0	
PAN_TILT_ SWAP	0x0602	Controller instructs responder to swap pan & tilt axes or queries same.	✗	✗	0	1	1	0	
REAL_TIME_ CLOCK	0x0603	Controller gets or sets responder's real time clock.	✗	✗	0	7	7	0	
Control									
IDENTIFY_ DEVICE	0x1000	Controller instructs responder visually identify itself or queries same.	✗	✗	0	1	1	0	✓
RESET_ DEVICE	0x1001	Controller instructs responder to reset itself.	✗	✗	✗	✗	1	0	
POWER_ STATE	0x1010	Controller retrieves or sets the current power state (standby, full power, etc) of the responder.	✗	✗	0	1	1	0	
SELF_TEST	0x1020	Controller instructs responder to enter self test or queries whether responder is in self test.	✗	✗	0	1	1	0	
SELF_TEST_ DESCRIPTION	0x1021	Controller requests text description of specified self test mode.	✗	✗	1	1-33	✗	✗	
CAPTURE_ PRESET	0x1030	Controller instructs responder to record current received levels and store to a preset.	✗	✗	✗	✗	2/8	0	
PLAYBACK_ PRESET	0x1031	Controller instructs responder to playback a specific preset or queries which preset is being played.	✗	✗	0	3	3	0	

Appendix L Wire Guages

Please note that the impedance figures are intended to be a rough guide. You should refer to the manufacturer's data sheet for the exact value of a specific cable.

AWG	Diameter	Cross Sectional Area	Approximate Impedance (Copper)	Nearest Metric Size
10	2.5900 mm	5.2600 mm^2	3 Ω /Km	
11	2.3000 mm	4.1700 mm^2	4 Ω /Km	
12	2.0500 mm	3.3100 mm^2	5 Ω /Km	
13	1.8300 mm	2.6200 mm^2	6 Ω /Km	
14	1.6300 mm	2.0800 mm^2	8 Ω /Km	
15	1.4500 mm	1.6500 mm^2	10 Ω /Km	
16	1.2900 mm	1.3100 mm^2	13 Ω /Km	26/0.25, 19/0.30
17	1.1500 mm	1.0400 mm^2	15 Ω /Km	
18	1.0200 mm	0.8230 mm^2	20 Ω /Km	1/1.02, 7/0.40, 16/0.25
19	0.9120 mm	0.6530 mm^2	25 Ω /Km	
20	0.8120 mm	0.5180 mm^2	35 Ω /Km	1/0.81, 7/0.32, 10/0.25, 19/0.20
21	0.7230 mm	0.4100 mm^2	45 Ω /Km	
22	0.6440 mm	0.3260 mm^2	55 Ω /Km	1/0.64, 7/0.25, 19/0.15
23	0.5730 mm	0.2580 mm^2	70 Ω /Km	
24	0.5110 mm	0.2050 mm^2	76 Ω /Km	1/0.50, 7/0.20
25	0.4550 mm	0.1620 mm^2	110 Ω /Km	
26	0.4050 mm	0.1290 mm^2	145 Ω /Km	1/0.40, 7/0.15, 19/0.10
27	0.3610 mm	0.1020 mm^2	170 Ω /Km	
28	0.3210 mm	0.0810 mm^2	230 Ω /Km	1/0.32, 7/0.13, 19/0.08
29	0.2860 mm	0.0642 mm^2	290 Ω /Km	
30	0.2550 mm	0.0509 mm^2	350 Ω /Km	1/0.25, 7/0.10
31	0.2270 mm	0.0404 mm^2	425 Ω /Km	
32	0.2020 mm	0.0320 mm^2	575 Ω /Km	1/0.2, 7/0.08

Appendix M Bibliography

ANSI E1.11 – USITT DMX512-A
Asynchronous Serial Digital Data Transmission Standard for Controlling Lighting Equipment and Accessories.

ANSI E1.27-1-2006, Entertainment Technology - Standard for Portable Control Cables for Use with USITT DMX512/1990 and E1.11 (DMX512-A) Products.

ANSI E1.20-2006, Entertainment Technology - Remote Device Management over USITT DMX512.

Karl Johan Astrom	Nyquist and his seminal papers University of California, Santa Barbara
Harry Nyquist	Certain factors affecting telegraph speed" (Bell System Technical Journal, 3, 324–346, 1924)
Wayne Howell	Rock Solid Ethernet (ISBN 1-904031-29-3)
Robert S. Simpson	Lighting Control (ISBN 0-240-51566-8)
Art Wittmann	Brush Up on Bluetooth
Charles D Knutson Ph.D.	Infrared Data Communications with IrDA.
Chambers	21st Century Dictionary (ISBN 0-550-10625-1).
Richard Pilbrow	Stage Lighting Design (ISBN 1-85459-273-4).
Frederick Bentham	The Art of Stage Lighting (ISBN 0-273-01544-3).
Lynne Truss	Eats, Shoots & Leaves (ISBN 1-86197-612-7)
Andy Ciddor	DMX Dialogue: The Device That Answers Back
Christa Jungnickel *Russel McCormmach*	Cavendish. (ISBN 0-87169-220-1)
Encyclopædia Britannica Inc	Encyclopædia Britannica (ISBN 1-59339-292-3)

Appendix N Web Resources

The Internet, as one would expect, provides a vast resource of information on the subject of communications.

The following list is by no means exhaustive, but does provide a useful starting point.

www.Plasa.org/Standards/	The Professional Light & Sound Association reference for technical information on Entertainment Technology standards.
www.Hinton.demon.co.uk/midi/promidi.html	A well written introduction to the subject of MIDI.
www.Midi.org	Home of the MIDI manufacturers' Association.
www.esta.org	The master reference for all questions related to ACN and DMX512
www.Usitt.org	The official home of DMX512 which includes a number of useful FAQs.
www.Standards.ieee.org/getieee802/	Download page for all IEEE802 Ethernet standards.
www.TiaOnline.org	Telecommunications Industry Association. This group manages standards such as RS485.
www.Wi-Fi.org	The WECA – Wireless Ethernet Compatibility Alliance.
www.Accutest.co.uk	Contains a range of tutorial material for the CAN (Controller Area Network) Bus protocol.
www.BlueTooth.com	The official Bluetooth web site.
www.irda.org	The official IrDA, Infrared communications web site.
www.cern.ch	European centre for high energy physics. Inventor of the World Wide Web.
www.esta.org/tsp/working_groups/CP/DMXoverCat5.htm	
	Report on DMX512 over CAT5 www.ArtisticLicence.com Inventor of Art-Net

Index

ENTERTAINMENT TECHNOLOGY PRESS

FREE SUBSCRIPTION SERVICE

Keeping Up To Date with

Control Freak

Entertainment Technology titles are continually up-dated, and all major changes and additions are listed in date order in the relevant dedicated area of the publisher's website. Simply go to the front page of www.etnow.com and click on the BOOKS button. From there you can locate the title and be connected through to the latest information and services related to the publication.

The author of the title welcomes comments and suggestions about the book and can be contacted by email at: wayne@artisticlicence.com

Titles Published by Entertainment Technology Press

ABC of Theatre Jargon *Francis Reid* **£9.95** ISBN 1904031099
This glossary of theatrical terminology explains the common words and phrases that are used in normal conversation between actors, directors, designers, technicians and managers.

Aluminium Structures in the Entertainment Industry *Peter Hind* **£24.95**
ISBN 1904031064
Aluminium Structures in the Entertainment Industry aims to educate the reader in all aspects of the design and safe usage of temporary and permanent aluminium structures specific to the entertainment industry – such as roof structures, PA towers, temporary staging, etc.

AutoCAD – A Handbook for Theatre Users *David Ripley* **£24.95** ISBN 1904031315
From 'Setting Up' to 'Drawing in Three Dimensions' via 'Drawings Within Drawings', this compact and fully illustrated guide to AutoCAD covers everything from the basics to full colour rendering and remote plotting.

Basics – A Beginner's Guide to Lighting Design *Peter Coleman* **£9.95** ISBN 1904031412
The fourth in the author's 'Basics' series, this title covers the subject area in four main sections: The Concept, Practical Matters, Related Issues and The Design Into Practice. In an area that is difficult to be definitive, there are several things that cross all the boundaries of all lighting design and it's these areas that the author seeks to help with.

Basics – A Beginner's Guide to Special Effects *Peter Coleman* **£9.95** ISBN 1904031331
This title introduces newcomers to the world of special effects. It describes all types of special effects including pyrotechnic, smoke and lighting effects, projections, noise machines, etc. It places emphasis on the safe storage, handling and use of pyrotechnics.

Basics – A Beginner's Guide to Stage Lighting *Peter Coleman* **£9.95** ISBN 190403120X
This title does what it says: it introduces newcomers to the world of stage lighting. It will not teach the reader the art of lighting design, but will teach beginners much about the 'nuts and bolts' of stage lighting.

Basics: A Beginner's Guide to Stage Management *Peter Coleman* **£7.95**
ISBN 9781904031475
The fifth in Peter Coleman's popular 'Basics' series, this title provides a practical insight into, and the definition of, the role of stage management. Further chapters describe Cueing or 'Calling' the Show (the Prompt Book), and the Hardware and Training for Stage Management. This is a book about people and systems, without which most of the technical equipment used by others in the performance workplace couldn't function.

Basics – A Beginner's Guide to Stage Sound *Peter Coleman* **£9.95** ISBN 1904031277
This title does what it says: it introduces newcomers to the world of stage sound. It will not teach the reader the art of sound design, but will teach beginners much about the background to sound reproduction in a theatrical environment.

Building Better Theaters *Michael Mell* **£16.95** 1904031404
A title within our Consultancy Series, this book describes the process of designing a theater, from the initial decision to build through to opening night. Michael Mell's book provides

a step-by-step guide to the design and construction of performing arts facilities. Chapters discuss: assembling your team, selecting an architect, different construction methods, the architectural design process, construction of the theater, theatrical systems and equipment, the stage, backstage, the auditorium, ADA requirements and the lobby. Each chapter clearly describes what to expect and how to avoid surprises. It is a must-read for architects, planners, performing arts groups, educators and anyone who may be considering building or renovating a theater.

Case Studies in Crowd Management
Chris Kemp, Iain Hill, Mick Upton, Mark Hamilton **£16.95** ISBN 9781904031482
This important work has been compiled from a series of research projects carried out by the staff of the Centre for Crowd Management and Security Studies at Buckinghamshire Chilterns University College, and seminar work carried out in Berlin and Groningen with partner Yourope. It includes case studies, reports and a crowd management safety plan for a major outdoor rock concert, safe management of rock concerts utilising a triple barrier safety system and pan-European Health & Safety Issues.

Close Protection – The Softer Skills *Geoffrey Padgham* **£11.95** ISBN 1904031390
This is the first educational book in a new 'Security Series' for Entertainment Technology Press, and it coincides with the launch of the new 'Protective Security Management' Foundation Degree at Buckinghamshire Chilterns University College (BCUC). The author is a former full-career Metropolitan Police Inspector from New Scotland Yard with 27 years' experience of close protection (CP). For 22 of those years he specialised in operations and senior management duties with the Royalty Protection Department at Buckingham Palace, followed by five years in the private security industry specialising in CP training design and delivery. His wealth of protection experience comes across throughout the text, which incorporates sound advice and exceptional practical guidance, subtly separating fact from fiction. This publication is an excellent form of reference material for experienced operatives, students and trainees.

A Comparative Study of Crowd Behaviour at Two Major Music Events
Chris Kemp, Iain Hill, Mick Upton **£7.95** ISBN 1904031250
A compilation of the findings of reports made at two major live music concerts, and in particular crowd behaviour, which is followed from ingress to egress.

Control Freak *Wayne Howell* **£28.95 ISBN 9781904031550**
Control Freak is the second book by Wayne Howell. It provides an in depth study of DMX512 and the new RDM (Remote Device Management) standards. The book is aimed at both users and developers and provides a wealth of real world information based on the author's twenty year experience of lighting control.

Copenhagen Opera House *Richard Brett and John Offord* **£32.00** ISBN 1904031420
Completed in a little over three years, the Copenhagen Opera House opened with a royal gala performance on 15th January 2005. Built on a spacious brown-field site, the building is a landmark venue and this book provides the complete technical background story to an opera house set to become a benchmark for future design and planning. Sixteen chapters by relevant experts involved with the project cover everything from the planning of the auditorium and studio stage, the stage engineering, stage lighting and control and architectural lighting through to acoustic design and sound technology plus technical summaries.

Electrical Safety for Live Events *Marco van Beek* **£16.95** ISBN 1904031285
This title covers electrical safety regulations and good pracitise pertinent to the
entertainment industries and includes some basic electrical theory as well as clarifying the
"do's and don't's" of working with electricity.

Entertainment in Production Volume 1: 1994-1999 *Rob Halliday* **£24.95**
ISBN 9781904031512

Entertainment in Production Volume 2: 2000-2006 *Rob Halliday* **£24.95**
ISBN 9781904031529
Rob Halliday has a dual career as a lighting designer/programmer and author and in these
two volumes he provides the intriguing but comprehensive technical background stories
behind the major musical productions and other notable projects spanning the period 1994 to
2005. Having been closely involved with the majority of the events described, the author is
able to present a first-hand and all-encompassing portrayal of how many of the major shows
across the past decade came into being. From *Oliver!* and *Miss Saigon* to *Mamma Mia!* and
Mary Poppins, here the complete technical story unfolds. The books, which are profusely
illustrated, are in large part an adapted selection of articles that first appeared in the magazine
Lighting&Sound International.

Entertainment Technology Yearbook 2008 *John Offord* **£14.95** **ISBN 9781904031543**
The new Entertainment Technology Yearbook 2008 covers the year 2007 and includes
picture coverage of major industry exhibitions in Europe compiled from the pages of
Entertainment Technology magazine and the etnow.com website, plus articles and pictures
of production, equipment and project highlights of the year. Also included is a major
European Trade Directory that will be regularly updated on line. A new edition will be
published each year at the ABTT Theatre Show in London in June.

The Exeter Theatre Fire *David Anderson* **£24.95** ISBN 1904031137
This title is a fascinating insight into the events that led up to the disaster at the Theatre Royal,
Exeter, on the night of September 5th 1887. The book details what went wrong, and the
lessons that were learned from the event.

Fading Light – A Year in Retirement *Francis Reid* **£14.95** ISBN 1904031358
Francis Reid, the lighting industry's favourite author, describes a full year in retirement. "Old
age is much more fun than I expected," he says. Fading Light describes visits and experiences
to the author's favourite theatres and opera houses, places of relaxation and re-visits to
scholarly institutions.

Focus on Lighting Technology *Richard Cadena* **£17.95** ISBN 1904031145
This concise work unravels the mechanics behind modern performance lighting and appeals to
designers and technicians alike. Packed with clear, easy-to-read diagrams, the book provides
excellent explanations behind the technology of performance lighting.

The Followspot Guide *Nick Mobsby* **£28.95** ISBN 9781904031499
The first in ETP's Equipment Series, Nick Mobsby's Followspot Guide tells you everything
you need to know about followspots, from their history through to maintenance and usage. It's
pages include a technical specification of 193 followspots from historical to the latest 2007
versions from major manufacturers.

From Ancient Rome to Rock 'n' Roll – a Review of the UK Leisure Security Industry
Mick Upton **£14.95** ISBN 9781904031505
From stewarding, close protection and crowd management through to his engagement as
a senior consultant Mick Upton has been ever present in the events industry. A founder of
ShowSec International in 1982 he was its chairman until 2000. The author has led the way on
training within the sector. He set up the ShowSec Training Centre and has acted as a consultant
at the Bramshill Police College. He has been prominent in the development of courses at
Buckinghamshire New University where he was awarded a Doctorate in 2005. Mick has
received numerous industry awards. His book is a personal account of the development and
professionalism of the sector across the past 50 years.

Health and Safety Aspects in the Live Music Industry *Chris Kemp, Iain Hill* **£30.00** ISBN
1904031226
This title includes chapters on various safety aspects of live event production and is written
by specialists in their particular areas of expertise.

Health and Safety Management in the Live Music and Events Industry *Chris Hannam*
£25.95 ISBN 1904031307
This title covers the health and safety regulations and their application regarding all aspects
of staging live entertainment events, and is an invaluable manual for production managers
and event organisers.

Hearing the Light – 50 Years Backstage *Francis Reid* **£24.95** ISBN 1904031188
This highly enjoyable memoir delves deeply into the theatricality of the industry. The
author's almost fanatical interest in opera, his formative period as lighting designer at
Glyndebourne and his experiences as a theatre administrator, writer and teacher make for a
broad and unique background.

An Introduction to Rigging in the Entertainment Industry *Chris Higgs* **£24.95**
ISBN 1904031129
This book is a practical guide to rigging techniques and practices and also thoroughly covers
safety issues and discusses the implications of working within recommended guidelines and
regulations.

Let There be Light – Entertainment Lighting Software Pioneers in Conversation
Robert Bell **£32.00** ISBN 1904031242
Robert Bell interviews a distinguished group of software engineers working on
entertainment lighting ideas and products.

Lighting for Roméo and Juliette *John Offord* **£26.95** ISBN 1904031161
John Offord describes the making of the Vienna State Opera production from the lighting
designer's viewpoint – from the point where director Jürgen Flimm made his decision not to
use scenery or sets and simply employ the expertise of LD Patrick Woodroffe.

Lighting Systems for TV Studios *Nick Mobsby* **£45.00** ISBN 1904031005
Lighting Systems for TV Studios, now in its second edition, is the first book specifically
written on the subject and has become the 'standard' resource work for studio planning
and design covering the key elements of system design, luminaires, dimming, control,
data networks and suspension systems as well as detailing the infrastructure items such as

cyclorama, electrical and ventilation. Sensibly TV lighting principles are explained and some history on TV broadcasting, camera technology and the equipment is provided to help set the scene! The second edition includes applications for sine wave and distributed dimming, moving lights, Ethernet and new cool lamp technology.

Lighting Techniques for Theatre-in-the-Round *Jackie Staines* **£24.95** ISBN 1904031013
Lighting Techniques for Theatre-in-the-Round is a unique reference source for those working on lighting design for theatre-in-the-round for the first time. It is the first title to be published specifically on the subject, it also provides some anecdotes and ideas for more challenging shows, and attempts to blow away some of the myths surrounding lighting in this format.

Lighting the Stage *Francis Reid* **£14.95** ISBN 1904031080
Lighting the Stage discusses the human relationships involved in lighting design – both between people, and between these people and technology. The book is written from a highly personal viewpoint and its 'thinking aloud' approach is one that Francis Reid has used in his writings over the past 30 years.

Model National Standard Conditions *ABTT/DSA/LGLA* **£20.00** ISBN 1904031110
These *Model National Standard Conditions* covers operational matters and complement *The Technical Standards for Places of Entertainment*, which describes the physical requirements for building and maintaining entertainment premises.

Mr Phipps' Theatre *Mark Jones, John Pick* **£17.95** ISBN: 1904031382
Mark Jones and John Pick describe "The Sensational Story of Eastbourne's Royal Hippodrome" – formerly Eastbourne Theatre Royal. An intriguing narrative, the book sets the story against a unique social history of the town. Peter Longman, former director of The Theatres Trust, provides the Foreword.

Pages From Stages *Anthony Field* **£17.95** ISBN 1904031269
Anthony Field explores the changing style of theatres including interior design, exterior design, ticket and seat prices, and levels of service, while questioning whether the theatre still exists as a place of entertainment for regular theatre-goers.

Performing Arts Technical Training Handbook 2007/2008 *ed: John Offord* **£19.95** ISBN 9781904031451
Published in association with the ABTT (Association of British Theatre Technicians), this important Handbook includes fully detailed and indexed entries describing courses on backstage crafts offered by over 100 universities and colleges across the UK. A completely new research project, with accompanying website, the title also includes articles with advice for those considering a career 'behind the scenes', together with contact information and descriptions of the major organisations involved with industry training – plus details of companies offering training within their own premises. The Handbook will be kept in print, with a major revision annually.

Practical Dimming *Nick Mobsby* **£22.95** ISBN 19040313447
This important and easy to read title covers the history of electrical and electronic dimming, how dimmers work, current dimmer types from around the world, planning of a dimming system, looking at new sine wave dimming technology and distributed dimming. Integration

of dimming into different performance venues as well as the necessary supporting electrical systems are fully detailed. Significant levels of information are provided on the many different forms and costs of potential solutions as well as how to plan specific solutions. Architectural dimming for the likes of hotels, museums and shopping centres is included. Practical Dimming is a companion book to Practical DMX and is designed for all involved in the use, operation and design of dimming systems.

Practical DMX *Nick Mobsby* **£16.95** ISBN 1904031368
In this highly topical and important title the author details the principles of DMX, how to plan a network, how to choose equipment and cables, with data on products from around the world, and how to install DMX networks for shows and on a permanently installed basis. The easy style of the book and the helpful fault finding tips, together with a review of different DMX testing devices provide an ideal companion for all lighting technicians and system designers. An introduction to Ethernet and Canbus networks are provided as well tips on analogue networks and protocol conversion. This title has been recently updated to include a new chapter on Remote Device Management that became an international standard in Summer 2006.

Practical Guide to Health and Safety in the Entertainment Industry
Marco van Beek **£14.95** ISBN 1904031048
This book is designed to provide a practical approach to Health and Safety within the Live Entertainment and Event industry. It gives industry-pertinent examples, and seeks to break down the myths surrounding Health and Safety.

Production Management *Joe Aveline* **£17.95** ISBN 1904031102
Joe Aveline's book is an in-depth guide to the role of the Production Manager, and includes real-life practical examples and 'Aveline's Fables' – anecdotes of his experiences with real messages behind them.

Rigging for Entertainment: Regulations and Practice *Chris Higgs* **£19.95**
ISBN 1904031218
Continuing where he left off with his highly successful *An Introduction to Rigging in the Entertainment Industry*, Chris Higgs' second title covers the regulations and use of equipment in greater detail.

Rock Solid Ethernet *Wayne Howell* **£24.95** ISBN 1904031293
Although aimed specifically at specifiers, installers and users of entertainment industry systems, this book will give the reader a thorough grounding in all aspects of computer networks, whatever industry they may work in. The inclusion of historical and technical 'sidebars' make for an enjoyable as well as informative read.

Sixty Years of Light Work *Fred Bentham* **£26.95** ISBN 1904031072
This title is an autobiography of one of the great names behind the development of modern stage lighting equipment and techniques.

Sound for the Stage *Patrick Finelli* **£24.95** ISBN 1904031153
Patrick Finelli's thorough manual covering all aspects of live and recorded sound for performance is a complete training course for anyone interested in working in the field of stage sound, and is a must for any student of sound.

Stage Lighting Design in Britain: The Emergence of the Lighting Designer, 1881-1950 *Nigel Morgan* **£17.95** ISBN 190403134X
This book sets out to ascertain the main course of events and the controlling factors that determined the emergence of the theatre lighting designer in Britain, starting with the introduction of incandescent electric light to the stage, and ending at the time of the first public lighting design credits around 1950. The book explores the practitioners, equipment, installations and techniques of lighting design.

Stage Lighting for Theatre Designers *Nigel Morgan* **£17.95** ISBN 1904031196
This is an updated second edition of Nigel Morgan's popular book for students of theatre design – outlining all the techniques of stage lighting design.

Technical Marketing Techniques *David Brooks, Andy Collier, Steve Norman* **£24.95** ISBN 190403103X
Technical Marketing is a novel concept, recently defined and elaborated by the authors of this book, with business-to-business companies competing in fast developing technical product sectors.

Technical Standards for Places of Entertainment *ABTT/DSA* **£45.00** ISBN 9781904031536
Technical Standards for Places of Entertainment details the necessary physical standards required for entertainment venues. New A4 revised edition June 2008.

Theatre Engineering and Stage Machinery *Toshiro Ogawa* **£30.00** ISBN 9781904031024
Theatre Engineering and Stage Machinery is a unique reference work covering every aspect of theatrical machinery and stage technology in global terms, and across the complete historical spectrum. Revised February 2007.

Theatre Lighting in the Age of Gas *Terence Rees* **£24.95** ISBN 190403117X
Entertainment Technology Press has republished this valuable historic work previously produced by the Society for Theatre Research in 1978. *Theatre Lighting in the Age of Gas* investigates the technological and artistic achievements of theatre lighting engineers from the 1700s to the late Victorian period.

Theatre Space: A Rediscovery Reported *Francis Reid* **£19.95** ISBN 1904031439
In the post-war world of the 1950s and 60s, the format of theatre space became a matter for a debate that aroused passions of an intensity unknown before or since. The proscenium arch was clearly identified as the enemy, accused of forming a barrier to disrupt the relations between the actor and audience. An uneasy fellow-traveller at the time, Francis Reid later recorded his impressions whilst enjoying performances or working in theatres old and new and this book is an important collection of his writings in various theatrical journals from 1969-2001 including his contribution to the Cambridge Guide to the Theatre in 1988. It reports some of the flavour of the period when theatre architecture was rediscovering its past in a search to establish its future.

Theatres of Achievement *John Higgins* **£29.95** ISBN: 1904031374
John Higgins affectionately describes the history of 40 distinguished UK theatres in a personal tribute, each uniquely illustrated by the author. Completing each profile is colour photography by Adrian Eggleston.

Theatric Tourist *Francis Reid* **£19.95** ISBN 9781904031468
Theatric Tourist is the delightful story of Francis Reid's visits across more than 50 years
to theatres, theatre museums, performances and even movie theme parks. In his inimi-
table style, the author involves the reader within a personal experience of venues from
the Legacy of Rome to theatres of the Renaissance and Eighteenth Century Baroque and
the Gustavian Theatres of Stockholm. His performance experiences include Wagner in
Beyreuth, the Pleasures of Tivoli and Wayang in Singapore. This is a 'must have' title for
those who are as "incurably stagestruck" as the author.

Walt Disney Concert Hall – The Backstage Story *Patricia MacKay & Richard Pilbrow*
£28.95 ISBN 1904031234
Spanning the 16-year history of the design and construction of the Walt Disney Concert
Hall, this book provides a fresh and detailed behind the scenes story of the design and
technology from a variety of viewpoints. This is the first book to reveal the "process" of the
design of a concert hall.

Yesterday's Lights – A Revolution Reported *Francis Reid* **£26.95** ISBN 1904031323
Set to help new generations to be aware of where the art and science of theatre lighting is
coming from – and stimulate a nostalgia trip for those who lived through the period, Francis
Reid's latest book has over 350 pages dedicated to the task, covering the 'revolution' from
the fifties through to the present day. Although this is a highly personal account of the
development of lighting design and technology and he admits that there are 'gaps', you'd be
hard put to find anything of significance missing.

Go to www.etbooks.co.uk for full details of above titles and secure online ordering facilities.